HNIQUES PRESENTED

able			
Several samples			
Independent			
Categorical	Ordinal	Categorical	
USKAL–WALLIS TEST 217–229 1.9, 4.1, 4.2, 4.3 LTIPLE COMPARISONS 160–165 4.4	JONCKHEERE TEST pp. 148–160 Ex. 1.12, 5.1, 5.2, 5.3, 5.4 KENDALL TEST pp. 183–190 Ex. 5.6, 5.8 MANN TEST p. 188 Ex. 5.7 SPEARMAN TEST pp. 190–194 Ex. 5.9 MEASURES OF ASSOCIATION (δ, γ, τ_b) pp. 195–209 Ex. 5.10, 5.11, 5.12	FRIEDMAN TEST pp. 170–183 Ex. 1.14, 6.1, 6.2 MULTIPLE COMPARISONS pp. 229–231 Ex. 6.3	COMBINED S TEST pp. 238–255 Ex. 1.16, 7.1, 7.2, 7.3 HOMOGENEITY TEST pp. 255–258 Ex. 7.9
SKAL–WALLIS EST or CHI-SQUARE EST FOR NDEPENDENCE) 59, 264–272 .10	JONCKHEERE TEST pp. 178–183 Ex. 1.13, 5.5 MEASURES OF ASSOCIATION (δ, γ, τ_b) pp. 255–258	COCHRAN TEST pp. 231–233 Ex. 1.15, 6.4	COMBINED S TEST pp. 245–255 Ex. 1.17, 7.4, 7.5, 7.6, 7.7 HOMOGENEITY TEST pp. 195–209 Ex. 7.8
SQUARE TEST OR INDEPENDENCE 64–272 .11, 8.2 SURES OF SSOCIATION (^{2}, C, λ_a, λ) 75–284 .5 SURE OF GREEMENT (κ) 85–289 .6			

Introduction

to

Statistics

Introduction to Statistics

A Nonparametric Approach for the Social Sciences

Chris Leach

Department of Psychology,
University of Newcastle upon Tyne

JOHN WILEY & SONS

Chichester · New York · Brisbane · Toronto

Library of Congress Cataloging in Publication Data:

Leach, Chris.
Introduction to statistics.

Includes bibliographical references and index.
1. Statistics. 2. Nonparametric statistics.
3. Social sciences–Statistical methods. I. Title.
HA29.L32 519.5′02′4301 78-10194
ISBN 0 471 99743 9 (cloth)
ISBN 0 471 99742 0 (paper)

Typeset in IBM Press Roman by Preface Ltd, Salisbury, Wilts
and printed in Great Britain by Unwin Brothers Ltd, The Gresham Press,
Old Woking, Surrey

For Smith

Contents

Preface

In this book, I have attempted to bring together some of the simplest and most useful nonparametric statistical techniques in a form that will be appropriate both as an introductory textbook for students with no previous background in statistics and as a handbook for researchers with little formal training in statistics. The book has grown out of undergraduate and postgraduate courses I have taught over the past six years to Psychology students, many of whom had very little knowledge of mathematical ways of thinking. Nonparametric techniques are particularly suitable for such students because their simplicity allows a fairly full understanding of standard statistical ideas to be gained without requiring a sophisticated knowledge of mathematics. Apart from being simple to understand, nonparametric techniques are particularly useful in social science applications, where the more stringent assumptions of parametric techniques are frequently inappropriate.

I have attempted to provide a coherent unified approach throughout, emphasizing the similarities between the tests presented. Nonparametric tests are usually taught as an afterthought once the basic parametric tests have been covered. The student is then confronted with a number of seemingly unrelated tests that are presented as poor relations of their parametric counterparts. I hope the framework presented here, which stresses the relations between the tests discussed, will redresss the balance somewhat. For this reason, I have chosen to concentrate on those tests that may profitably be viewed within the framework of Fisher's method of randomization. This decision has led to some omissions. Most importantly, I have not discussed tests of the Kolmogorov-Smirnov variety. However, while these tests are important conceptually for theoretical statisticians, they do not seem to have sufficient applications in the social sciences to justify their inclusion and the consequent bending of the framework.

I have maintained uniformity of approach and notation wherever possible. This is most noticeable in the use of Kendall's S statistic as the test statistic for the Rank-Sum Test, the Fisher Exact Test, the Jonckheere Test, as well as the Kendall Test for Correlation. In addition to the obvious conceptual advantage, this considerably simplifies the use of tables of the test statistics, which is a frequent cause of difficulty among students. In the Appendix, I have tabulated selected critical values of the test statistics throughout, for reasons both of space and uniformity. The only exception to this is the standard normal distribution, for which both critical values (Table B(ii)) and the upper half of the distribution (Table B(i)) are tabulated.

The most frequent cause of difficulty for all users of statistics is knowing which techniques to use in a particular situation. Although no easy solution to this problem is possible, I hope the framework developed here and illustrated in the table at the front of the book will help make the choice of a test a little less arduous. Once Sections 1.4–1.6 have been understood, this table should make it easy to locate a potentially appropriate test. Each technique covered has at least one completely worked example (listed in the table) that illustrates the calculations involved and its appropriate usage. In addition, the summaries at the end of each chapter (apart from the first) should give a fairly quick indication of whether a test is appropriate and how to carry it out.

Most of the basic ideas necessary for understanding the workings of the techniques that form the main part of the book are introduced in Chapter 1 and the first three sections of Chapter 2. Once these ideas have been grasped a number of routes through the book are possible. Some of the routes are illustrated in the diagram below, which shows the dependencies between the chapters.

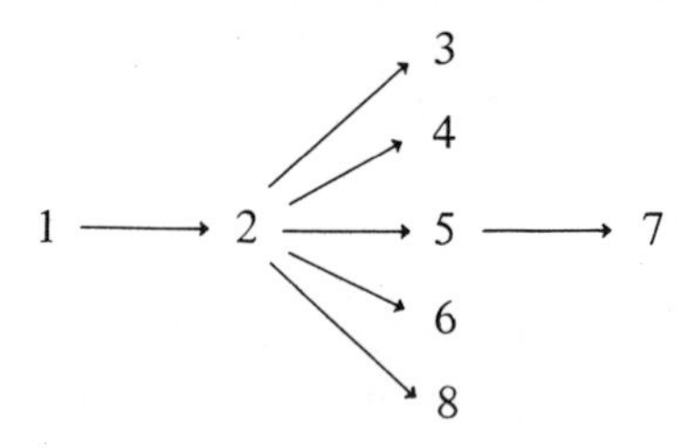

The book is intended to provide a self-contained introduction to nonparametric techniques. However, for those interested in following up some of the ideas in more detail, I have included references to other books and journal articles that give a fuller account. These are intended mainly for the researcher with some knowledge of mathematics and statistics beyond that assumed in the main parts of the book. For the enthusiastic student wanting to learn more about statistics, the references provided in Chapter 9 may be useful.

Acknowledgements

I originally had the idea of writing an introductory textbook when preparing material for the Refresher Course in Distribution-free and Nonparametric Statistics organized by the Mathematical and Statistical Psychology Section of the British Psychological Society at the University of Lancaster in January 1975. The framework presented here emerged from discussions with Thomas Green, Godfrey Harrison, A. R. Jonckheere, Philip Levy, and Sandy MacRae, all of whom taught on the course. I owe a particular debt to A. R. Jonckheere, whose excellent lectures made me appreciate the general usefulness of Kendall's S statistic.

Since then, many people have had to fight their way through very incomplete drafts. The first and second year Psychology students at the University of Newcastle upon Tyne since 1975 have been particularly patient in teaching me how to put ideas across comprehensibly. Several of these students have been kind enough to allow me to use data from their final year projects as examples. Apart from my students, several other people have been involved at various stages. Douglas Carroll, Jeremy Coyle, and Adrian Simpson provided helpful criticisms of the lectures notes from which the book evolved. Harry Fisher, Thomas Green, Paul Jackson, and Edward W. Minium all spent a great amount of time and effort carefully reading the penultimate version; their detailed comments are responsible for many of the good things here. The only person who has been forced to read every word is Linda Smith, who typed the final two versions with unbelievable care and accuracy. Much of the credit for any of this finally getting into print must go to Linda as well as to Valerie Byle, who typed the original lecture notes. Without such good typists I would have given up long ago. Finally, Elspeth Stirling deserves a special mention for providing encouragement and support throughout the writing of this book. She read and commented on much of the book as it emerged and despite having done this, agreed to help in the arduous task of proof-reading. She also helped to convince me that there are more things in life than writing books.

Newcastle upon Tyne,
June, 1978

CHRIS LEACH

CHAPTER 1

'I'm not very good at problems,' admitted Milo.

'What a shame,' sighed the Dodecahedron. 'They're so very useful. Why, did you know that if a beaver two feet long with a tail a foot and a half long can build a dam twelve feet high and six feet wide in two days, all you would need to build the Kariba Dam is a beaver sixty-eight feet long with a fifty-one-foot tail?'

'Where would you find a beaver as big as that?' grumbled the Humbug as his pencil point snapped.

'I'm sure I don't know,' he replied, 'but if you did, you'd certainly know what to do with him.'

'That's absurd,' objected Milo, whose head was spinning from all the numbers and questions.

'That may be true,' he acknowledged, 'but it's completely accurate, and as long as the answer is right, who cares if the question is wrong? If you want sense, you'll have to make it yourself.'

Norton Juster, *The Phantom Tollbooth*

Some Introductory Concepts

Statistics is generally thought of as serving two functions. One is to describe sets of data; the other is to help in drawing inferences. As an example of the descriptive use, we might want to know how many left-handed women were imprisoned in Holloway Jail in 1976. To answer this question, we should obtain information about the handedness of all the prisoners in 1976 and simply count how many were left-handed. To illustrate the inferential use, we might be interested in finding out whether people who drive big cars are more likely to be aggressive than those who drive small cars. Because of the number of people involved, it would normally be out of the question to investigate every car driver. We should need to study a sample of people, and use the results of our sample to draw inferences that we hope will apply to all car drivers. Because we are studying only a sample, there is the possibility that our conclusions may not be accurate and we can never be certain that we have drawn the correct inference. For this reason the inferential use of statistics may be thought of as helping us to make decisions under conditions of uncertainty. It is different from guessing, however, since statistics also provides us with a method of estimating how reliable our conclusions are. With each statistical statement that we make, we indicate the probability that findings like ours could have been the result of chance factors.

More often than not, a study of statistics will not help you ask sensible questions; asking sensible questions can only come about as a result of knowledge of the subject matter. However, statistics will frequently help you decide on ways of posing a particular question. Alfred Hitchcock was once asked what he thought of the fact that a man committed a murder immediately after seeing *Psycho.* He replied by asking how many people had committed murder after seeing *The Sound of Music.* A knowledge of statistics might have prevented the interviewer from asking the question in that way before having adequate evidence.

In this book, we shall be mainly concerned with the inferential use of statistics. However, we need to make use of a few of the techniques of descriptive statistics, which will be discussed briefly below.

1.1 DESCRIBING SETS OF DATA

When we collect a set of data in an experiment, it is often useful to find a way of representing the data that makes it easy to see what is going on. Also, we frequently need ways of summarizing the most important features of the data. The methods of this section will help us to do this.

The method we choose to represent our data will be determined in part by whether the data are *continuous* or *discrete. Continuous* data are such that the value of what is being measured may (theoretically) take on an unlimited number of intermediate values. For example, reaction time data are normally considered continuous. We may record a person's reaction time only to the nearest hundredth of a second, but with a more refined measuring instrument, we can attain greater accuracy. One important property of continuous data is that it is not possible to obtain two exactly equal values. If we record two identical reaction times in an experiment, this tells us only that our measuring device is not sensitive enough; with a better timer we should have been able to distinguish between the two reaction times. In some cases, we may be quite happy to use a crude measuring device with continuous data. For example, we may record simply whether a person passes or fails an examination and still regard performance on the examination as continuous; we know that some people classified as passing may have passed easily while others have just scraped through. In all cases, what defines continuous data is not the number we record, but the underlying theoretical scale.

In contrast, *discrete* data take on only a limited set of values. The number of students in a class or the number of times a head comes up when we toss a coin are both examples of discrete data. It makes no sense to talk of 30.2 students in a class, or to say that if two classes of 30 students each had been measured on a more refined scale, we should have been able to say that one class had more students than the other. In the case of discrete data we may well get ties or equal values which are not the result of poor measurement, but which mean exact equality in some sense.

Frequency Distributions

Discrete data

Suppose that, as part of a study investigating various aspects of the style of crime writers, we decide to focus on the lengths of words used. We may tabulate this information most straightforwardly in the form of a *frequency distribution*, which associates with each possible word-length the frequency or number of words of that length. For example, Table 1.1 shows the frequency distribution of word-lengths in Chapter 2 of Rex Stout's novel *More Deaths Than One*. Counting word-lengths gives us discrete data, since it is not possible to have, say, a word containing 2½ letters. In the case of discrete data, we can also draw a graph like the one in Figure 1.1 to represent the frequency distribution. Either way of representing the data shows that a large proportion of the 391 words in that chapter is fairly short, with 3 or 4 letters, and there are relatively few long words. To convey this sort of information more directly, it is often useful to record the *relative frequency* or proportion of words of a particular length. This is done by dividing the frequency of words of a particular length by the total number of words in the chapter. For example, the relative frequency of words 3 letters long is 80/391 or 0.205. The resulting *relative frequency distribution* for our example data is shown in Table 1.2 and Figure 1.2.

Sometimes we might be interested not just in how many words there are of a particular length but in how many words there are of that length or longer. We can see from Table 1.1 that there are 6 words with 11 or more letters, but we can simplify matters by recording this information directly in what is known as a *cumulative frequency distribution.* For each word-length we record the number of words with that many letters or more. Finally we may also find it useful to tabulate a *cumulative relative frequency distribution*, in which, for each word-length, we record the proportion of words that length or longer. For our example data, these two distributions are presented together in Table 1.3. From the cumulative relative frequency distribution, for example, we can see immediately that only 0.373 or 37.3% of the words are 5 letters long or longer. Notice that, instead of recording our cumulative distributions this way round, we could have tabulated for each word length, the number of words of that length or shorter, if that information is more useful to us.

Table 1.1. Frequency distribution of word length in Chapter 2 of Rex Stout's *More Deaths Than One*

Word-length in letters	1	2	3	4	5	6	7	8	9	10	11	12	13	Total number of words = 391
Frequency of words of that length	23	66	80	76	41	31	34	20	9	5	4	0	2	

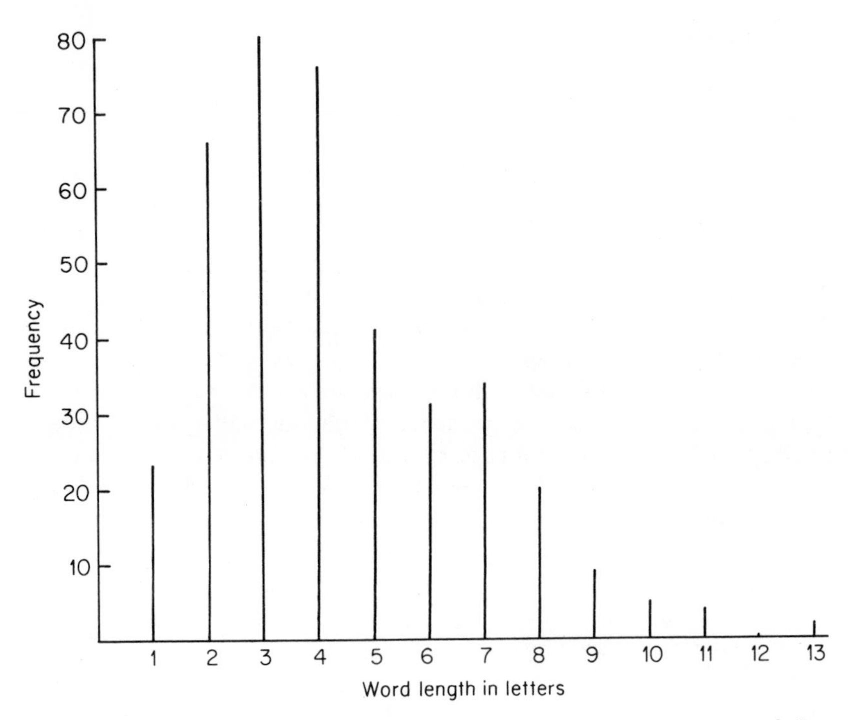

Figure 1.1. Frequency distribution of word length in Chapter 2 of Rex Stout's *More Deaths Than One*

Continuous data

As an example of continuous data, suppose we have measured the heights of 200 people. Measuring height gives us continuous data, since with sufficiently precise measurement, we should not be able to find two people with *exactly* the same height. This means that, if we attempt to draw up a frequency distribution, we should have a table of 200 distinct heights each with a frequency of one, which doesn't help us interpret the data at all. The normal solution to this is to simplify the data by grouping together people with similar heights. For example, we count the number of people with heights between 145 cm and 155 cm and group them together to form one 'cell' of the frequency distribution. The interval chosen for grouping (145–155 cm in our example) is known as the *class-interval*. It is usual to choose equal class-intervals throughout the range of heights. We can then tabulate a frequency distribution such as the one in Table 1.4. In this table we have also recorded the relative frequencies, cumulative frequencies and cumulative relative frequencies associated with each class-interval; each of these is calculated as shown above for the discrete case. There are a lot of problems associated with this procedure such as choosing the most appropriate size of class-interval for the data at hand, but for our present purposes, we shall not need to go into these.

Table 1.2. Relative frequency distribution for the Rex Stout example

Word-length in letters	1	2	3	4	5	6	7	8	9	10	11	12	13
Relative frequency of words of that length	0.059	0.169	0.205	0.194	0.105	0.079	0.087	0.051	0.023	0.013	0.010	0.000	0.005

Table 1.3. Cumulative frequency distribution and cumulative relative frequency distribution for the Rex Stout example

Word-length in letters	1	2	3	4	5	6	7	8	9	10	11	12	13
Cumulative frequency of words of that length or longer	391	368	302	222	146	105	74	40	20	11	6	2	2
Cumulative relative frequency of words of that length or longer	1.000	0.941	0.772	0.568	0.373	0.269	0.189	0.102	0.051	0.028	0.015	0.005	0.005

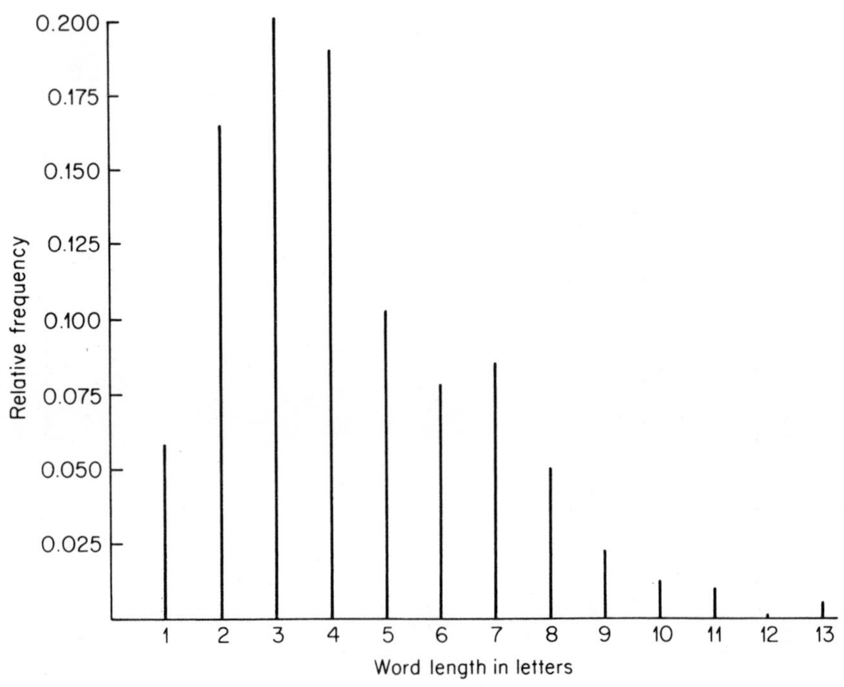

Figure 1.2. Relative frequency distribution of word length in Chapter 2 of Rex Stout's *More Deaths Than One*

As with the discrete case, it is often helpful to display the information in the form of a graph. For continuous data, to remind us that the recorded frequencies occurred throughout the class-interval and not just at one point we normally draw a bar right across the class-interval at the appropriate frequency. Such a method of displaying the frequency distribution is known as a *histogram*. The frequency histogram for the height data is shown in Figure 1.3. An alternative method of displaying the same information is the *frequency polygon* shown in Figure 1.4. Here, the frequencies are plotted against the midpoint of each class-interval; for

Table 1.4. Distribution of heights of 200 people (in cm)

Class-interval	Frequency	Relative frequency	Cumulative frequency	Cumulative relative frequency
145–155	7	0.035	200	1.000
155–165	50	0.250	193	0.965
165–175	65	0.325	143	0.715
175–185	55	0.275	78	0.390
185–195	20	0.100	23	0.115
195–205	3	0.015	3	0.015
	200			

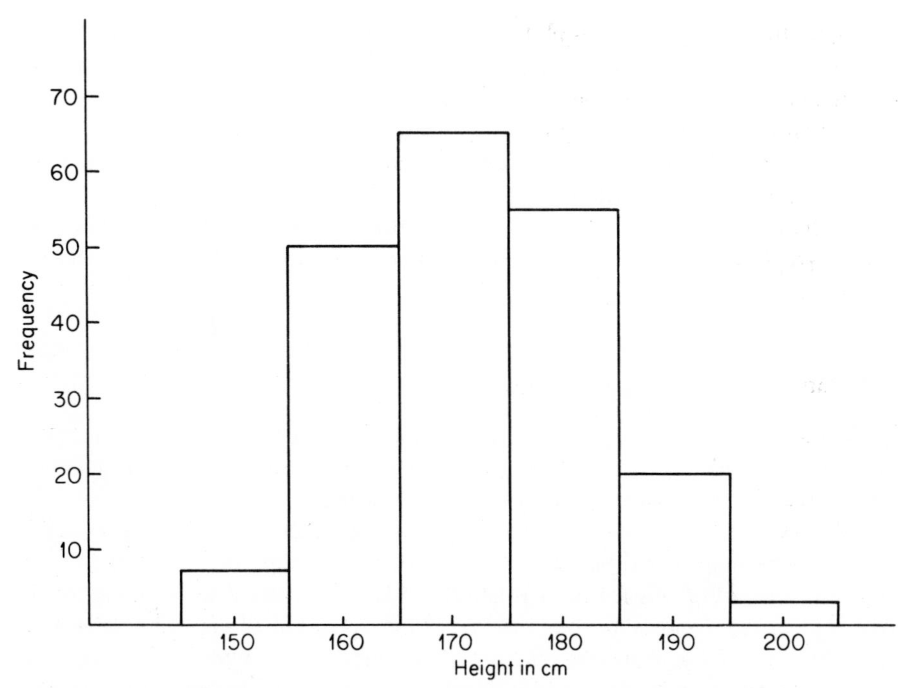

Figure 1.3. Histogram of height of 200 people

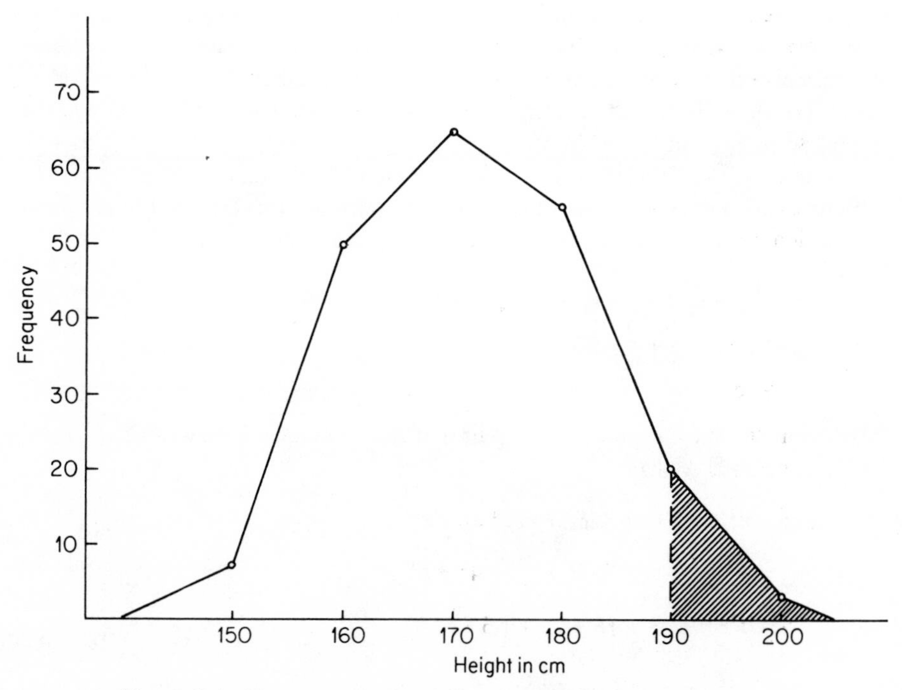

Figure 1.4. Frequency polygon for the height data in Table 1.4

example, the frequency of 7 is plotted against 150 cm, which is the midpoint of the interval 145–155. The resulting points are then joined up. In the polygon or histogram, the frequencies are represented by a certain area. For example, the shaded area in the polygon gives us an estimate of the number of people taller than 190 cm; it is only an estimate because we simplified the data by grouping when forming the frequency distribution.

As before, it is normally useful to display the relative frequency information as well in graphical form and this can easily be done by drawing a histogram or relative frequency polygon.

Σ Notation

So far, we have seen several ways of representing an entire set of data. In many situations it is also useful to have ways of summarizing the most important features of the data. In the following sections, the two most commonly used features of a set of scores will be introduced. These are the average value and the degree to which the scores are spread out. Some of the ways of summarizing the data require a lot of calculations. For this reason it is helpful to have a simple way of saying things like 'add all the numbers' or 'find the sum of the squares of all the numbers'. I shall use a simplified form of standard mathematical notation for saying such things.

Suppose we ask a group of seven people to solve a set of difficult problems and we note the number of problems solved by each person. Suppose further that these people solved 3, 3, 5, 4, 5, 4, and 4 problems. Rather than writing out all the scores every time we want to say what calculation we are doing, it is helpful to represent all the scores from a particular group by a common symbol, say x. The individual scores are then distinguished using subscripts: the first score is labelled x_1, the second score x_2, and so on. In our example, $x_1 = 3, x_2 = 3, x_3 = 5, x_4 = 4, x_5 = 5$, $x_6 = 4$ and $x_7 = 4$. Then the symbol Σx_i says 'add all the numbers in group x'. The subscript i takes on each of the values from 1 upward in turn. Σ is used to represent summation, since it is the Greek capital S, read 'sigma'. Thus, we have

$$\begin{aligned}\Sigma x_i &= x_1 + x_2 + x_3 + x_4 + x_5 + x_6 + x_7 \\ &= 3 + 3 + 5 + 4 + 5 + 4 + 4 \\ &= 28.\end{aligned}$$

If we want to find the sum of the squares of all our numbers, we write Σx_i^2. Thus, for the same data, we have

$$\begin{aligned}\Sigma x_i^2 &= x_1^2 + x_2^2 + x_3^2 + x_4^2 + x_5^2 + x_6^2 + x_7^2 \\ &= 3^2 + 3^2 + 5^2 + 4^2 + 5^2 + 4^2 + 4^2 \\ &= 9 + 9 + 25 + 16 + 25 + 16 + 16 \\ &= 116\end{aligned}$$

If we want first to add all the numbers and then to square the result, we write $(\Sigma x_i)^2$. Thus,

$$(\Sigma x_i)^2 = (x_1 + x_2 + x_3 + x_4 + x_5 + x_6 + x_7)^2$$
$$= (3 + 3 + 5 + 4 + 5 + 4 + 4)^2$$
$$= 28^2 = 784$$

Note that brackets are used to say 'do everything inside the brackets first and then do anything left over'. In this case, we first add the numbers, Σx_i, and then square the result to give $(\Sigma x_i)^2$.

We can use these simple conventions to specify much more complicated calculations. For example, the expression

$$\tfrac{1}{7}\Sigma(x_i - 2)^2$$

says 'subtract 2 from every observation, square the result and add these squared scores together; when you've done that, divide the result by 7'. With our data this gives

$$\tfrac{1}{7}\Sigma(x_i - 2)^2 = \tfrac{1}{7}(1^2 + 1^2 + 3^2 + 2^2 + 3^2 + 2^2 + 2^2)$$
$$= \tfrac{1}{7}(1 + 1 + 9 + 4 + 9 + 4 + 4)$$
$$= \tfrac{32}{7} = 4.57$$

Once you have grasped the convention about brackets, this notation provides a simple, concise way of specifying how a series of calculations can be carried out.

It is worth noting that we don't have to label our set of data *x*'s. We could call them *y*'s or *z*'s or anything, as long as we use the labels consistently. The only exception to this is that the letters N and n are normally used only to refer to the number of scores or the number of people.

> 'How terribly confusing', he cried. 'Everything here is called exactly what it is. The triangles are called triangles, the circles are called circles, and even the same numbers have the same name. Why, can you imagine what would happen if we named all the twos Henry or George or Robert or John or lots of other things? You'd have to say Robert plus John equals four, and if the four's name were Albert, things would be hopeless.'
>
> Norton Juster, *The Phantom Tollbooth.*

Measures of Location

Suppose we ask a further group of seven people to solve the set of problems and these people solve 4, 6, 6, 4, 5, 5, and 5 problems. The results from each group are plotted as separate frequency distributions in Figure 1.5. We can see immediately that the distribution of scores from our new group (Group 2) has exactly the same

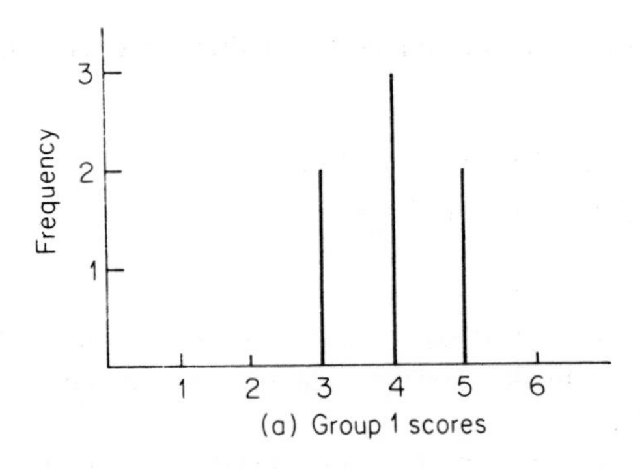

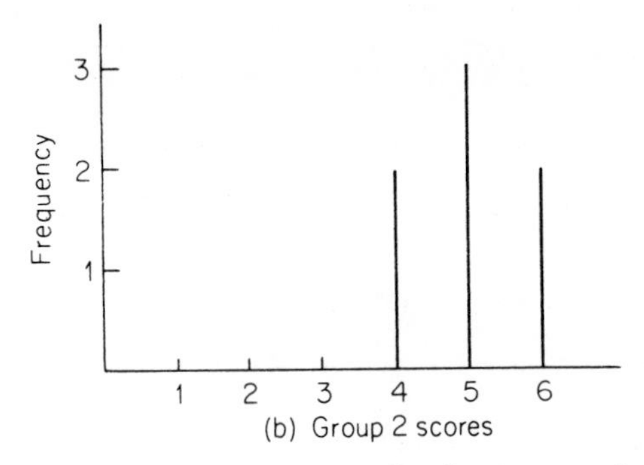

Figure 1.5. Frequency distributions of number of problems solved by each of two groups

shape as that of the first group (Group 1), but the scores tend to be higher. The whole distribution for Group 2 has moved up the axis representing number of problems solved. We normally say that the *locations* of the two distributions differ. It is frequently useful to have a simple numerical way of representing the location of a distribution that will allow us to identify location differences between distributions that are more complicated than the ones illustrated. There are three common ways of doing this.

Mean. One way is to compute the arithmetic mean of the set of scores, usually referred to simply as the mean. This is calculated by finding the sum of the scores and dividing by the number of scores. For scores labelled x_i, the mean is frequently labelled $\bar{x}$ (read 'x bar'). So, for the Group 1 scores, with $N = 7$ (the number of scores), we have

$$\text{Mean} = \bar{x} = \frac{1}{N} \Sigma x_i$$

$$= \tfrac{1}{7}(3 + 3 + 4 + 4 + 4 + 5 + 5)$$

$$= 4$$

For the data from Group 2, the mean is 5. By comparing the values 4 and 5 obtained in this way, we have a simple numerical statement of our observation that the two distributions differ in location.

Median. A second commonly used measure of location is the median, which is the midpoint of the distribution of scores. More precisely, the median is the score above which half the remaining scores are located and below which the other half are located. For our two examples, the medians are 4 and 5. In both cases, however, there is an odd number of scores, so there will always be a middle score. With an even number of scores, the median is defined to be half the sum of the middle two scores. Thus, with the scores 3, 5, 5, 8, 9, and 10, the two middle scores are 5 and 8, so the median is $(5 + 8)/2 = 6.5$. In general, if n is the number of scores, the median is the $(n + 1)/2$th smallest score when n is odd or halfway between the $n/2$th score and the $(n + 1)/2$th score when n is even.

Mode. The third measure of location is the mode, which is the most frequent or typical value of the distribution, i.e. the score that occurs most often. For our examples, the modes are 4 and 5. In some cases, there will be more than one such typical score, in which case there is no uniquely defined mode and the distribution is referred to as multimodal.

Why do we need to bother with three measures of location if they all give the same result? The problem is that they don't always. For the data shown in Figure 1.6, the mean is 7 (indicated by the arrow), while the median is 4 and there is no single well-defined mode. Which one to choose in any particular case will depend on what is required from the data. Notice that the mean is very sensitive to extreme values or outliers such as the single score of 28 in Figure 1.6. If that score had been 7, as in Figure 1.7, then the mean (indicated again by an arrow) would be drastically changed to 4. The median, on the other hand, is relatively unaffected by outliers, and in the example would stay at a value of 4.

The reason the mean, unlike the median, is very sensitive to outliers is that it is the centre of gravity of the distribution and is thus determined both by how many

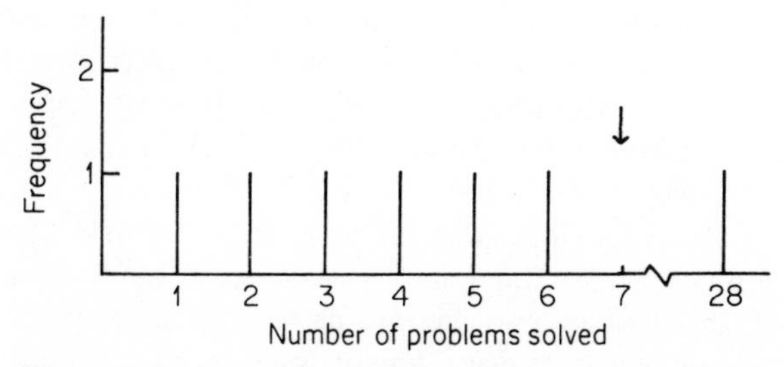

Figure 1.6. A multimodal distribution with a single outlier

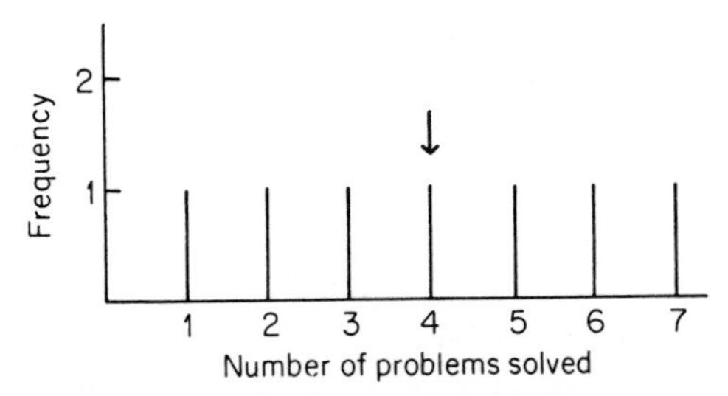

Figure 1.7. A multimodal distribution with no outliers

scores are on either side of it and by how far out they are. The mean is rather like the centre or fulcrum of a seesaw (or teeter-board): a very light person a long way from the centre (an outlier) can balance two heavy people close to the centre. The median, on the other hand, is determined only by how many scores are on either side of it.

This implies that the mean should be used if you want to pay particular attention to the numerical properties of the data, while the median should be used if the numerical properties are not important or if they are likely to be misleading. For example, when measuring reaction times, it sometimes happens that a task typically produces fast reaction times but that a few large times are recorded simply as a result of the subject not paying attention. If these outliers are the result of a different process, computing the mean is likely to give a misleading impression of the average reaction time, so in such cases the median might be preferable.

The mode is useful mainly when a quick, rough measure is desired or when we are only interested in the typical case.

A further aspect of a distribution that we shall make frequent use of is whether or not it is *symmetrical* about its midpoint. The Group 1 distribution in Figure 1.5 is symmetrical about its midpoint of 4. If a distribution is symmetrical and unimodal (i.e. has only one mode), then the three measures of location will agree, otherwise they will have different values. We shall also refer to the ends of a distribution as its *lower* and *upper* tails. Both tails will be identically shaped in a symmetrical distribution. In an asymmetrical distribution, the tails will have different shapes. The Rex Stout example (Figure 1.1) gives us an example of such a distribution. There are a large number of short words, which makes the lower tail short and fat. As word-length increases, so the frequencies decrease relatively slowly, which makes the upper tail long and thin. This will result in the three measures of location taking different values; the mean of the distribution in Figure 1.1 is 4.32, while the median is 4 and the mode is 3.

The rules given above for calculating the measures of location apply equally to discrete and continuous data. There are straightforward ways of simplifying the calculations when the data are presented in the form of a frequency distribution; however, we shall not need to make use of these in what follows. The reader interested in such methods is referred to Haber and Runyon (1973).

Measures of Dispersion

The measures of location discussed above look at only one aspect of a frequency distribution, namely its average value, and do not summarize all of the information depicted – what can you expect from a single number! Thus the distribution of the Group 1 scores in Figure 1.5 has the same mean value of 4 as the distribution in Figure 1.7 but the two distributions are very different in shape The Group 1 distribution is rather squashed up around its central value of 4, which is therefore a fairly representative value for this set of scores. The distribution in Figure 1.7 is relatively spread out, so the central value of 4 is not representative. There are several ways of finding a numerical value that characterises this difference in shape. Such numbers are called measures of dispersion and we shall discuss just two of them.

Range. The simplest measure of dispersion is the range of the scores, which is the difference between the largest and the smallest values. The Group 1 scores in Figure 1.5 have a range of 5 – 3 = 2; so do the Group 2 scores, which is reasonable, since both distributions in Figure 1.5 have the same shape. The scores in Figure 1.6 have a range of 27 while those in Figure 1.7 have a range of 6. The more spread out the scores are, the larger the range.

Variance. This measure is slightly more complex since it makes use of all the numbers in the distribution. The variance reflects the distances of the scores from the mean. To compute it, we first need to know the mean of the distribution. The mean is then subtracted from each of the scores in turn. This is illustrated for the Group 1 data in the second column of Table 1.5. If the mean is representative of the distribution, this column will contain mainly small numbers, as in this case. If the distribution is spread out, as in the case of Figure 1.6, this column will contain mainly large numbers. We want to reduce this column of numbers to a single score that captures how small or large they are. Averaging these deviation scores as they stand will not help, however, since the numbers in this column will always add to 0, no matter what numbers we started from. One solution is to square each of the

Table 1.5. Steps towards calculating the variance

x_i	$(x_i - \bar{x})$	$(x_i - \bar{x})^2$
3	−1	1
3	−1	1
4	0	0
4	0	0
4	0	0
5	1	1
5	1	1
$\Sigma x_i = 28$		$\Sigma(x_i - \bar{x})^2 = 4$

N = Number of scores = 7

$$\text{Mean} = \bar{x} = \frac{\Sigma x_i}{N} = \frac{28}{7} = 4$$

$$\text{Variance} = \frac{1}{N}\Sigma(x_i - \bar{x})^2 = \frac{4}{7}$$

$$\text{Standard deviation} = \sqrt{\frac{4}{7}}$$

numbers before averaging them. This solution preserves the magnitude of the numbers but gets rid of any minus signs, since the square of a negative number is always positive, e.g. $(-2)^2 = 4$. The final step is to find the mean of these squared deviation scores. Summarizing the steps involved using the Σ notation, we have

$$\text{Variance} = \frac{1}{N}\Sigma(x_i - \bar{x})^2 \tag{1.1}$$

In the example in Table 1.5, the sum of the seven squared deviation scores is 4, so the variance is 4/7 or 0.57. The variance for the data in Figure 1.6, calculated in the same way, is 76; the large value reflects the fact that this distribution of scores is very spread out.

Notice that, because we have squared the deviation scores, the variance we have computed will be in squared units. It is often helpful to have our measure of dispersion in the same units as the original scores. To do this we simply compute the square root of the variance. Since this measure is so frequently used rather than the variance, it has a name of its own and is known as the *standard deviation*, which we shall frequently abbreviate to S.D. In symbolic form,

$$\text{S.D.} = \sqrt{\frac{1}{N}\Sigma(x_i - \bar{x})^2} \tag{1.2}$$

The S.D. for the data in Table 1.5 is $\sqrt{4/7} = 0.76$, and the S.D. for the data in Figure 1.6 is $\sqrt{76} = 8.72$. The S.D. still retains the same properties as the variance, with small numbers reflecting squashed up distributions and large numbers reflecting spread out distributions.

It is worth noting that the amount of computation involved in calculating a variance can be reduced somewhat by using a different, but equivalent, formula. Instead of computing the deviation scores as we did above, we can simply find the sum of the squares of the original scores, divide this by the number of scores and subtract from the result the square of the mean. So the simpler formula is

$$\text{Variance} = \frac{1}{N}\Sigma x_i^2 - \bar{x}^2 \tag{1.3}$$

A helpful way of remembering this is 'Variance equals the mean of the squares minus the square of the means'. The use of this formula is illustrated in Table 1.6. Although this method is much simpler, the first method is still worth remembering, since it shows most clearly the logic behind the variance – namely, that it is an average measure of how much each individual score deviates from the mean.

Although the variance is more difficult to calculate than the range, it tends to be used more frequently, since it takes into account all the scores under consideration. The range ignores all but two of the scores.

Both the range and the variance (or S.D.) are greatly affected by outliers. The variance for the data in Figure 1.6 is 76, while that for Figure 1.7 is only 4, and the corresponding ranges are 27 and 6. There are other measures of dispersion that do not have this property, but we shall not need to make use of them For the time

Table 1.6. A simpler way of calculating the variance

x_i	x_i^2
3	9
3	9
4	16
4	16
4	16
5	25
5	25
$\Sigma x_i = 28$	$116 = \Sigma x_i^2$

$$\text{Variance} = \frac{1}{N}\Sigma x_i^2 - \bar{x}^2 = \frac{116}{7} - 4^2 = \frac{116}{7} - 16 = \frac{4}{7}$$

being, all you need to know is that there are several reasonable ways of assigning a number to the vague concepts of location and dispersion. Because of their different properties, some of these may be more appropriate than others in a particular situation. Once you have chosen one method of measuring location or dispersion of a distribution of scores, you should not close your mind to the fact that there are other possibilities that might be sensitive to different aspects of the data, and that might be answering different questions about the data. (A fuller discussion of these ideas may be found in Haber and Runyon, 1973.)

1.2 PROBABILITY

In each of the following chapters, we shall be making a lot of use of the concept of probability. Most of the time, we shall want to know how likely it is that a particular set of results has occurred merely by chance. There is no definition of probability that is completely satisfactory. However, for our purposes, a simple definition will suffice. *The probability of an event is the relative frequency of that event within a reference class of similar events.* This sounds complicated but it's not really. Some examples will help. For the Rex Stout example, suppose we are interested in the probability of selecting any word three letters long from the chapter. Here the event we are interested in is the occurrence of a three-letter word and the reference class of similar events is the total number of words of any length in the chapter. Thus, the relative frequency distribution given in Table 1.2 immediately tells us that the probability of selecting a three-letter word is 0.205; this probability will only be accurate if the selection is made strictly at random (see section 1.3 below). The cumulative relative frequency distribution of Table 1.3 allows us to state that the probability of selecting a word of seven letters or more is 0.189.

Similarly, the probability of throwing a five in a single throw of an unbiased die is one-sixth, since each of the six possible faces (our reference class) is equally likely to show and there is only one face labelled five. The probability of the first card dealt from a pack being a club is 13/52, because 13 of the 52 possible cards are clubs. The probability of an unbiased coin falling heads is one-half, and so on.

Our definition of probability as relative frequency will always result in any probability calculated being a number between 0 and 1. If an event is certain to occur its probability is 1; thus, the probability of selecting a word containing at least one letter in the Rex Stout example is 1, since all words contain one letter or more (see Table 1.3). If an event is certain not to occur, its probability is 0; Table 1.2 shows us that the probability of selecting a 12-letter word is 0, since there are no 12-letter words in the chapter concerned.

Frequently we shall want to combine probabilities in various ways, so that, for example, we can calculate the probability of either a four or a five showing in a single throw of a die. There are some simple laws of probability that will frequently speed up the calculations.

The Addition Law of Probability for Mutually Exclusive Events

The *addition law* states that if A and B are two mutually exclusive events, then the probability that *either A or B* will occur is equal to the sum of their separate probabilities. Two events are *mutually exclusive* if they cannot both occur simultaneously. Thus, a die cannot come up with both a one and a two on a single throw, so the events 'one shows' and 'two shows' are mutually exclusive; therefore, the probability that either a one or a two shows is given by $1/6 + 1/6 = 2/6$. Similarly, the probability of getting either a head or a tail on a single toss of a coin is $\frac{1}{2} + \frac{1}{2} = 1$: in other words, a coin must come down heads or tails.

Modifying the Addition Law when the Events are not Mutually Exclusive

The simple *addition law* of probability only holds when the events concerned are mutually exclusive. If the two events are not mutually exclusive, we need a slightly more elaborate formula. For example, in throwing a die we might want to know the probability of throwing a number divisible by *either* 2 *or* 3. In this simple case we know the answer to be 2/3 since any of the four faces 2, 3, 4, and 6 meet our requirements and the probability of any one of the four is $4/6 = 2/3$. Our simple law will not hold, because the occurrence of a 6 simultaneously satisfies *both* of our requirements, so the two events ('divisible by 2' and 'divisible by 3') are not mutually exclusive. Had we used our simple law, it would have given a probability that was too large, because it doesn't take account of the 6 satisfying both requirements – our answer with the addition law would have been $2/6 + 3/6 = 5/6$, which is clearly wrong. The reason it is wrong is that we have included the possible occurrence of 6 twice in our computations – the simple law gives us prob (3 *or* 6) + prob (2 *or* 4 *or* 6). We can easily modify our formula by subtracting one of the offending probabilities – since a 6 occurs with a probability of 1/6, we simply subtract this from the result given by the addition law to give $5/6 - 1/6 = 4/6$, which is the answer dictated by reason. In subtracting this value, we have simply taken account of the overlap between our two events. A more general formula for the probability of either A or B occurring is therefore

$$\text{prob}\ (A\ \textit{or}\ B) = \text{prob}\ (A) + \text{prob}\ (B) - \text{prob}\ (A\ \textit{and}\ B)$$

This formula is known as the *joint probability* of A and B. In our example, A is the event 'number divisible by 2', B is the event 'number divisible by 3', with A *and* B occurring only when a 6 is thrown, so that prob (A *and* B) = 1/6. Thus, in our case, prob (A *or* B) = 2/6 + 3/6 – 1/6 = 4/6, as required.

Notice that when the two events are mutually exclusive, the formula is still applicable, since prob (A *and* B) will be zero. For example, the probability of throwing a one or a two is simply 1/6 + 1/6 – 0 = 2/6, since a one and a two cannot both be thrown simultaneously with a single throw of a die. Thus, the simple law of addition for mutually exclusive events is a special case of the more general formula.

The Multiplication Law of Probability for Independent Events

Suppose we want to find the probability of getting two heads when we toss two unbiased coins. Four distinct things can happen that are all equally likely – the first coin can come down either heads or tails and for each of these two possibilities the second coin can come down either heads or tails. Thus the possible outcomes are HH, HT, TH, and TT. Therefore, the probability of getting two heads, Prob (HH), is simply ¼.

The *multiplication law* gives us a simpler way of arriving at the same result. It states that if two events are independent then the probability of both occurring is the product of the probabilities of each. Two events are *independent* if the occurrence of one in no way affects the occurrence of the other. In our example, the result of tossing one coin should not affect the result of tossing the second coin so we can use the multiplication law, to give

prob (HH) = prob (H with first coin) x prob (H with second coin)
= ½ x ½ = ¼, as before.

What about the probability of getting only one head when two coins are tossed? To answer this, we use both laws. We know that the event 'one head' can occur in two ways – either the first coin comes up heads and the second tails or the first comes up tails and the second heads. These two events, HT and TH, cannot both occur simultaneously, so they are mutually exclusive; therefore prob (one head) = prob (HT *or* TH) = prob (HT) + prob (TH). Now, the multiplication law will give us each of these probabilities: prob (HT) = prob (H) x prob (T) = ½ x ½ = ¼, and prob (TH) = prob (T) x prob (H) = ½ x ½ = ¼. So our result is simply prob (one head) = ¼ + ¼ = ½. Therefore, on half the occasions when we toss two coins, we should expect only one head to show.

Modifying the Multiplication Law when the Events are not Independent

The *multiplication law* in its turn needs adjustment if the events A and B are not independent. For example, the probability of dealing a club from a pack of cards is 13/52 = ¼. The probability of the second card dealt being a club is not ¼, but

12/51, since we've already taken one club out of the pack. So the probability of the first two cards dealt being clubs is 13/52 x 12/51 = 0.059. The 12/51 involved here is the probability of getting a club, given that one club has already been dealt. It is different from 13/52 because the two events are not independent. In general we can modify our multiplication law to take account of non-independence in the following way. The probability of two events A and B *both* occurring is given by the probability of A occurring multiplied by the probability of B occurring, given that A has already occurred. In symbolic form:

$$\text{prob } (A \text{ and } B) = \text{prob } (A) \times \text{prob } (B \mid A)$$

The symbol prob $(B \mid A)$ stands for the probability of B given that A has already occurred – it is called the *conditional probability* of B given A. In our example, A is the event 'first card is a club' and B is the event 'second card is a club'.

As another example, what is the probability of obtaining a number divisible by *both* 2 *and* 3 when we throw a die? We know the answer to be 1/6, since only one face of the die, namely 6, meets the requirements. To show how to get the same result with the formula, let A be the event 'number divisible by 2' and B the event 'number divisible by 3'. Three faces of the die, 2, 4, and 6, satisfy the requirements of event A, so prob $(A) = 3/6$. Of these three faces, only one, the 6 satisfies also the requirements of event B, so prob $(B \mid A) = 1/3$. Therefore, prob $(A$ *and* $B) = 3/6 \times 1/3 = 1/6$, as required.

Notice that the simple multiplication law for events that are independent is a special case of this formula. If two events are independent, then by definition, the occurrence of one does not affect the occurrence of the other – in other words, learning that A has occurred does not affect the probability that B will also occur. In this case, prob $(B \mid A)$ will be the same as prob (B).

1.3 POPULATIONS, SAMPLES, AND RANDOMNESS

The techniques discussed above apply to any set of events that might interest us. We now need to distinguish between two types of set. A *population* is the entire set of events being considered. Our population of interest might be the set of all people, or the set of all people resident in London in 1976, or the set of all children of school age who come from a broken home. A population in its statistical usage does not have to consist of people. We might be interested in the population of Iron Age artefacts, or the population of pocket calculators made by a certain company or the population of words in Rex Stout's novel, or the population of scores in the first year Psychology examination for 1968 in the University of Newcastle upon Tyne. Any entire set of people, objects or scores having some common observable characteristic defines a population.

A *sample* is simply a part of a population. Thus, the set of words in Chapter 2 of Rex Stout's novel is a sample from the population of words in the entire novel.

When carrying out an investigation, we normally wish to generalize our results beyond the particular conditions of the investigation. In our first example of a study to investigate the relation between size of car driven and aggression, although we might only be able to select a small sample of car-drivers to take part in the study, we wanted to be able to generalize our results to the whole population of car-drivers. The statistical techniques we shall be studying all allow us to make this sort of generalization, as long as the sample that we use in our experiment is a *random sample* from the population of interest. For a sample to be random, every member of the population must have an equal chance of being incorporated in the sample. Thus, if we select our sample of car-drivers from the telephone book, we should not have a random sample, since there are car drivers who do not have telephones and these people would not be considered for inclusion in our sample. My choice of Chapter 2 for the sample of words in the Rex Stout example is not random either – I chose that chapter because it is one of the shortest in the book.

To turn the problem around the other way, if we carry out an experiment with a ready-made group of subjects, such as the members of a practical class, any conclusions we draw will be reliable when referred to that group of subjects, but it will not be possible straightforwardly to generalize the results of the experiment, since this ready-made group of subjects may not be a representative sample of any population and will certainly not be a random sample.

In some cases, such as twin studies, it is difficult to obtain a random sample. The twins used in such studies are frequently *all* those that come to the attention of the investigator, so they are not a random sample from the population of twins, or any other population. But this doesn't detract from the value of twin studies; it just means that great caution must be exercised in generalizing the results of such studies.

The concept of randomness crops up indirectly in almost everything we shall be doing. We have already seen its application in probability statements in the last section, where we stated that the probability of selecting a three-letter word from the Rex Stout chapter is 0.205, if the selection is made at random. In this context, it means that every word of the chapter must have an equal chance of being selected. Thus, if we closed our eyes and used a pencil to point to a particular word, the longer words are more likely to be selected, so the probability of 0.205 will be inaccurate. We can make the selection more random here by writing each of the 391 words on a separate slip of paper and shuffling them thoroughly before selecting one.

1.4 DISTINCTION BETWEEN ATTRIBUTES AND TREATMENTS

Each of the statistical techniques we shall be discussing may be applied in two rather different situations, which differ in the degree of experimental control we have and in the type of conclusion that may be drawn. To illustrate the difference, we shall consider two ways in which our study relating size of car driven to aggression might be carried out.

In the first situation, we take a random sample of people who drive big cars and a second random sample of people who drive small cars. We then give the members of each sample a questionnaire that reflects aggression, and note whether the big car drivers score higher than the small car drivers. In such a study, the size of car driven is not under experimental control, but rather it is an *attribute* of each person taking part in the study; it is inseparably attached to each of the subjects as far as the investigator is concerned. In this situation it is not possible to establish a causal relation between size of car and aggression but only an association between them. Thus, if a difference is found between the two samples, we are not entitled to say that owning big cars makes people aggressive. It is quite possible that the association could be caused by other traits or environmental factors which predispose a person towards both owning a big car and aggression. In fact, it is not even possible in such a study to rule out the possibility of aggression causing people to own big cars rather than the other way round. Such studies are frequently called *correlational studies*.

The second situation gets around this problem by experimentally controlling size of car driven. In this situation, we handle size of car driven as a *treatment* rather than an attribute. We take a random sample from our population of interest and randomly assign each person to one of two groups, the members of one group being given a big car to drive, while the members of the other group are each given a small car. After a certain amount of time driving their cars, they are given the aggression questionnaire. Then, even if there were, for example, certain traits that cause both a desire to drive big cars and a tendency towards aggression, these would be balanced by the random assignment of subjects to the two treatments. In this case, if the big car drivers scored higher on the aggression questionnaire than the small car drivers, this would indicate size of car as the cause. Thus, in the second situation, we are entitled to draw causal conclusions, while in the first we are not. Studies of the second type are frequently called *experimental studies*.

In some cases, we may be able to choose which of the two types of study to carry out. In other cases, it may be difficult or impossible to carry out the second type of study. Most of the work investigating the relation between smoking and cancer, for example, handles smoking as an attribute. A sample of smokers is compared with a sample of non-smokers in terms of tendency towards cancer. Such studies can therefore not conclude that smoking causes cancer but can merely demonstrate an association between the two. It would be very difficult to handle smoking and non-smoking as two treatments; this would necessitate finding a group of volunteers willing to be assigned at random to either the smoking or the non-smoking treatment on a long-term basis.

In some cases, it is even impossible to carry out an experimental study. If we are investigating differences between men and women in problem solving ability, for example, it is not possible to regard the sex of the person studied as a treatment. We cannot take a sample of people and make half of them into men and half into women. Such studies of sex differences therefore only look for an association between sex and problem-solving ability. This means that it is very often difficult to decide whether any such differences discovered are a result of sex differences *per se* or are due to environmental or cultural differences between men and women.

This distinction between attributes and treatments is extremely important, since each of the statistical tests that we shall be looking at may be applied equally well in both situations. The distinction is at the level of designing and carrying out the experiment, not at the level of analysing the data, but it determines what sort of conclusion may be drawn. In correlational studies we may only conclude that there is an association between the variables being investigated, while in experimental studies we may go further and talk about causal relations between the variables.

1.5 TYPES OF DATA

One of the most difficult questions for both the novice and the experienced researcher is deciding which statistical test is most appropriate for a given set of data. No straightforward answer to this question can be given without a detailed knowledge of what is being investigated. Even with this detailed knowledge it is frequently a difficult question to answer. However, there are some generally applicable guidelines that may help make the question more manageable. These guidelines turn on the type of data collected in a study and the sort of question asked of the data. The aim of this section is to suggest some broad distinctions between various types of data that will be used throughout the book to introduce the different tests. It is worth emphasizing at this stage that these distinctions should be borne in mind from the very outset of an investigation. Whenever possible it is wise to design an experiment with a particular analysis in mind rather than unthinkingly to collect a large amount of data and then to search for a method of analysis. The latter approach frequently results in the collection of data that are unanalysable.

Explanatory and Response Variables

Any measurable quantity that can vary from one individual to another is called a *variable*. In the Rex Stout example, the variable we were interested in was word-length; each individual word has a particular length, and length can vary from word to word.

In our study relating car-driving and aggression, we were comparing the two variables size of car driven and score on an aggression questionnaire. In such studies relating two variables we are usually interested in explaining an individual's score on one variable in terms of his or her score on the other variable; thus, we wanted to explain an individual's score on the aggression questionnaire by his or her 'score' on the size of car variable, i.e. whether that person drives a large car or a small one. For this reason, it is helpful to distinguish between *explanatory variables* and *response variables*, explanatory variables being used to explain or predict variation in response variables. (These are sometimes referred to as *independent* and *dependent* variables, respectively.) Thus, size of car is an explanatory variable, while score on the aggression questionnaire is a response variable. For the reasons mentioned in the previous section, such a distinction will only be strictly accurate if any explanatory variable we are interested in is handled as a treatment rather than an attribute. However, we shall adopt the distinction for both situations, since it will help us equally well in both situations to choose an appropriate test. So we must always remember that when an explanatory variable is handled as an attribute, we may not be justified in concluding that any variation in the explanatory variable 'explains' variation in the response variable. In this situation, the terminology is just a convenient way of differentiating between the variables being studied.

Categorical and Ordinal Data

Suppose we are interested in whether the number of men and women on a psychology course reflect the relative numbers of men and women in the country as a whole. For each person on the course, the only datum we have is whether he/she is a man or a woman. In other words, we have only information about the category membership of each person. Such data are known as *categorical data*. Categorical data result when we sort the observations in an experiment into a number of distinct categories, such as men, women, or children; successes or failures; whether a rat turns left or right in a T-maze; and so on. To be useful our categories must be mutually exclusive – once we have classified a person as a man, for example, we should not also be able to classify him as a child, if we want to use the categories men, women, and children.

In other cases, we may want to pay particular attention to whether one individual has more or less of the variable under consideration than another. Thus, in comparing the heights of a number of people it makes sense to say that one person is taller or shorter than another. In such situations, where it is meaningful to rank order the individuals in an experiment in terms of the variable, the data are referred to as *ordinal data*.

Ordinal data can arise in a number of different ways. For example, we may rank order a group of people according to height by lining them up and moving them around. Alternatively, we may measure each person's height using a tape measure; these measurements may then be used to rank order the individuals. In treating these measurements as ordinal data, we are of course ignoring a lot of the numerical information contained in them, since ordering implies that one person is taller than the next but does not tell you by how much.

Most of the tests to be discussed in this book assume that the data collected are either categorical or ordinal. As in the height example, even when more refined measurements are available, we shall usually reduce these measurements to rank orders.

Independent and Related Data

When we collect a set of data, it is always necessary to keep track of whether one measurement has influenced another or not. If all the measurements can be assumed not to have influenced one another, the data are said to be *independent*. Thus, in our study of car driving and aggression, it may be reasonable to assume that the scores of different people on the aggression questionnaire are independent, unless we know that the participants in the study have told each other of the contents of the questionnaire.

Data that are not independent are called *related* or *dependent.* If we measure a person's reaction time twice, the second reaction time cannot normally be assumed to be independent of the first, since the person has already been exposed to the task. Related data may arise as an integral part of the design of an experiment. Thus, if we suspect that level of income may be an important factor in our study of car driving and aggression, we may wish to control for it by selecting pairs of people with comparable incomes, and then asking one member of each pair to drive a large car and the other member to drive a small car. The scores of each matched pair on the later aggression questionnaire are then best thought of as related. There are, therefore, two common ways in which related data arise: repeated observations on the same subjects and subjects matched in some way thought to be relevant.

1.6 CHOOSING A STATISTICAL TEST

We are now in a position to discuss a general framework for thinking about the different statistical tests that will be presented below. This framework will aid us in the difficult task of choosing a test. In this book we shall only consider problems involving one or two variables.

Problems involving one variable, which is best thought of as a response variable, will be called *one-sample* problems. These involve taking a single sample of individuals from the population of interest and obtaining a response for each member of the sample. For example, suppose a linguistic theory predicts that a particular sentence should take on average 350 msec to process. We could test the theory by obtaining the processing time for each of a sample of people; the median time should be close to 350 msec if the theory is correct.

In problems involving two variables, it is normally useful to distinguish between the explanatory variable and the response variable as suggested in the previous section. The initial classification is then based on the number of levels or values that the explanatory variable takes in the study. In our car-driving and aggression example, size of car driven was the explanatory variable and score on the aggression questionnaire was the response variable. Size of car could be large or small, so the explanatory variable has two levels. This sort of problem is known as a *two-sample* problem; the two samples are determined by the two levels of the explanatory variable.

When the explanatory variable has more than two levels, we shall call the problem a *several sample* problem. Thus, if we had included a third group of people who drove medium sized cars, our car-driving example would become a several sample problem, with the explanatory variable taking the three values large, medium or small car.

Given this initial classification, we can now add the other two distinctions made in the previous section, which involve deciding whether the data are independent or related, and whether they are categorical or ordinal. We shall not consider all possibilities, but shall limit our discussion to the sorts of data that occur most frequently in practice. The combinations we shall be interested in are shown in

Table 1.7. Framework for choosing a test

		Explanatory variable							
		One-sample	Two-sample		Several samples			
			Independent	Related	Independent		Related	
					Categorical	Ordinal	Categorical	Ordinal
Response variable	Ordinal	Example 1.1	Example 1.4	Example 1.7	Example 1.9	Example 1.12	Example 1.14	Example 1.16
	Two categories	Example 1.2	Example 1.5	Example 1.8	Example 1.10	Example 1.13	Example 1.15	Example 1.17
	More than two categories	Example 1.3	Example 1.6		Example 1.11			

Table 1.7. These are also listed below together with examples of the sort of problem that may be considered. For the beginner, this classification may seem particularly difficult at first reading, when the concepts introduced earlier are still relatively unfamiliar. The separate parts of this classification relate to later chapters, where the situations discussed here are spelt out in greater detail. For this reason, it is not necessary to understand all the details here before proceeding further. I suggest that the rest of this section be read quickly initially and the relevant examples returned to at the beginning of each subsequent chapter.

For reference, the classification shown in Table 1.7 is repeated in the table at the front of the book, which suggests which of the tests discussed in later chapters might be appropriate for each of the examples.

One-Sample Situation

Example 1.1–Ordinal Response Variable

Suppose that, on the basis of extensive work in North America, it is concluded that the median score on a particular dogmatism scale is 30. We wish to use the scale in Britain. A random sample of 100 British people is selected and the score of each person on the dogmatism scale is obtained. Are these British data consistent with a median of 30, or are we justified in concluding that British people differ in terms of score on this test from North Americans? Scores on such a scale may usually be regarded as ordinal data: they are constructed in such a way that if one person scores higher than another, then the first person is considered more dogmatic than the second.

This is a one-sample situation, since we have selected a single sample of people and we are interested in testing the prediction that the median score of the population from which the sample was obtained is 30. Notice that, in this situation, the only information we have about the North American population is that its median score is 30. So we are not comparing two samples.

Example 1.2–Categorical Response Variable (Two categories)

Fifty art critics are each shown two paintings, one by Modigliani and one by an art forger in the style of Modigliani, and are asked to choose the 'real' Modigliani. Thirty of them choose correctly, while the others all select the forgery. Would these findings reassure a person who is sceptical of the judgement of art critics?

These data are one-sample data, since we have obtained one response from each member of a single sample of critics. The response is categorical; each critic says either 'real' or 'forgery'.

Example 1.3–Categorical Response Variable (More than two categories)

Four cat-food manufacturers each claim to produce the 'food that cats love best'. One hundred cats are each confronted with four bowls of food, each bowl containing food from one of the manufacturers. For each cat, the name of the food eaten first is noted. Do the resulting data indicate any consistent preference among the four foods or are they are equally popular?

This is again a one-sample situation, with the response variable taking four different categorical values, these being the names of the four foods.

Two Independent Samples

Example 1.4–Ordinal Response Variable

Suppose that the study in Example 1.1 had been carried out in a rather different way and we had obtained dogmatism scores from a sample of North Americans and a sample of British people. This time we are comparing results from two samples rather than comparing results from a single sample with a predicted median. This would be a two-sample situation, asking a similar question to that in Example 1.1.

Example 1.5 – Categorical Response Variable (Two categories)

Ten men and twelve women are known to have contracted a rare disease. One of the men and seven of the women died as a result of the disease. Can we reliably conclude that the chances of survival are higher for men than for women?

The two samples here are men and women, with the response 'survived' or 'died' recorded for each of the men and each of the women.

Example 1.6 – Categorical Response Variable (More than two categories)

Thirty boys and thirty girls each name their favourite colour. Ten boys name blue; five brown; five red and ten black. Of the girls five name blue; six brown; eight red; ten black and one white. Do the girls have different preferences from the boys?

Here the two samples are boys and girls, while the response variable has the five categorical values: blue, brown, red, black, and white. Each of the boys and girls names only one colour. Thus, each person in the study has one 'score' on the explanatory variable (boy or girl) and one 'score' on the response variable, colour chosen.

Two Related Samples

Example 1.7 – Ordinal Response Variable

As part of a rehabilitation scheme for the mentally handicapped, fifteen men who have lived in a hospital for longer than ten years are rehoused in the community. They are rated on a social skills questionnaire both before they leave the hospital and after a year living in the community. The questionnaire provides a single numerical score that is supposed to reflect ability in social situations. Do these data suggest that living in the community has increased the men's social skills?

This is a two-sample situation, the two samples being before and after living in the community. Scores on the two samples are related since each man is assessed both before and after.

Example 1.8 – Categorical Response Variable (Two categories)

A theory of problem solving predicts that two particular problems, A and B, should be of equal difficulty. The problems are both given to 100 people and it is recorded whether each person solved or failed to solve them. If the theory is correct, most of the people should solve or fail to solve both problems; of those who solve only one problem, there should be as many who solve problem A only as there are who solve problem B only.

The two samples here are the two problems. We have related data since each person attempts both problems and the response for each problem is one of the two categories 'solve' or 'fail to solve'.

Several Independent Samples – Categorical Explanatory Variable

Example 1.9 – Ordinal Response Variable

As part of an investigation of the differences between four type-faces, forty people are asked to read a passage. The people are randomly divided into four groups of 10, each group being asked to read the passage typed in one of the type-faces. Time taken to read the passage is recorded for each person.

The explanatory variable in this example has four different categorical values, these being the four different type-faces. Each person reads the passage typed in only one style, so the four samples can reasonably be assumed independent, if the experiment is conducted properly. The response variable is the time taken to read the passage, which we can treat as ordinal data.

Example 1.10 – Categorical Response Variable (Two categories)

Responding to growing pressure from the anarchist lobby for complete decentralisation of all decision-making bodies, the Government decides to hold a referendum on whether Parliament should be dissolved. Three alternative ways of phrasing the question to be asked in the referendum are suggested. To test the implications of these alternative phrasings, a random sample of 3000 people is selected. 1000 of the people are asked the question in its first form; 1000 are asked the question in its second form and the final 1000 are asked the question in its third form. Each person answers by saying 'yes' or 'no'. Do the different ways of phrasing the question lead to different proportions of 'yes' responses?

The explanatory variable has three categorical values, these being the three ways of phrasing the question. Each person responds to only one form of the question and gives a single response, so the samples are independent. The response variable has the two values 'yes' and 'no'.

Example 1.11 – Categorical Response Variable (More than two categories)

If in the previous example the researcher had allowed the responses 'yes', 'no' or 'don't know', the response variable would now have three categorical values.

Several Independent Samples – Ordinal Explanatory Variable

Example 1.12 – Ordinal Response Variable

The reaction time of each of forty volunteers is measured after being given different dosages of a particular drug. Ten of the people received 5 mg of the drug, a further ten received 10 mg, ten received 15 mg, and the remainder were given 20 mg. Does reaction time increase with increasing dosage levels?

Each person is assessed under only one of the dosage level conditions, so we have four independent samples. The explanatory variable takes on the four different values determined by the dosage levels. Since we are interested in whether reaction time increases as the dosage level increases, the explanatory variable is best treated as an ordinal variable.

Example 1.13 – Categorical Response Variable (Two categories)

A theory predicts that, for young children, performance on a volume conservation task should improve with age. Thirty children, ten 5 year-olds, ten 6 year-olds and ten 7 year-olds, are tested on the task, and each is judged either to have or not to have conservation. Do the data support the theory?

The explanatory variable here takes the three values 5, 6, and 7 years old. We wish to know whether performance improves with age, so we treat the explanatory variable as ordinal. Each child either has or does not have conservation, so the response variable has just two categories.

Several Related Samples – Categorical Explanatory Variable

Example 1.14 – Ordinal Response Variable

One hundred students each attend three courses. At the end of the year they rate each course on a 100-point scale of enjoyment. Do the courses differ in student appeal?

The explanatory variable here has three categorical values, these being the names of the courses. Each student gives three ratings, one for each course, so the data are related.

Example 1.15 – Categorical Response Variable (Two categories)

The cat-lover of Example 1.3 tries a different method of comparing the four cat-foods. Ten cats volunteer to take part in this experiment. Each cat tries all four foods, one at a time, and the experimenter simply notes whether the cat eats or refuses to eat each of the foods.

The four cat-foods now form the four categorical values of the explanatory variable, while the response variable has the two categories 'eats' or 'does not eat'. The data are related since each cat tries each of the foods.

Several Related Samples – Ordinal Explanatory Variable

Example 1.16 – Ordinal Response Variable

Six people take part in a learning experiment. A list of items is presented on each of five trials. After presentation, each person recalls as much of the list as possible. The number of items correctly recalled on each trial is recorded. Do the people show evidence of learning?

In this example, the explanatory variable is the trial number, with five different values. We predict that if learning occurs, as the trial number increases, so should the number of items correctly recalled. We have related data, since each subject gives five responses, one for each trial. Number of items correctly recalled is an indicator of memory for the list, and we may treat it as an ordinal variable, i.e. the more items recalled, the better the memory. The explanatory variable is considered ordinal in this case, since we predict better recall as trial number increases.

Example 1.17 – Categorical Response Variable (Two categories)

Three tasks are given to each of ten people, and it is recorded whether each person succeeds or fails at the tasks. It is predicted that Task *A* should be easier than Task *B*, which should be easier than Task *C*.

The explanatory variable, type of task, is ordinal in this case because of the prediction we make that *A* should be better than *B* and *B* should be better than *C*. The response variable has the two categories, 'success' or 'failure'. The data are related, since each person attempts each of the three tasks.

One of the most important things to realize in choosing a statistical test is that the test selected depends on the question being asked of the data. This is what makes the choice of test difficult in most cases. The same data may frequently be analysed in several different ways, each way corresponding to a different question. This may most simply be illustrated with our Example 1.17, in which we were interested in testing the difference between three tasks. We treated the explanatory variable as ordinal in that example, since we wanted to test the ordered prediction that Task *A* should be the easiest and Task *C* the most difficult of the three. Had we not made that prediction there would be no sense in treating the explanatory variable as ordinal; we should then have a categorical explanatory variable, and the analysis would be asking the question whether there was any difference at all between the three tasks, not just a difference in the predicted direction.

1.7 THE LOGIC OF A STATISTICAL TEST

Null Hypothesis and Alternative Hypothesis

The logic used in the statistical tests that we shall be discussing is similar to that used in many courts of law, where the accused person is assumed to be innocent and the prosecutor must produce evidence that establishes guilt beyond a reasonable doubt. In carrying out a statistical test, we usually start by assuming that the effect we wish to demonstrate is absent and hope that the data we have collected will provide the evidence to establish beyond a reasonable doubt that the effect really is present.

Thus, in our study attempting to relate size of car driven to aggression, we wished to demonstrate that people who drive large cars tend to score high on the aggression questionnaire. In order to do this, we first assume there is no such relation. Having collected the data, a statistical test will allow us to state how likely the data were to have been obtained if there is no relation. If they were extremely unlikely, we conclude that our initial assumption of no relation was incorrect and that there really is a relation. In doing this, we are weighing the odds against our prediction, so that the evidence has to be really strong before we are prepared to say our prediction is correct.

The assumption that there is no relation is usually called the *null hypothesis*, since it nullifies our prediction. The effect we wish to demonstrate is called the *alternative hypothesis* or the *research hypothesis*. Carrying out a statistical test thus involves stating a sensible null hypothesis for the question being asked and assessing how likely the data were to have been obtained if the null hypothesis really is true. Only if the data were very unlikely to have been obtained do we conclude that the alternative hypothesis is true. In our example, the alternative hypothesis is that drivers of large cars score high on the aggression questionnaire, while the null hypothesis is that there is no relation between the two variables.

As another example, suppose I suggest a game to you which involves me tossing a coin – if the coin comes up tails I give you £5; if it comes up heads you give me £1. You might be rather suspicious of such a game, but suppose further that you have reason to believe I am very generous and eager to give my money away. Since you stand to gain a lot of money, you are prepared to give me the benefit of the doubt and play the game with me. We play the game three times and each time the coin shows heads. In such a situation you might start to suspect that my coin is weighted in a biased manner; this is your alternative hypothesis. As soon as you have good grounds for your alternative hypothesis, you will want to stop playing. The null hypothesis is that the coin is unbiased, so that heads and tails are equally likely to show. Even if the null hypothesis is true, it is quite likely that three heads in a row could occur, so you might be prepared to go on playing. By the time five heads in a row have been obtained the null hypothesis is starting to seem very unlikely to be true and most people would want to stop playing, concluding that the null hypothesis should be rejected in favour of the alternative hypothesis.

This example illustrates also that there is room for a lot of subjective judgement in all statistical decisions. Different people playing the game will probably not agree when to stop; some people will give up even after one or two heads have shown, while others will go on until seven or eight heads in a row turn up.

Type I and Type II Errors

In a court of law, there are two types of mistake that can be made. The first type is that an innocent person is convicted, while the second type is that a guilty person is acquitted. The two types of error have different consequences and costs associated with them. Most people would agree that the first type of error is worse than the second type, particularly when the sentences are tough. The possibility of the first type of error being made is one of the strongest and most frequently used arguments against capital punishment.

Both types of error can occur in science as well. The first type, known as a *Type I* error, involves falsely rejecting the null hypothesis. It would occur, for example, if we concluded from our data that there is a relation between size of car driven and aggression, when in fact there isn't. The second type, known as a *Type II* error, involves falsely accepting the null hypothesis. This would occur if our data led us to conclude that there is no relation between size of car driven and aggression, when in fact there is.

As in a law-court, we can never be certain about any conclusions we draw on the basis of statistical tests. What we attempt to do, however, is to keep the probability of making both types of error as low as possible. In addition, we attempt to estimate what these error rates are likely to be in any particular situation.

Simplified Example

To show how these ideas are used, I shall illustrate the main stages in constructing a statistical test using the simple coin-tossing example. These stages are common to all the statistical tests discussed in this book, so once you have appreciated the logic for this example, the ideas will carry over to all the other tests.

Suppose we agree to play the coin-tossing game four times, no matter what the outcomes are. This is a one-sample situation, since we obtain a single sample of four observations, with a two-category response, heads (H) or tails (T). The test we shall now proceed to construct is the Binomial Test that will be discussed in more detail in Section 3.4.

The first stage in constructing a statistical test appropriate for this situation is to list all the possible outcomes. This is done in Table 1.8. Now, if the coin is in fact unbiased, i.e. the null hypothesis is true, then each of these 16 possible outcomes is equally likely to be obtained. This means that each has a probability of 1/16 of occurring if the null hypothesis is true. On the other hand if the coin really is biased in favour of heads, i.e. the alternative hypothesis is true, then the outcomes at the top of Table 1.8 are more likely to occur than those at the bottom. Thus, the probabilities calculated in the null case will no longer be accurate.

Test Statistic – *B*

For our purposes, we are only interested in the relative number of heads and tails obtained, so outcome 2 (HHHT) gives no more information than outcome 3 (HHTH) or outcome 4 (HTHH) or outcome 5 (THHH). Each of these four outcomes has three heads and one tail; the only thing distinguishing them is the throw on which the tail was obtained. As long as we assume that the four throws are independent and the coin does not change its properties, these four outcomes

Table 1.8. The 16 possible outcomes for 4 trials of the coin-tossing game and associated values of B (number of heads)

	Trial				
	1	2	3	4	B
1.	H	H	H	H	4
2.	H	H	H	T	3
3.	H	H	T	H	3
4.	H	T	H	H	3
5.	T	H	H	H	3
6.	H	H	T	T	2
7.	H	T	H	T	2
8.	T	H	H	T	2
9.	H	T	T	H	2
10.	T	H	T	H	2
11.	T	T	H	H	2
12.	H	T	T	T	1
13.	T	H	T	T	1
14.	T	T	H	T	1
15.	T	T	T	H	1
16.	T	T	T	T	0

should be treated as equivalent. Similarly, outcomes 6 to 11 each have two heads and two tails and so give us identical information. For this reason, instead of continuing to talk in terms of the 16 possible outcomes, it is helpful to replace each outcome by a number reflecting the relative numbers of heads and tails obtained, this being the crucial information. Such a number is known as the *test statistic*.

In this case, we simply count the number of heads associated with each outcome. This gives the test statistic for this test, which we label B (for binomial). The relevant value of B is shown alongside each outcome in Table 1.8. (Notice that we could have chosen to count the number of tails instead and use this as the test statistic. This would give exactly the same test since it is reflecting exactly the same aspect of the outcomes as the number of heads.)

Null Distribution of B

As we have argued above, if the null hypothesis is true, each of the possible outcomes has a probability of 1/16 of occurring. Since we now wish to talk in terms of our test statistic B and not the individual outcomes, we can compute the probability associated with each value of B rather than that associated with each outcome. B takes the value 4 for only one outcome (HHHH), so the probability that $B = 4$ if the null hypothesis is true is just 1/16 or 0.0625. B takes the value 3 for 4 of the outcomes, so the probability that $B = 3$ is 4/16 or 0.25. The probability associated with each value of B can be worked out in this way and the results of these calculations are shown in Table 1.9. Such a table is known as the *null*

Table 1.9. The null distribution of B for 4 trials of the coin-tossing game

B	0	1	2	3	4
Probability	0.0625	0.2500	0.3750	0.2500	0.0625

distribution of B since it represents the probabilities associated with each possible value of B if the null hypothesis is true.

Decision Rule

The next stage is to choose a rule that we can use to decide either in favour of the null hypothesis or in favour of the alternative hypothesis. The arguments used in choosing such a rule go roughly as follows. We know from the null distribution that large values of B are relatively unlikely to occur if the null hypothesis is true. We also know that if the alternative hypothesis is true then large values of B *are* likely to occur. Therefore, one possible rule for our example might be that if we obtain, say, 3 or 4 heads, then we shall decide that the coin is biased (the alternative hypothesis); otherwise we shall decide that the coin is fair (the null hypothesis). Notice that using this rule means that we know how often we are likely to reject the null hypothesis by mistake; the null distribution tells us that a B of 3 or 4 can occur $0.2500 + 0.0625 = 0.3125$ or 31.25% of the time even if the null hypothesis is true. This value of 0.3125 therefore represents the probability of committing a Type I error and is normally referred to as the *significance level* of the test. It is usually labelled α, the Greek letter alpha.

In practice, the procedure described above is carried out in reverse order. We first decide on a significance level α that reflects what risk we are willing to take of making a Type I error. We then use the significance level to find a *critical value* of the test statistic B. The critical value is usually determined so that under the null hypothesis the probability of obtaining a value of B as large as this critical value or larger is equal to α. In our case, with $\alpha = 0.3125$, the critical value is 3, since the null distribution of B tells us that under the null hypothesis the probability of getting 3 or more heads is 0.3125. Our decision rule is therefore to reject the null hypothesis in favour of the alternative hypothesis if we actually obtain data associated with a B value greater than or equal to the critical value of 3 (i.e. if we get 3 or more heads in the 4 trials).

Significance Levels

For most practical purposes a significance level as high as 0.3125 would not generally be acceptable, since a 31% chance of committing a Type I error is too high. The actual level to use in practice depends on the experimenter's purpose. If, as here, the experiment is a strictly personal matter in which only you stand to gain or lose as a consequence of a wrong decision, then the significance level can be chosen to coincide with your own judgement of the costs entailed. In this case people not prepared to go on playing the game beyond the four trials agreed upon unless they were certain the null hypothesis is true would choose a high significance level. Those people who are happy to go on playing until they have very convincing evidence that the null hypothesis is false would choose a low significance level.

More often than not, however, the reason for carrying out an experiment is to convince others that your pet theory works. Thus if you wish to convince a judge and jury that the coin is biased, you would need to use a low significance level. While there are no hard and fast rules governing the choice of significance levels, most people would be prepared to accept a verdict in favour of the alternative hypothesis if a significance level as low as 0.05 or 0.01 is used.

If we had selected $\alpha = 0.05$ for our example, we should never reject the null hypothesis no matter what the outcome, since each of the possible values of B has a probability of at least 0.0625 of occurring by chance. With only four observations, each outcome is relatively likely to be obtained even if the null hypothesis is true, so none of the possible results would be surprising. To convince an impartial observer that the coin really is biased, we should collect sufficient evidence to enable us to use a low significance level.

Suppose we agreed to play the coin-tossing game five times instead of four. In this case, the possible outcomes will be different from those shown in Table 1.8 and consequently the null distribution of B will also differ. In general the null distribution will be different for different numbers of trials. The null distribution for this new example with 5 trials will in fact be as shown below.

B	0	1	2	3	4	5
Probability	0.031	0.156	0.313	0.313	0.156	0.031

This shows, for example, that the probability of getting as many as five heads is 0.031. Thus, by increasing the number of trials to five, we could use a sensibly small significance level such as 0.05, since it is actually possible to obtain results that have such a low probability. In this case, 5 would be the critical value for a test with $\alpha = 0.05$. Notice that there is no value of B associated with a probability exactly equal to the desired α of 0.05. Such a situation frequently occurs in the tests we shall be discussing. When this occurs, we choose the critical value to be that value of the test statistic with the largest probability smaller than α. Hence the critical value of 5 for a test with $\alpha = 0.05$. Had we chosen α to be 0.4 for this example, the critical value of B would be 4 (not 3) since the probability of obtaining a B of 4 or larger is 0.187 (= 0.156 + 0.31) while the probability of obtaining a B of 3 or larger is 0.5, which is larger than α.

These examples illustrate the fact that with very small amounts of data, none of the possible results are very surprising under the null hypothesis. By increasing the amount of data obtained, some of the more extreme results start to become very unlikely under the null hypothesis.

1.8 THE POWER OF A TEST

In discussing our simplified example above, we considered only Type I errors. There is also the possibility of making a Type II error, i.e. failing to reject the null hypothesis when it is false (acquitting the guilty). If we are able to keep the probability of a Type II error small, then we say we have a *powerful* test. A powerful test is thus one that has a large probability of rejecting the null hypothesis when it is actually false (convicting the guilty). Unfortunately, it is usually rather difficult to estimate the power of a test, so it will only be possible here to give some rough indications of the ways power can be varied. To give a complete coverage of the tests discussed later, we should need to take up the concept of power separately for each test. This will not be done because of the difficulty of computing power in all but the simplest cases. However, the discussion here should be adequate for most purposes. For a fuller discussion and further references the reader is referred to Lehmann (1975).

The probability of making a Type II error is normally labelled β, the Greek letter beta. Thus, when β is small, the power of the test is large, and vice versa. In some cases, it is helpful to put a numerical value on the power of a test; this value is given as $1 - \beta$.

The major ideas involved in estimating power can again be illustrated using the coin-tossing example of the previous section. The null distribution of B for five trials of the game is shown again in pictorial form in Figure 1.8(a), which also shows the critical value of 5 associated with a significance level of 0.05. With a critical value of 5, values to the right of the line will lead us to conclude that the null hypothesis is false. If the null hypothesis is in fact true, this conclusion will be wrong. On the other hand, the conclusion will be correct if the null hypothesis is false. But in this latter case, the null distribution will not be appropriate. One of the problems in calculating power is deciding what is the appropriate distribution. To do this we need to be more specific about the alternative hypothesis we wish to be able to detect. Suppose you believe I have obtained my coin from a dealer who makes coins that show heads three-quarters of the time, so that prob (H) = 3/4. (In general, of course, we should not have such specific knowledge about the alternative hypothesis.) If this represents the true state of affairs, then outcomes that have a large proportion of heads would be more likely than those having few heads. This means that low values of the test statistic B will be relatively unlikely, while higher values of B will be more likely. Thus, the null distribution will not be accurate and the true distribution of possible values of B will be as shown in Figure 1.8(b). (The way these probabilities are calculated is not important for present purposes, but the interested reader should be able to reconstruct them once the methods of Section 3.4 have been studied.) This is known as the *alternative* or *non-null distribution* of the test statistic. In this case, the critical value of 5 means that we shall correctly reject the null hypothesis 0.237 of the time if the coin is in fact biased in such a way that prob (H) = 3/4. The probability of accepting a false null hypothesis, i.e. the probability of a Type II error, is the sum of the probabilities to the left of the line representing the critical value, since if any of these

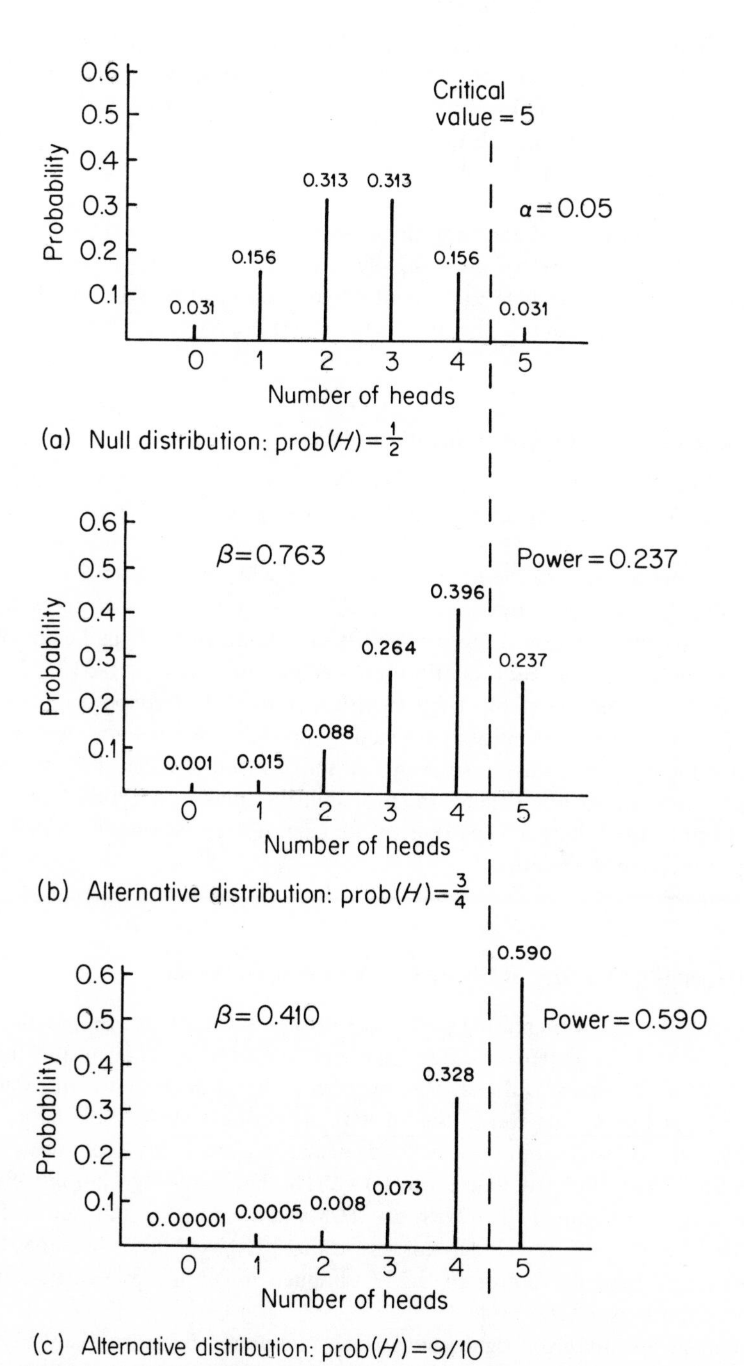

Figure 1.8. Null distribution and two possible alternative distributions of B for five trials of the coin-tossing game

values is obtained we conclude that there is not sufficient evidence to reject the null hypothesis. In this case, $\beta = 0.763$. This is rather a large value for β. Equivalently, we can say that the probability of $0.237 (1 - \beta)$ of rejecting a false null hypothesis represents a very low power. Ideally we should like to make the power as large as possible. In practice, power values of 0.90 or larger are thought of as being desirable.

There are three ways of changing the power of a test, which will be discussed in turn below in the context of our example. The first is to change the significance level. The second is to change the size of departure from the null hypothesis that you wish to be able to detect. The third is to change the number of observations.

Power Depends on the Choice of Significance Level

We can increase the power of our test by using a less stringent critical value. Thus if we had used a critical value of 3 instead of 5, we should have increased the power of the test from 0.237 to 0.897, since the probability of obtaining a B of 3 or larger if the alternative distribution (b) is true will be $0.264 + 0.396 + 0.237 = 0.897$. This has increased the power to a value nearly large enough to be acceptable, but it has also increased the probability of committing a Type I error. With a critical value of 3, the null distribution (a) tells us that $\alpha = 0.313 + 0.156 + 0.031 = 0.500$, an unacceptably large significance level. In terms of our law-court analogy, power is the probability of convicting the guilty. We can increase power by convicting more people, but by so doing we increase our chances of convicting the innocent. Thus, we have to balance the probability of making a Type I error against the probability of making a Type II error; we cannot decrease one of these without causing an increase in the other.

Power Depends on the Size of Effect That You Wish to Detect

The second way of increasing power is to resign ourselves to the possibility of detecting only gross departures from the null hypothesis. This means that we should have a more powerful test if we were content to detect only an extremely biased coin and were not too bothered with detecting a slightly biased coin. To see why this is so, suppose a second dealer makes coins that show heads nine-tenths of the time, so that prob (H) = 9/10. The resulting alternative hypothesis is shown in Figure 1.8(c). With $\alpha = 0.05$ and the corresponding critical value of 5, the power of the test under this new alternative hypothesis becomes 0.590, which is larger than the power of 0.237 obtained under the previous alternative hypothesis (with prob (H) = 3/4).

In general, for any given significance level, you would be more likely to detect the extremely biased coins made by the second dealer than the moderately biased coins made by the first.

Power Depends on the Number of Observations

The third way of increasing power is to collect more data. If you were prepared to play the coin-tossing game for eleven trials, the resulting null distribution and alternative distribution (calculated only for the first dealer, with prob (H) = 3/4) are shown in Figure 1.9. Using a significance level of 0.05, the critical value of B is 9, since the probability of getting 9 or more heads on eleven trials if the null hypothesis is true is 0.027 + 0.005 + 0.000 = 0.032, which is the closest we can get to an α of 0.05 in this situation. From the alternative distribution shown in Figure 1.9(b), we can see that this choice of significance level implies a power of 0.455, which is larger than the power of 0.237 for the same alternative with only five trials (Figure 1.8(b)).

This result holds in general, so that it is always possible to obtain a more powerful test by collecting more data.

The general conclusions about power drawn in this section apply to all the statistical tests discussed in this book. To illustrate how these conclusions can be used in practice, we need again to question the reason for carrying out the particular experiment.

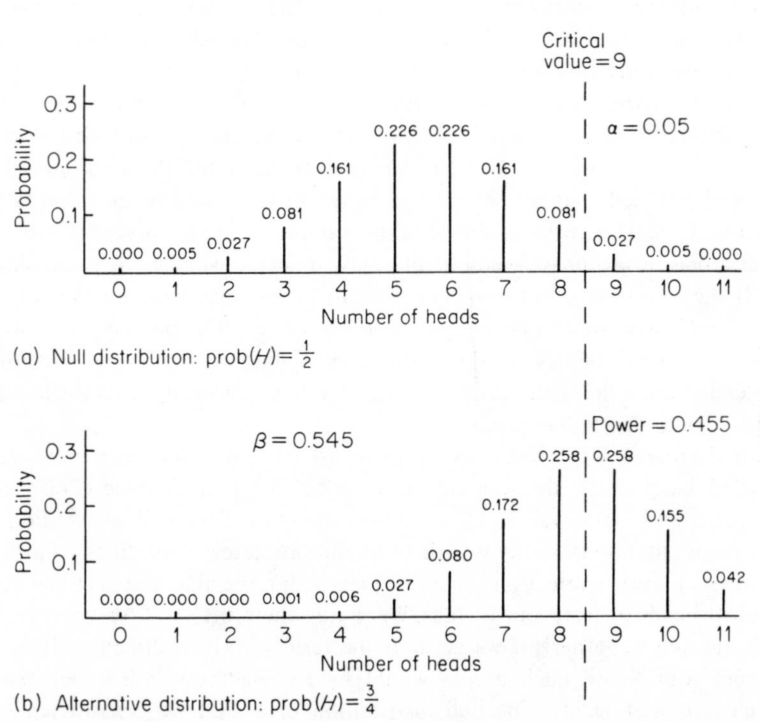

Figure 1.9. Null distribution and a possible alternative distribution of B for eleven trials of the coin-tossing game

If it costs a great deal of effort or money (as in our example it might) to collect a lot of data, but we still need a powerful test that will detect small effects (e.g. a very slightly biased coin), then the only possibility is to increase the significance level. This may be reasonable if we only have to persuade ourselves that the coin is biased, but we shall find it more difficult to convince impartial observers using a high significance level, since they can rightly claim that the results obtained have a large probability of occurring even if the coin is unbiased.

On the other hand, if we are particularly concerned to persuade others to accept an alternative hypothesis, we should start by setting a sufficiently low significance level (such as 0.05). If the effect we wish to be able to detect is large (such as an extremely biased coin) we may still have a test powerful enough to detect it even with relatively few observations. If the effect we wish to be able to detect is small (such as a slightly biased coin) the only way of ensuring that our test is powerful enough to detect it is to collect a large amount of data.

1.9 ONE-TAILED AND TWO-TAILED TESTS

In our coin-tossing example we were only interested in detecting whether the coin was biased in favour of heads. This was our alternative hypothesis and the decision rule we constructed reflected this. We decided to reject the null hypothesis that the coin was unbiased only if we obtained large values of B. Using this decision rule there are only two possible conclusions that may be drawn from any given set of data: *either* the coin is biased in favour of heads *or* there is no evidence that the coin is biased in favour of heads. We should never be able to conclude that the coin is biased in favour of tails. Our alternative hypothesis and the associated decision rule have assumed that we should not be at all interested in detecting a bias in favour of tails. This is reasonable for this example, since we only wish to be able to detect a bias in favour of heads to allow us to decide whether to go on playing or not. If the coin favours heads we should want to stop playing, since this will cost us money; otherwise we should be quite content to continue playing, since we stand to win a lot of money whether the coin is fair or whether it favours tails. (Remember the rule of the game was that I give you £5 if the coin shows tails and you give me £1 if it shows heads.)

Our alternative hypothesis has led us to use what is known as a *one-tailed test*, so called because the decision rule is to reject the null hypothesis only if large values of B were obtained, i.e. values at the upper tail of the null distribution.

In many situations we may wish to be able to detect departures from the null hypothesis in either direction. Thus, we may wish to be able to detect bias either in favour of heads or in favour of tails. We should therefore want our decision rule to reject the null hypothesis if we get extreme results in either direction. If we tossed the coin four times, such a rule would be to reject the null hypothesis if we obtained 0 or 4 heads. The null distribution of B that we constructed for this situation by considering all the possible outcomes (listed in Table 1.8) is still appropriate. The null distribution in Table 1.9 shows that the significance level associated with this new rule is 0.1250, since the probability of getting no heads and the probability of getting 4 heads are both equal to 0.0625. Thus we have a 12½% chance of falsely rejecting the null hypothesis. With this decision rule we are using both the upper and lower tails of the null distribution. For this reason, we have constructed what is known as a *two-tailed test.* Notice that we have two critical values, 0 and 4, for a two-tailed test, instead of the single critical value used for a one-tailed test. The two critical values are generally chosen to reflect equal departure from the null hypothesis in either direction. The values may be chosen straightforwardly by noticing that the mean of the null distribution in Table 1.9 is 2: the values 0 and 4 are both two points away from the mean, but in opposite directions. So if we use the critical value of 4 for the upper tail, we also use the critical value of 0 for the lower tail. Similarly, if 3 were the upper tail critical value, then 1 would be the relevant lower tail value, since both depart by one from the mean of the distribution.

To use a two-tailed test in practice, the standard procedure is to select the significance level α first and then choose the critical values as above in such a way that the combined probability of getting a value of B larger than or equal to the upper tail value or smaller than or equal to the lower tail value is α. In some cases, we may not be able to find critical values such that the combined probability is exactly equal to our desired α: we then choose critical values so that the combined probability is as close as possible to α without being larger.

To illustrate, suppose we played the coin-tossing game for eleven trials. Then the null distribution is given in Figure 1.9(a). If we wish to be able to detect bias in the coin in either direction, we need a two-tailed test. Suppose we select α to be 0.05. We now proceed to find the critical values. Let's try out a few until we reach the most appropriate one. If 11 is the upper tail value, then 0 will be the lower tail value, since both are equidistant from the mean of 5½ for this distribution. The probability of getting as many as 11 heads or as few as 0 heads is $0.000 + 0.000 = 0.000$, which is less than α. So we can try a less extreme possibility. Selecting 10 as the upper tail value implies that the lower tail value should be 1, with associated probability of $0.000 + 0.005 + 0.005 + 0.000 = 0.010$, which is still less than α. Trying 9 as the upper tail value gives 2 as the lower tail value, with associated probability of $0.000 + 0.005 + 0.027 + 0.027 + 0.005 + 0.000 = 0.064$. This time, the probability is larger than α, so we have gone too far. The relevant critical values associated with a significance level of 0.05 are therefore 1 and 10, so the decision rule is to reject the null hypothesis that the coin is biased if we obtain *either* 1 or fewer heads *or* 10 or more heads in eleven trials.

Notice that the decision rule for a *one-tailed test* with $\alpha = 0.05$ is to reject the null hypothesis if 9 or more heads are obtained (see Figure 1.9(a)). So had we actually obtained 9 heads, this one-tailed test would lead us to reject the null hypothesis, concluding that the coin is biased in favour of heads. For a two-tailed test, the same outcome with the same significance level would lead us to accept the null hypothesis, and we should have to conclude that there is no evidence that the coin is biased. The reason for this is that the two-tailed test is looking for evidence of bias in either direction and so cannot be as sensitive in any particular direction as the one-tailed test. Because of this difference between the one-tailed and two-tailed versions of the test, it is crucial that the decision as to which of the two to use should be made independently of the actual data obtained. Otherwise, you would be open to the charge of biasing the test in your favour. In the original version of our example, it was natural to use a one-tailed test, since we were interested only in detecting whether the coin favoured heads and were not interested in the possibility of it favouring tails. In general, if you are unsure in any particular case whether to use a one- or a two-tailed test, it is wise always to choose the two-tailed version, since this is more conservative. As with the choice of significance level, the best guide is to decide whether you will be able to convince an impartial observer that your choice is reasonable.

1.10 ESTIMATING THE SIZE OF AN EFFECT

In carrying out an experiment we frequently wish to go beyond merely demonstrating that an effect exists; we also want to know how large the effect is. Thus we may wish not merely to state that the coin is biased but also to estimate how biased it is. This may be important for the conclusions we draw, since one of the implications of our discussion of power in Section 1.8 is that, with enough observations, we should be able to detect even a slight departure from the null hypothesis. Such a slight departure, although statistically significant, may be totally unimportant for the question being asked. If our coin is only very slightly biased (prob (H) = 51/100, say), we should probably be happy to continue playing with it even if a statistical test detects this slight bias. In other words, the substantive significance of a test may differ from the statistical significance. Calculating an estimate of the size of an effect may help us assess the substantive significance of a result.

Notice that we can never know exactly what the probability of heads is for our coin, since we only observe a small sample of coin-tosses, so we must be content with an estimate. This is a general problem. We want to be able to estimate the size of an effect in the population from knowledge of only the sample data. We shall discuss only the simplest problems of estimation in this book, such as estimating the difference between two treatments or the strength of an association. In this section I shall introduce very briefly some of the basic ideas.

A natural way of estimating the probability of heads for our coin is to use the proportion of heads actually obtained in the sample of observations. Thus, if we obtained ten heads and one tail in eleven trials, our estimate of the probability of obtaining a head with this coin would be 10/11. This turns out to be a good way of estimating the true probability in this case, but such obvious methods may not always be best.

There is no easy answer to what constitutes a good way of estimating an effect, but several criteria are commonly used. Before turning to them, it is helpful to distinguish the method of obtaining an estimate from the estimate itself. The method is referred to as an *estimator*. In our example, the *estimator* is 'calculate the proportion of heads'; the *estimate* is 10/11.

An Estimator Should Be Unbiased

One commonly used criterion for a good estimator is that it should be *unbiased*. Suppose we play our coin-tossing game many times, each time playing it for eleven trials. Each time we play, we estimate the probability of a head for this coin by calculating the proportion of heads obtained in the eleven trials. These estimates will not all be the same, but on average they should be equal to the true probability. If this is so, the estimator is said to be unbiased. Our estimator in this case is in fact unbiased, so we can be confident that even though the estimate we obtain from one sample may not be exactly right, on average we should get close to the true value; overestimates will occur as frequently as underestimates.

As another example, suppose we wish to estimate the mean length of the words in Rex Stout's book, but cannot be bothered to count the lengths of all the words. If we take a random sample of words from the book, the obvious estimator is to calculate the mean of the sample. This again is an unbiased estimator. In general the mean of the sample provides an unbiased estimate of the mean of the population. But the sample median is also an unbiased estimator of the population mean, so on average calculating the median value for our sample of words will give us a good idea of the mean word-length of the population. In this case, we have two ways of estimating the population mean, both of which are unbiased, so we shall have to use other criteria for choosing between them. We need to choose between them, since they will not always give the same answer.

As an example of a biased estimator, suppose we wish to estimate the variance of the word-lengths in the book. In this case, calculating the variance of the sample gives a biased estimator, since it tends to underestimate the true variance. We can obtain an unbiased estimator by multiplying the sample variance by $n/(n-1)$, where n is the sample size; this has the effect of increasing the estimates and thereby overcomes the bias towards underestimation.

An Estimator Should Be Efficient

A second criterion for a good estimator is that it should be *efficient*. This is in effect a guarantee that any particular estimate will not be wildly out. If we played our coin-tossing game many times, each time obtaining an estimate for prob (H), these estimates will not always be the same. Calculating the standard deviation of these estimates will give us an idea of how close any particular estimate is likely to be to the true value. An estimator is said to be efficient if this standard deviation is small. Because the standard deviation of an estimate obtained from repeated samples is commonly required, it is convenient to have a special name for this quantity. It is usually called the *standard error*. Thus an efficient estimator is one for which the standard error is small.

This is not an absolute criterion, since we have not said how small the standard error should be, but it does allow us to compare two estimators in some circumstances. For example, in many situations, the sample mean tends to be a more efficient estimator of the population mean than the sample median, although there are situations for which the reverse is true (see, for example, Bradley, 1968, pp. 20–21).

An Estimator Should Make Use of All the Information Available

Had we chosen to estimate prob (H) after playing our game for eleven trials by using only the proportion of heads in the first five trials, then we are ignoring a lot of potentially useful information. Our original suggestion of using the proportion of heads in all eleven trials will provide a better estimator, since it uses all the available information. This criterion for a good estimator is usually referred to as the criterion of *sufficiency*.

An Estimator Should Be Consistent

A further criterion is that the estimator should be *consistent.* This means that the estimator should get increasingly better as the sample size increases. Thus we expect to get a better estimate of prob (H) if we play the game for 100 trials than if we play it for only 10 trials.

If, instead of counting the proportion of heads across all the trials observed, we used as our estimate the proportion of heads in the first five trials only, then the estimate would not be better for 100 trials of the game than for 10. This alternative estimator is not consistent (as well as not making use of all the information).

The sample mean and median are both consistent estimators of the population mean.

An Estimator Should Be Resistant

The final criterion is that the estimator should be *resistant*. This means that it should not be affected too much by gross errors in the data. For example, in measuring reaction times, it frequently happens that several unusually large times are recorded during a session. These large times result from factors such as lack of attention and so may not accurately reflect the process we are interested in. If we want to estimate the mean of the population of reaction times, we will tend to overestimate the true value if we use the mean of the sample, since we know from Section 1.1 that the mean is greatly affected by outlying observations. The median provides a better estimator here since it is not so greatly affected by outliers. In such a situation, then, the median is a more resistant estimator than the mean.

The criteria mentioned above provide useful ways of evaluating estimators, but they should not be regarded as necessary properties for all estimators. In some situations, it might be preferable to use a biased estimator rather than an unbiased one if, for example, the biased estimator is more efficient than the only available unbiased one, since it may then give a more precise estimate despite being biased. In this book, we shall pay particular attention to resistant estimators, since gross errors occur so frequently in practice that it is important to stress this criterion.

I have introduced these ideas only to make you aware of some of the things that need to be considered in choosing an estimator for a particular problem. You should also by now realize that the most obvious estimator may not always be the best. A complete understanding of the ideas is not necessary to be able to use the estimators introduced later on in the book. For those interested in going beyond the very brief discussion given here, there is fuller coverage in the books by Wonnacott and Wonnacott (1972, pp. 141–161) and Hays (1963, Chapter 7).

1.11 PARAMETRIC AND NONPARAMETRIC STATISTICS

There is generally a large number of statistical techniques available for analysing any given set of data. I have chosen to concentrate in this book on those techniques known as *nonparametric* or alternatively as *distribution-free*. These techniques may be contrasted with others known as *parametric* techniques. Parametric techniques make a large number of assumptions regarding the nature of the underlying population distribution; for example, in our car-driving and aggression study, they will make specific assumptions about the entire population of car drivers, not just the sample under investigation. Thus, if we were able to obtain scores from the whole population, parametric techniques will only be strictly valid if the population frequency distribution has a particular specified shape. By their very nature, such assumptions are frequently untestable, so in using parametric techniques of data analysis we are taking a gamble. If the population assumptions are correct or approximately correct, then we should have a very good test and in most cases parametric techniques would be preferable to their nonparametric counterparts. On the other hand, if the population assumptions are false, then a nonparametric test may well give us a more accurate result. Nonparametric tests make relatively few assumptions about the nature of the population distribution (hence the alternative name distribution-free), and so they are widely applicable.

A further advantage of nonparametric methods over parametric methods is that they are generally very easy to understand. A knowledge of only the most elementary mathematics is all that is necessary to gain a relatively full understanding of most nonparametric techniques.

The major disadvantage of nonparametric techniques is that they are not readily applicable to complex experiments in which a large number of variables are manipulated, whereas parametric techniques such as the analysis of variance are easily usable in such situations.

For those readers interested in using analysis of variance, Keppel (1973) gives a very readable and complete account of the basic methods of interest to social scientists. For those familiar with analysis of variance and other parametric techniques, Bradley (1968, Chapter 2) gives a detailed comparison of nonparametric and parametric statistics.

1.12 SOME MORE NOTATION

Apart from the summation sign Σ introduced in Section 1.1, we shall also make use of some other convenient pieces of notation.

The *inequality* signs $<$, $>$, $\leqslant$ and $\geqslant$ will be used quite a lot, so it's worth getting to grips with them as soon as possible. They allow us to say things like '4 is less than 5' or 'the first number is less than or equal to the second number', without writing it out in full. Their interpretation is as follows. For any two numbers, say x and y, we write,

$x < y$ for 'x is less than y'; e.g. $4 < 5$;

$x \leqslant y$ for 'x is less than or equal to y'; e.g. $4 \leqslant 5$;

$x > y$ for 'x is greater than y'; e.g. $5 > 4$;

$x \geqslant y$ for 'x is greater than or equal to y'; e.g. $5 \geqslant 4$.

People frequently get confused about which way round to write these signs; it is useful to remember that the tip of the arrow always points to the smaller number – thus, in $4 < 5$, the tip of the arrow is pointing at 4.

The inequality signs will be used mainly to say things like 'the probability of selecting a word at random of 10 or more letters long is 0.028'. This statement would be written

$$\text{prob (word-length} \geqslant 10) = 0.028$$

We shall also occasionally make use of *factorial* notation when we want to say things like 'multiply 4, 3, 2, and 1 together' or 'multiply all the numbers less than or equal to 100 together'. We simply write the largest of the numbers being multiplied followed by an exclamation mark. Thus,

$$4! = 4 \times 3 \times 2 \times 1 = 24$$

$$100! = 100 \times 99 \times 98 \times 97 \times \ldots \times 3 \times 2 \times 1$$

These expressions are read '4-factorial' and '100-factorial'. In general, for any number N, we have

$$N\text{-factorial} = N! = N \times (N-1) \times (N-2) \times \ldots \times 3 \times 2 \times 1$$

The use of the factorial notation saves writing out all the terms on the right.

Finally, the notation for ***absolute value*** will occasionally be used to say 'ignore the sign of this result'. For example, if we want to subtract two numbers, say x and y, and ignore the sign of the result, we write $|x - y|$. If $x = 5$ and $y = 6$, we have $|x - y| = 1$. If $x = 6$ and $y = 5$, we also have $|x - y| = 1$.

1.13 EXERCISES

Section 1.1

1. For each of the following, state whether what is being measured leads to continuous or discrete data.
   (a) The time taken to cook a meal.
   (b) The weight lost by a person on a slimming course.

(c) The number of problems solved in an hour.
(d) The time taken to cook a meal, measured correct to the nearest five minutes.
(e) The number of moves in a chess game.
(f) The length of a piece of material.
(g) Whether a piece of material is longer or shorter than 6 cm.

2. Twenty people were each asked to state the number of times they had visited a doctor's surgery in the previous twelve months. Their responses were as follows: 0, 1, 6, 5, 3, 2, 2, 5, 5, 6, 0, 0, 1, 4, 4, 0, 6, 5, 5, 2.
   (a) Construct a frequency distribution and a relative frequency distribution for these data.
   (b) What proportion of people visited a doctor more than 5 times?
   (c) Compute the mean, median and mode of the data.
   (d) Compute the range and the standard deviation.
3. (a) Calculate the mean and variance of the following set of scores: 1, 2, 2, 4, 6.
   (b) Add 3 to each of the scores in (a) and calculate the mean and variance of the new scores.
   (c) What effect does adding a constant value to each score have on the mean?
   (d) What effect does adding a constant have on the variance?
   (e) Multiply each of the scores in (a) by 2 and calculate the mean and variance of the new scores.
   (f) Multiply each of the scores in (a) by 3 and calculate the mean and variance of the new scores.
   (g) What effect does multiplying a set of scores by a constant have on the mean?
   (h) What effect does multiplying a set of scores by a constant have on the variance?
4. The time taken, in seconds, to solve a problem for each of 25 people is as follows: 15, 19, 25, 26, 29, 31, 32, 36, 37, 38, 40, 42, 43, 44, 47, 47, 48, 49, 49, 53, 58, 59, 59, 60, 64.
   (a) Construct a frequency distribution for these data, using a class-interval of 10 seconds.
   (b) Draw a histogram to represent the frequency distribution.
   (c) Calculate the mean and variance for these data.
   (d) What is the median score?

Section 1.2

5. Suppose one of the people of Exercise 2 were selected at random:
   (a) What is the probability of selecting a person who did not visit a doctor?
   (b) What is the probability of selecting a person who visited a doctor more than 3 times?
6. For the data of Exercise 4:
   (a) What is the probability of a randomly selected person taking longer than 30 seconds to solve the problem?

(b) What is the probability of a randomly selected person taking either less than 25 seconds or more than 60 seconds?

(c) Suppose two different people are selected. What is the probability of both of them taking longer than 60 seconds to solve the problem?

(d) What is the probability of both of them taking longer than 58 seconds?

Section 1.4

7. For each of the following studies, decide whether it is best described as a correlational study or an experimental study.

(a) The body images of 12 anorexic women and 12 non-anorexic women are compared in an attempt to assess whether the anorexic women have more distorted body images than the non-anorexics.

(b) In a study of the relation between alcohol intake and reaction time, half of a sample of 50 people are randomly selected to be given the equivalent of two double whiskies while the remainder are given the equivalent of a single whisky. One hour after imbibing the alcohol, the reaction time of each person is measured.

(c) In a study investigating the potential benefit of wearing car seat-belts, 1000 accidents were classified according to whether the people involved were wearing seat-belts and also according to whether they sustained fatal injuries.

CHAPTER 2

Independence is the first condition of dialogue between people

Graffiti in Paris, May 1968

Tests for Two Independent Samples – Ordinal or Two Category Response Variable

In this chapter we shall discuss two tests that are applicable when two independent samples of data have been collected and when the response variable may be thought of as either ordinal or categorical with two categories (see Examples 1.4 and 1.5 of Chapter 1). A discussion of the more general categorical case when there are more than two categories of response (see Example 1.6) will be postponed until Chapter 8. The most important assumption common to each of these tests is that of independence. Each person in the experiment must contribute only one score on the response variable and one score on the explanatory variable, and should not be able to influence the scores of any other person.

This chapter and the ones to follow have the same format. Each test is introduced with a grossly oversimplified example that is used to illustrate the rationale of the test in detail. At the end of each section some more realistic examples are worked through to suggest how the test may most straightforwardly be carried out in practice and how the results of the test should be presented.

2.1 THE WILCOXON RANK-SUM TEST – ORDINAL RESPONSE VARIABLE

The *Rank-Sum Test*, devised by Frank Wilcoxon, is one of the most frequently used of the tests presented in this book. An exactly equivalent test was also devised by Mann and Whitney, so you will sometimes see the test described below referred to as the *Mann–Whitney Test*. The test is normally used to decide whether the response scores from one of the samples tend to be higher than those from the other. In other words, the test attempts to decide whether the two sets of scores come from the same population (the null hypothesis) or whether they come from two populations that differ in location (the alternative hypothesis). The test may in fact pick up differences between the two populations other than a difference in location. However, it is particularly sensitive to location differences and so provides a simple method of testing for such differences. As we shall see, it assumes that the data collected are independent and that the scores on the response variable consist of ordinal data which are continuous. This means that each person in the study should provide us with a single score on the response variable and all the resulting response scores should be orderable with no ties. We shall discuss what happens when ties actually occur in Section 2.3.

Simplified Example

Suppose we wish to compare two methods of teaching reading, Method *A* and Method *B*, to see whether one tends to be more effective than the other. We take a random sample of five from a population of children who cannot read and randomly select three of these children to be taught by Method *A* while the other two are taught by Method *B*. At the end of the course, we assess the five children's reading abilities on a reading test, with large numbers indicating greater ability. The scores obtained are shown below.

Method *A*	Method *B*
70	80
90	100
50	

In this example, the explanatory variable is method of teaching, which has the two possible 'scores', Method *A* and Method *B*. The response variable consists of the scores on the reading test. It will be helpful at this stage to introduce some simple notation. First, we shall call the total number of children taking part in the experiment n: in our case, $n = 5$. The number of children in the larger sample (i.e. number taught by Method *A*) will be called t_1 and the number in the smaller sample (i.e. number taught by Method *B*) will be called t_2: in our case, $t_1 = 3$ and $t_2 = 2$. Obviously, $t_1 + t_2 = n$.

For the Rank-Sum Test to be appropriate, the independence assumption must hold. If the children taught by Method *A* were taught by the same teacher in the same class, while the other children were taught by different teachers, the scores of the *A* children might best be considered dependent. In such a case, the Rank-Sum Test could give misleading results. For the results not to be misleading, each of the children must have been taught in an equivalent manner and the score of one child should not influence in any way the score of any other child.

If the reading test used in this example is at all adequate, it may be reasonable to regard it as providing an ordering of the five children in terms of reading ability; a child who scores higher than another might sensibly be regarded as being a better reader. So the scores on the response variable may be assumed to be ordinal. Further, it seems appropriate to regard reading ability as a continuous variable. If two children scored identically on the test, we might still wish to say that it is possible for one of them to be a better reader than the other, but that the test is not sensitive enough to reflect this difference. For the time being, however, we shall assume that identical scores cannot occur; I shall suggest what to do when ties occur in Section 2.3.

Rather than collecting the scores of the five children on the reading test, we could simply have rank ordered the children in terms of reading ability, noting by careful observation which of the five children was the poorest reader at the end of the course, which was the next poorest and so on. Either method of providing scores on the response variable would satisfy the ordinal requirements of the Rank-Sum Test, even though the two methods have different implications. For example, reliable tests of reading are difficult to construct and so the conclusions drawn from the first method of collecting the data might have to do more with the properties of the reading test than with differences between the two methods of teaching. On the other hand, observational techniques may be unreliable in different ways. With such techniques, care must be taken that the person assessing reading ability does so in a 'blind' manner, not knowing which child has been taught by which method.

No matter which method of collecting the data was used, we can string the reading scores out in increasing order and assign a rank to each score; the score with the lowest rank is the one obtained by the poorest reader and the score with the highest rank was obtained by the best reader. Each score is also labelled A or B according to whether that reading score was associated with a child taught by Method A or Method B. This is done below:

Reading Score	50	70	80	90	100
Rank	1	2	3	4	5
Teaching Method	A	A	B	A	B

Suppose that the two methods have no differential effect, i.e. suppose that the null hypothesis is true. In this case, a child's reading score and hence the rank assigned to the child is determined solely by reading ability, so that the ranking of the children does not depend on which of them were taught by Method A and which by Method B. We may therefore think of a rank being attached to each child even before the assignments to Method A and Method B are made. Thus, if the null hypothesis is correct, the rank scores associated with Method B are determined simply by the random assignment of two children to be taught by that method. Since the assignment was random, any two of the five children, and hence any two of the five scores, could have been selected. Each possible selection can then be thought of as labelling two of the rank scores Method B and the other three Method A. The results of all possible such selections are shown in Table 2.1. The pattern of results actually obtained in our simplified example forms the second row of this table. Since the two children receiving Method B were chosen at random, it follows that this pattern was as likely to have been obtained as any of the other patterns. This means that each of the 10 possible patterns of results has a probability of 1/10 of occurring if the null hypothesis is true. On the other hand, suppose that one of the methods really is superior in that it leads to higher reading scores. This is the

Table 2.1. The 10 possible patterns of results when $n = 5$, $t_1 = 3$, $t_2 = 2$

	Rank of response variable						
	1	2	3	4	5	R	S
1.	*A*	*A*	*A*	*B*	*B*	9	6
2.	*A*	*A*	*B*	*A*	*B*	8	4
3.	*A*	*B*	*A*	*A*	*B*	7	2
4.	*A*	*A*	*B*	*B*	*A*	7	2
5.	*A*	*B*	*A*	*B*	*A*	6	0
6.	*B*	*A*	*A*	*A*	*B*	6	0
7.	*A*	*B*	*B*	*A*	*A*	5	−2
8.	*B*	*A*	*A*	*B*	*A*	5	−2
9.	*B*	*A*	*B*	*A*	*A*	4	−4
10.	*B*	*B*	*A*	*A*	*A*	3	−6

alternative hypothesis. In this case, even though the children bring different abilities to the experiment, we should expect the ranks of the children taught by the better method to be higher. Table 2.1 will still reflect the patterns of results that are possible, but we should expect those patterns at the top or bottom of the table to be more likely to occur than those in the middle. Thus the probability of 1/10 calculated for each pattern in the null case will no longer be accurate.

Test Statistic – *S*

Instead of continuing to talk about patterns of results, we wish to find a test statistic that reflects just how much larger or smaller the *B* ranks are than the *A* ranks.

The first step towards obtaining a test statistic for the Rank-Sum Test is to find the sum of the ranks associated with children in the smaller sample, i.e. those taught by Method *B*. This is done in the column labelled R in Table 2.1 for the 10 possible patterns of results in our example. In the first pattern, the *B* children have ranks 4 and 5, so $R = 4 + 5 = 9$. In pattern 5, the *B* children have ranks 2 and 4, so $R = 6$. These rank-sums adequately reflect the differences in the patterns of results – hence the name of the test. Patterns with high values of R occur when the *B* children score higher than the *A* children, while patterns with low values of R have the *B* children scoring lower. Patterns with the *A*'s and *B*'s most completely jumbled (i.e. patterns 5 and 6) are associated with intermediate values of R.

R is frequently used as the test statistic for the Rank-Sum Test. However, it is more convenient to go a little further and use a test statistic that reflects the amount by which the value of R deviates from the mean of the possible values. Now the mean of the possible values of R is simply $(9 + 8 + 7 + 7 + 6 + 6 + 5 + 5 + 4 + 3)/10$ or 6. Our test statistic is then given by twice the amount by which the value of R deviates from this mean value. We label this test statistic S and the values of S for each of the 10 possible patterns are shown in the final column of

Table 2.1. Thus the S value of 6 associated with pattern 1 is given by $2 \times (9 - 6)$. The main reason S is useful as a test statistic is that the most obviously jumbled patterns of results end up with values close to or equal to zero, while patterns more in line with the alternative hypothesis receive either large positive or large negative values of S, as can be seen in Table 2.1. Large positive values will occur if Method B is better than Method A, while large negative values will occur if Method A is better than Method B.

In general, it is helpful to have a way of calculating S for any pattern that does not depend on knowing all the values of R, which we needed to know to compute the mean. Such a method is given by the formula

$$S = 2R - t_2(n + 1),$$

where n is the total number of scores and t_2 is the number of scores in the smaller sample. In our case $n = 5$ and $t_2 = 2$, so the S values are given by $S = 2R - 12$. Thus, the S value for pattern 1 is $2 \times 9 - 12 = 6$, while that for pattern 9 is $2 \times 4 - 12 = -4$.

It is worth noting that S is a discrete variable even though the response scores on which it is based were assumed to be continuous. Because we have assumed that the response scores are continuous, tied values cannot occur and so the patterns of results shown in Table 2.1 are the only possible ones. This means that our test statistic S can take only the discrete values −6, −4, −2, 0, 2, 4, and 6. It is not possible with continuous data to obtain an S of 4½, for example.

Null Distribution of S

As we have argued above, if the null hypothesis is true, each of the 10 possible patterns of results recorded in Table 2.1 is equally likely to have occurred, and so each has a probability of 1/10 of occurring. We can therefore immediately write down the null distribution of S for this situation, as shown in Table 2.2; for example, the probability that $S = 0$ is 2/10 or 0.2, since S takes the value 0 for two of the 10 equally likely patterns.

We can now use this null distribution to complete our test following the procedure outlined in Chapter 1. To do this we need to decide whether to use a one- or a two-tailed test and to choose a significance level. For our example a two-tailed test is appropriate, since we are interested in identifying situations resulting in either abnormally large or abnormally small values of S, i.e. we are interested both in the possibility of Method A being the more effective and in the possibility of Method B being the more effective . Suppose we choose a significance level of 0.05, which is a reasonable choice for this example where we might need such a small probability of making a Type I error to be able to convince anyone that

Table 2.2. Null distribution of S for the case $t_1 = 3$, $t_2 = 2$

S	−6	−4	−2	0	2	4	6
Probability	0.1	0.1	0.2	0.2	0.2	0.1	0.1

the methods are differentially effective. With $\alpha = 0.05$, the null distribution of S in Table 2.2 shows that there are no relevant critical values With such small sample sizes as $t_1 = 3$ and $t_2 = 2$, none of the possible patterns of results would be surprising even if there were no difference between the two methods, each of the S values having a probability of at least 0.1 of occurring by chance.

Had we been prepared to use a two-tailed test with a significance level as large as 0.2, the relevant critical values of S would be 6 and –6. Our decision would then be to reject the null hypothesis if we obtained a value of S as large as 6 (or larger) or if we obtained a value of S as small as –6 (or smaller). The value of S actually obtained was 4, so even with such a large significance level as 0.2, we should not reject the null hypothesis. We should need to choose a significance level as large as 0.4 (for which the critical values of S are shown in Table 2.2 to be 4 and –4) before being able to reject the null hypothesis in this case.

Thus, for any reasonable choice of significance level, we should not reject the null hypothesis for our example data. We therefore conclude that there is no reliable evidence that the two methods of teaching differ..

To illustrate the use of a one-tailed test, suppose we had carried out the same study to compare a new method of teaching reading (Method *B*) with a standard method (Method *A*). If *B* is better than *A*, we might be prepared to use it as the standard method in future; but if *A* is better than *B* this has no more consequences for action than if there were no difference, since in either case we should probably not replace *A* as the standard method. In such a situation, a one-tailed test would be appropriate. We wish to detect only whether *B* is better than *A*, so our attention focuses on the upper tail of the null distribution of S since large positive values of S are associated with *B* being better than *A* (see Table 2.1). As in the two-tailed case, there is no critical value corresponding to a sensibly small significance level such as 0.05. To be able to reject the null hypothesis for our example data with $S = 4$, using a one-tailed test, we should need to use a significance level as large as 0.2. As this example illustrates, with a one-tailed test, the decision whether to use an upper tail or a lower tail version depends on whether the prediction being tested leads us to expect large positive or large negative values of S. If the prediction implies large positive values of S then an upper tail test should be used. If the prediction implies large negative values then a lower tail test should be used.

Table of the Null Distribution of *S* (Appendix Table A)

The null distribution of S is determined by the sample sizes, t_1 and t_2. If $t_1 = 3$ and $t_2 = 2$, then Table 2.2 shows the appropriate null distribution; but if $t_1 = 3$ and $t_2 = 3$ Table 2.2 is not appropriate since Table 2.1 will no longer show the possible patterns of results. Therefore, to carry out a test with different sample sizes, we should need to go through the whole tedious procedure of constructing an appropriate null distribution before making our decision rule. However, to make the decision rule, we do not use all the null distribution, only the tails. Once we have worked out critical values associated with a given significance level and a given combination of sample sizes, we can use these values for any study involving the same significance level and sample sizes. It is therefore possible to construct a table of critical values of S for the most commonly used significance levels and sample sizes, and thereby cut down the amount of work necessary in any particular application of the Rank-Sum Test. This has been done in Table A in the Appendix. Since S is a discrete variable the null distribution may not contain a value of S that is exactly appropriate for a given significance level. Where this is the case, Table A gives that value of S with the largest probability smaller than the given α. In some cases, then, the actual probability will be slightly smaller than the required α and the resulting test will be more conservative than we wish. However, with this procedure, the Type I error probability will never be larger than the required α.

To use Table A we first find the appropriate sample sizes; t_1 refers to the number of scores in the larger of the two samples, t_2 to the smaller. This determines the relevant row of the table. We then decide whether we want to use a one-tailed or a two-tailed test and select α, the significance level. These decisions determine the relevant column. The entry in the body of the table pointed to by this choice of row and column gives the upper tail critical value of S. Thus, if we have sample sizes of 7 and 6 and wish to do a two-tailed test with $\alpha = 0.01$, the relevant critical values are 36 and -36; we should therefore reject the null hypothesis if the S obtained from our data is larger than or equal to 36, or if it is smaller than or equal to -36. For a one-tailed test with $t_1 = 5, t_2 = 3$ and $\alpha = 0.05$, the upper tail critical value is 13. We should therefore reject the null hypothesis if our obtained S is larger than or equal to 13 for an upper tail test. For a lower tail one-tailed test, we should reject the null hypothesis only if the obtained S is smaller than or equal to -13.

Alternative Methods of Computing *S*

The method of computing S that we have used until now is rather tedious when we have a large amount of data. It involves stringing out the scores in order, assigning a rank to each score, finding the rank-sum associated with the scores from one sample and then converting this into the test statistic S. We shall see in this section two ways of arriving at S that may speed things up. In Section 2.3 a third method is discussed that is particularly appropriate when there are extensive ties in the response variable. The three alternative methods always give the same result. This means that we can use whichever method is most convenient for a particular set of data.

Computing Rank-Sums

The first method is not really different from our original method – it just tidies up the calculations. Instead of stringing out the scores in order and then assigning a rank, we can do the ranking directly in the original table of results. This is shown for our simplified example in Table 2.3. This makes the calculation of R, the rank-sum of the B scores, more straightforward, since it involves simply adding a column of ranks. We then convert this rank-sum into S in the usual manner. This method is generally the most straightforward to use with large sample sizes.

Table 2.3. Tidying up the calculation of R

Method A		Method B	
Score	Rank	Score	Rank
70	2	80	3
90	4	100	5
50	1		
			$R = 3 + 5 = 8$

Computing S directly

Rather than first computing R and then converting it into S, it is possible to compute S directly. This method is particularly useful, since it throws light on some important properties of S. In this method, we take one of the A scores and count how many of the B scores are larger – this is the positive contribution of that A score to S, and we label it p. We also count how many B scores are smaller than our chosen A score – this is the negative contribution to S, which we label q. We do this for each of the A scores. S is then given by summing the p scores to give P, summing the q scores to give Q, and subtracting the latter from the former. That is,

$$S = P - Q.$$

The calculation of S for our example using this method is shown in Table 2.4. Thus, when the A score of 70 is compared with the two B scores, $p = 2$ and $q = 0$, since both B scores are larger than 70; for the A score of 90, $p = 1$ and $q = 1$, since one B score is larger than 90 and one is smaller; for the A score of 50, $p = 2$ and $q = 0$. P is therefore 5 and Q is 1, so that $S = 5 - 1$, which agrees with our previous method.

Using this method, we can see that if the B scores are larger than the A scores, then the p's will all be large while the q's will be small, resulting in a large positive S. On the other hand, if the B scores are smaller than the A scores, then the p's will be small and q's will be large, resulting in a large negative S. If there is no difference between the A and the B scores, the p's and q's will tend to cancel each other out, with the result that S will be close to zero.

This method is usually the quickest way of computing S with small sample sizes.

Table 2.4. Direct calculation of S

Method A			Method B	
Score	p	q	Score	
70	2	0	80	
90	1	1	100	$S = P - Q$
50	2	0		$= 5 - 1$
	$P = 5$	$Q = 1$		$= 4$

Further Comments

In introducing the Rank-Sum Test, I stated that the test may pick up differences between the two populations other than a difference in location. It is possible to construct examples of populations having the same location but differing in other respects for which the Rank-Sum Test would tend to reject the null hypothesis, but such examples occur very infrequently in practice (see Bradley, 1968, p. 106 for examples and a discussion of this point). In most applications of the Rank-Sum Test it is reasonable to expect that rejection of the null hypothesis implies that the two populations differ in location. To be more precise, suppose in our simplified example that we select two children at random, one having been taught by Method A and one by Method B, and compare their reading scores. Then, given reasonable sample sizes and significance levels, the Rank-Sum Test will tend to accept the null hypothesis if the probability of the A child's score being higher than the B child's is ½; and it will reject the null hypothesis if the probability of the A child's score being higher than the B child's is different from ½. This latter situation usually implies that the A and the B populations differ in location.

In some cases, instead of wanting a test that is sensitive to location differences, we may be more interested in whether the scores of one sample are more spread out than those of the other sample. In other words, we may want a test that is particularly sensitive to dispersion differences between the two populations rather than location differences. For example, we may wish to test the prediction that the speed at which extraverts drive under alcohol will not differ much from their normal driving speed, while the driving speed of introverts will be affected – some will drive faster than normal and others will drive slower. A simple way of testing this would be to obtain a sample of introverts and a sample of extraverts and ask each of them to drive in a driving simulator, once while sober and once after imbibing alcohol. We could then use as the response variable the percentage difference between the speeds under the two conditions, a positive difference indicating that the person was driving faster under alcohol than normal. We should then want to test whether the introverts' difference scores are more spread out than the extraverts'. The Rank-Sum Test is not particularly sensitive to such differences and so should not be used in this situation. For a discussion of two-sample tests sensitive to dispersion differences, see Lehmann (1975, Chapter 1), Bradley (1968, Section 5.11) or Hollander and Wolfe (1973, Chapter 5).

Example 2.1 The Wilcoxon Rank-Sum Test (without ties)

In a study of the effects of 'set' on problem-solving, a sample of ten people is randomly divided into two groups of five. Group 1 is given a set of training problems, for which the solution involves a common principle which is similar to that required to solve a subsequently given test problem. Group 2 is given a different set of training problems, which involve no common principle. It is predicted that Group 1 should solve the test problem quicker than Group 2. All people worked alone in solving the problems, so their performances are independent. The

Table 2.5. Hypothetical data and calculations for Example 2.1

Group 1			Group 2	
Time	p	q	Time	
20	5	0	120	
100	3	2	94	
90	5	0	91	$S = P - Q$
40	5	0	105	$= 23 - 2$
65	5	0	130	$= 21$
$P = 23$	$Q = 2$			

time to solution, in seconds, for each person is shown in Table 2.5 together with the calculations required for the direct computation of S; with small samples this is usually the quickest method of computing S. Suppose we decide to use a significance level of 0.05. Our prediction leads us to carry out a one-tailed test. With this prediction and the results set out as in Table 2.5, we should want to reject the null hypothesis that there is no difference between the two groups in time taken to solve the test problem if we obtain a large positive value of S. Entering Table A with $t_1 = 5$, $t_2 = 5$ we obtain a critical value for S of 17 for a one-tailed test with $\alpha = 0.05$. Our obtained value of 21 is larger than this, so we reject the null hypothesis and conclude that Group 1 do solve the problems reliably faster than Group 2, as predicted. We shall see how to estimate how much faster Group 1 are in Example 2.6.

2.2 THE NORMAL APPROXIMATION TO THE RANK-SUM TEST

The Shape of the Null Distribution of S

It is only possible to use Table A to find critical values for the null distribution of the Rank-Sum statistic S when each sample contains 25 or fewer observations. However, for large sample sizes we can obtain a very good approximation to the null distribution of S. It is based on a distribution known as the *standard normal distribution* which is easy to tabulate and which thereby allows us to bypass the tedious task of constructing an exact distribution of S each time we want to use the Rank-Sum Test for situations beyond the scope of Table A. In this section, we shall see how the approximation works. To introduce the rationale, we shall first look at the shape of the null distribution of S.

We have already derived the complete null distribution of S for the case $t_1 = 3$, $t_2 = 2$, which is shown in Table 2.2. This is shown again in graphical form in Figure 2.1(a). The distribution is symmetrical about 0, with large probabilities of getting

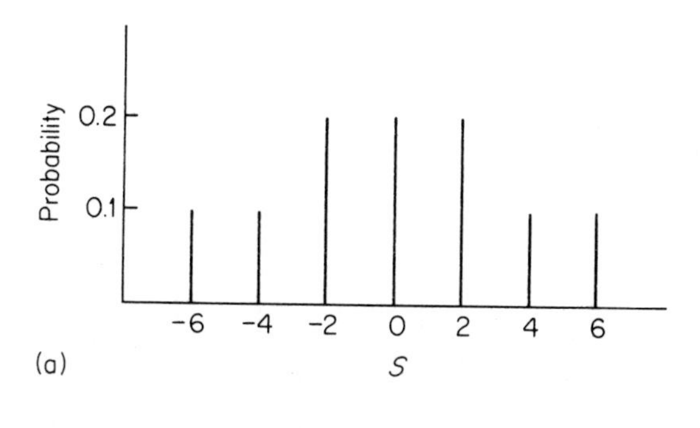

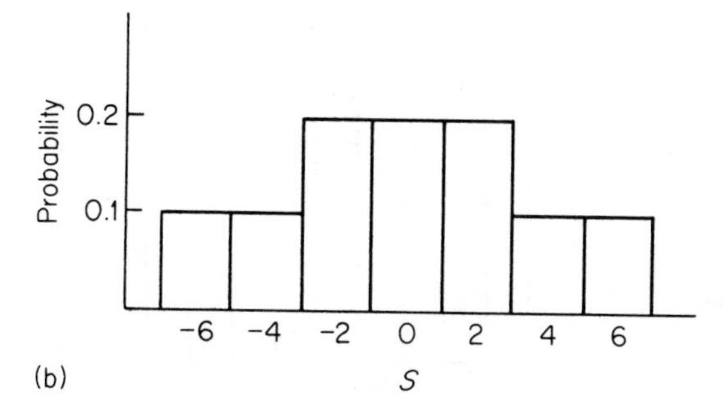

Figure 2.1. Two ways of drawing the null distribution of S for the case $t_1 = 3, t_2 = 2$

an S close to 0 and small probabilities of getting an S far away from 0 in either direction. S clearly can take only discrete values; in this case the only possible values for S are the even integers from −6 to +6. The first step in obtaining an approximation is to ignore this fact and pretend that S is really a continuous variable. If S were continuous, then we could fill in the gaps in the distribution and represent it as a histogram, as shown in Figure 2.1(b). We can then think of the probabilities shown in the histogram as being represented by areas of the histogram (see section 1.1 above). So the probability of getting an S of 4 or larger is the area represented by the two rectangles centred at 4 and 6 in the histogram.

We know that the distribution of S is different for different sample sizes. As the sample sizes increase, the null distribution of S becomes progressively more bell-shaped. Thus the null distribution shown in Figure 2.2 for the case $t_1 = 5, t_2 = 5$ is symmetrical about 0 and looks approximately like a bell. This distribution has also been drawn as a histogram, maintaining our pretence about the continuity of S. If we do not make such a pretence, there would be holes in the bell between the consecutive possible values of S, which in this case are the odd integers between −25 and 25. The exact probability of getting an S of 13 or larger is then the area represented by the rectangles labelled 13 – 25 in the histogram, which we can find to be 0.1111.

The main idea behind the approximation is to attempt to approximate the areas in the histogram by the areas under a continuous bell-shaped curve. We should not

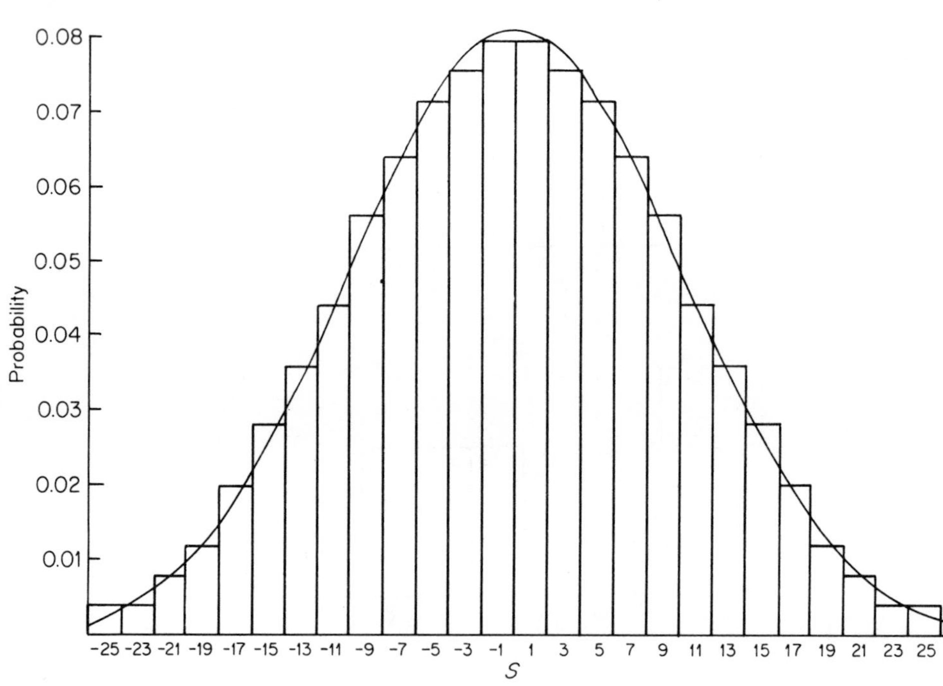

Figure 2.2. Null distribution of S for the case $t_1 = 5$, $t_2 = 5$

expect this to be successful for small sample sizes such as $t_1 = 3$, $t_2 = 2$, since the null distribution for that case does not look much like a bell, but it should be reasonable for those cases where the null distribution does look something like a bell. Since the bell-shape is apparent in Figure 2.2 for the case $t_1 = 5$, $t_2 = 5$ and since the null distribution of S becomes progressively more bell-shaped as the sample sizes increase, the approximation has a good chance of being reasonable for cases beyond the scope of Table A.

One class of bell-shaped curves has been extensively investigated and is known to have simple mathematical properties that makes it very useful in statistics. These curves are usually referred to as *normal distribution* curves. One important property of a normal distribution is that it is completely specified by its mean and standard deviation. This means that it is possible to draw the complete curve once these two values are known. To be able to draw a normal distribution, we should need to know its equation, which is rather complicated. Fortunately, we can exploit the simple properties of normal distributions without having to draw them, so the equation will not be given here.

If we know the mean and standard deviation of the possible values that S can take for a particular case, we can use these to draw the normal distribution curve that most closely approximates the null distribution of S.

Now it is easy to find the mean and variance of S in any particular case, and we know that the standard deviation is just the square root of the variance. The mean and variance are always given by

$$\text{Mean of } S = 0$$

$$\text{Variance of } S = \frac{t_1 t_2 (n+1)}{3} \tag{2.1}$$

To show that these formulae work, we can compute the mean and variance for the case $t_1 = 3$, $t_2 = 2$ directly using the methods of selection 1.1. In this case we know from Table 2.1 that the 10 possible S values are 6, 4, 2, 2, 0, 0, −2, −2, −4, and −6, for which the mean is 0 and the variance is 12. The formula also gives the variance as 3 x 2 x 6/3 = 12 (since $n = t_1 + t_2$). In general, we shall not know all the possible S values, so the formula is essential.

For the case $t_1 = 5$, $t_2 = 5$, the mean is 0 and the variance is 5 x 5 x 11/3 = 91.67, so the standard deviation is $\sqrt{91.67} = 9.57$. The appropriate normal distribution with the same mean and S.D. has been superimposed over the exact distribution shown in Figure 2.2, in which it can be seen that the shapes of the two distributions are very similar. So, if the exact distribution were not available, we should be able to get a good approximation to the probabilities by finding the corresponding area under the normal curve. For example, we should be able to approximate the probability of getting an S of 13 or larger (which we know to be 0.1111) by finding the area under the normal distribution to the right of 13. This of course will only be a worthwhile exercise if the work involved in finding areas under normal curves is considerably less than that involved in computing the exact distribution anew for each case.

The Standard Normal Distribution (Appendix Table B)

Fortunately, it is very easy to find areas under normal curves by making use of a table of areas under the *standard normal distribution*, which is that particular normal distribution with a mean of 0 and a standard deviation of 1. In this section we shall indicate how to find areas under the standard normal distribution and in the next section we shall see how to use this information to find areas under normal curves with different means and standard deviations.

The standard normal distribution is illustrated in Figure 2.3, which shows it to be symmetrical about its mean of 0. It also has the property that the total area under the curve is 1. (We should need calculus to prove this, so we shan't try!) This means that it makes sense to think of the area under a part of the curve as representing the proportion of scores occurring under that part of the curve, or, equivalently, as the probability of obtaining such a score. The scores on the horizontal axis of the standard normal distribution are generally referred to as *z-scores* or *standard scores*. A table showing the areas in the upper tail of the distribution associated with positive z-scores is provided as Table B(i) in the Appendix. This shows, for example, that the probability of getting a z-score of 1.96 or larger is 0.025. This is the area shaded on the right in Figure 2.3. Since the distribution is symmetrical about zero, we can also use the table for negative z-scores. For example, since the probability of obtaining a $z \geqslant 1.96$ is 0.025, the probability of obtaining a $z \leqslant -1.96$ is also 0.025, as shown in the area shaded in the lower tail of Figure 2.3. The symmetry of the distribution about zero also allows us to use the table to obtain two-tailed probabilities. Thus, the two-tailed probability of getting a z of larger magnitude than 1.96 in either direction is 0.025 + 0.025 or 0.05.

In Table B(ii) the standard normal distribution is shown in an alternative form; here the critical values of z corresponding to the commonly used one- and two-tailed significance levels are given. For example, the upper tail critical value of z for a one-tailed test with a significance level of 0.01 is 2.326. Similarly, the critical values associated with a two-tailed test with a significance level of 0.01 are −2.576 and 2.576.

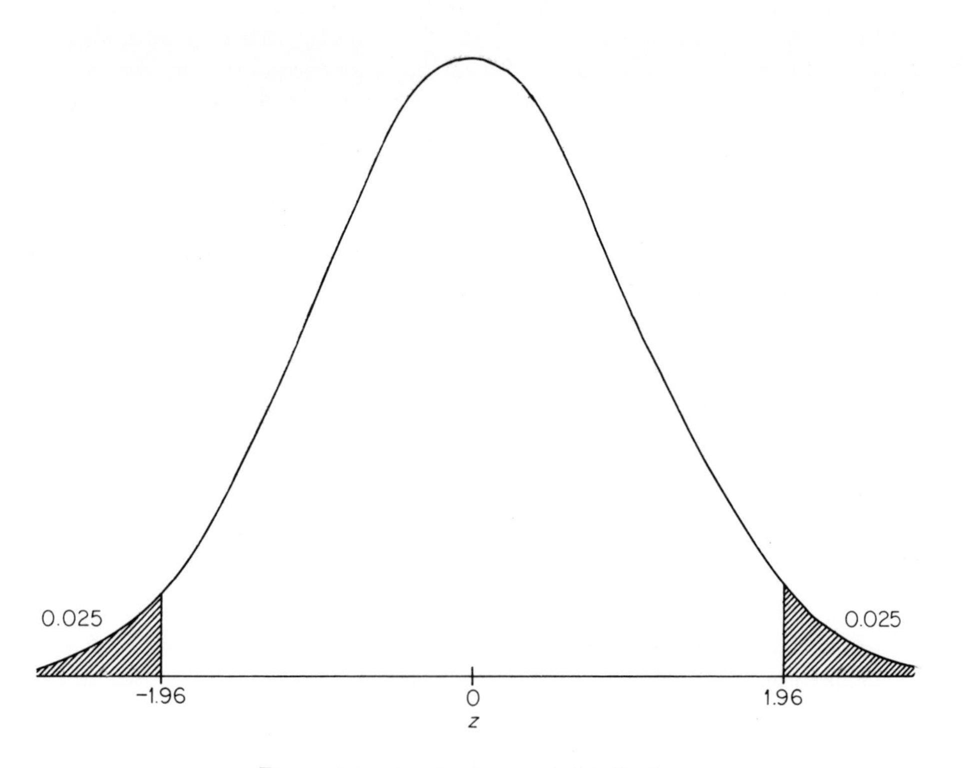

Figure 2.3. Standard normal distribution

The Normal Approximation to S

Returning to our example with $t_1 = 5, t_2 = 5$ shown in Figure 2.2, we wish to find the area under the normal distribution shown there to the right of an S of 13. We can use Table B for this purpose by converting the S scores shown on the horizontal axis of Figure 2.2 into z-scores. To do this we first subtract the mean of the S scores from each score and divide by the standard deviation. Thus, an S of 13 is converted into a z-score as follows:

$$z = \frac{S - \text{Mean}}{\text{S.D.}}$$

$$= \frac{13 - 0}{9.57}$$

$$= 1.36$$

The mean and standard deviation used here are given in formula 2.1 above. This process is known as *standardizing* the S scores and it has the effect of converting them into a distribution with a mean of 0 and a standard deviation of 1. Such standardization does not change the information we are interested in, which is the proportion of the curve beyond a certain score – it merely changes the scale and thereby allows us to use Table B. In this respect, it is like changing from a Centigrade scale of temperature to a Fahrenheit one – both scales give exactly the same information, but in a different form.

Having standardized the S scores, we can now use Table B directly. From Table B(i) we find that the probability of getting a z-score larger than or equal to 1.36 is 0.0869. This is an approximation to the probability of getting an S of 13 or larger, which we know in this case to be 0.1111. So the approximation given by the normal distribution is a bit lower than the true probability, but it is fairly close. We shall see in the next section a simple technique for improving the approximation. However, we only really need an approximation for those cases that are outside the range of Table A, so such a close fit for this case is quite heartening, since the approximation gets better for larger sample sizes.

Improving the Approximation – a Continuity Correction

To make use of the normal distribution as an approximation to the null distribution of S, we have pretended that S is a continuous variable, whereas in fact we know it to be discrete. In our example for the case $t_1 = 5$, $t_2 = 5$, we are approximating the areas represented by the rectangles labelled 13–25 in the histogram in Figure 2.2 by the area to the right of the z-score corresponding to 13. Now, by pretending S is continuous, we have assumed that the rectangle labelled 13 in fact spreads from 12 to 14, being centred at 13, as can be seen in Figure 2.2. So we might do better at approximating the probability of getting an S of 13 or larger by converting 12, and not 13, into a z-score. If we do this, the z-score will be 1.25 and from Table B(i), we find prob ($z \geqslant 1.25$) = 0.1056, which is very close to the exact value of 0.1111 that we are trying to approximate.

To use this device in general, we note that in all cases, the interval between possible S values is 2. Thus, when $t_1 = 5$ and $t_2 = 5$, S takes all the odd integers between −25 and +25. When $t_1 = 3$ and $t_2 = 2$, S takes all the even integers between −6 and +6 (see Figure 2.1) while for $t_1 = 3$ and $t_2 = 3$, S takes all the odd integers between −9 and +9 (see Exercise 2.4). If we constructed a histogram for each case, the rectangle for any particular value would stretch from that value minus 1 to that value plus 1, just as in our example the rectangle centred at 13 stretched from 12 to 14. Therefore, to find the appropriate z-score corresponding to a positive S value, we subtract 1 from the S value before doing the conversion. For a negative S value, we first add 1 before converting to a z-score. This device is known as a *continuity correction*, since it is an attempt to correct for the fact that we are using a continuous distribution as an approximation to a discrete distribution. In many cases, a continuity correction improves the approximation produced.

As a further illustration of its accuracy, suppose we have 25 observations in each sample, i.e. $t_1 = 25$, $t_2 = 25$. Table A shows that in this case the exact critical value of S corresponding to a one-tailed significance level of 0.05 is 171. From formula 2.1, we find that the mean of the possible values of S in this case will be 0 (as in all cases) while the variance will be $25 \times 25 \times 51/3 = 10625$, so, using the continuity correction of 1 we have S_c, the value of S with continuity correction subtracted, equal to 170.

$$z = \frac{S_c - \text{MEAN}}{\text{S.D.}}$$

$$= \frac{170 - 0}{\sqrt{10625}}$$

$$= 1.649$$

This z-score of 1.649 agrees almost exactly with the 0.05 one-tailed critical value shown in Table B(ii) which is 1.645.

When to Use the Normal Approximation

We have seen that the normal approximation together with the continuity correction leads to fairly accurate results even when there are only 5 observations in each sample, and I have stated that the approximation gets better as sample sizes increase. As a rough guide, the normal approximation will be poor and should not be used if the smaller of the two samples has 3 or fewer observations (i.e. $t_2 \leqslant 3$). In other cases, the approximation should be adequate for most purposes. Of course, the exact Table A should always be used in preference to the normal approximation for those cases where *both* t_1 *and* t_2 are less than 26.

> The word 'normal' in normal distribution must not be thought of in its everyday sense of 'usual' or 'to be expected'. Distributions other than the normal are not abnormal . . . . Sometimes the normal distribution is called Gaussian, especially in engineering and physics. In France it is called Laplacean. These names are probably used because the distribution was invented by de Moivre.
>
> Mosteller, Rourke and Thomas, 1970, p. 266.

Example 2.2 Using the Normal Approximation to the Rank-Sum Test

52 overweight people take part in a study comparing the relative effectiveness of two simple methods of weight reduction. 24 of the people simply keep a detailed record of all the food they consume together with calorie counts, which they bring every week for six months to a clinic where they are weighed and interviewed by a psychologist. The remaining 28 people are required in addition to

Table 2.6. Hypothetical data for Example 2.2 and calculation of S and z

Group 1		Group 2	
% weight-loss	Rank	% weight-loss	Rank
−18.30	4	−16.11	5
3.33	32	2.42	18
3.42	33	2.76	25
−2.19	10	3.71	40
2.69	22	3.78	41
−20.34	1	5.93	48
−20.01	2	6.80	49
2.71	23	15.69	51
2.62	20	3.21	31
−19.50	3	3.79	42
2.59	19	3.80	43
2.30	17	10.12	50
1.28	13	3.58	35
1.34	14	3.44	34
2.77	26	−9.54	7
2.75	24	3.59	36
2.68	21	3.61	37
1.99	16	21.32	52
1.56	15	5.42	47
−5.13	8	3.65	38
3.13	30	−4.88	9
−15.23	6	4.83	45
0.15	12	4.85	46
2.79	28	3.92	44
		3.66	39
		2.78	27
		3.01	29
		−1.86	11
	$R = 399$		

n = Total no. of observations $= 52$

t_1 = Size of larger group $= 28$

t_2 = Size of smaller group $= 24$

$$S = 2R - t_2(n+1) = 2 \times 399 - 24 \times 53 = 798 - 1272 = -474$$

$$S_c = S + 1 = -473$$

$$\text{MEAN} = 0$$

$$\text{S.D.} = \sqrt{\frac{t_1 t_2 (n+1)}{3}} = \sqrt{\frac{28 \times 24 \times 53}{3}} = \sqrt{11872} = 108.96$$

$$z = \frac{S_c - \text{MEAN}}{\text{S.D.}} = \frac{-473 - 0}{108.96} = -4.34$$

(The continuity correction is +1 since the obtained S is negative)

ensure that all food is consumed in exactly the same room, sitting at a table, even if they only want to nibble a biscuit. Neither group is instructed specifically to stop eating certain things. One year after the end of the treatment, each person's percentage weight-loss is recorded. Do the two treatments differ in effectiveness? The data are recorded in Table 2.6 (a negative score meaning that the person put on weight). The most straightforward way of computing S with large samples is usually the rank-sum method and the calculations for this are shown with the data. A two-tailed test is appropriate, since we are interested in detecting differences between the two treatments in either direction. Suppose we decide to use a significance level of 0.01. The large sample sizes of 24 and 28 mean that we cannot use the exact Table A. We therefore use the normal approximation together with a continuity correction, since both samples have more than 3 observations. Table B tells us that the relevant critical values for a two-tailed test with $\alpha = 0.01$ are -2.576 and $+2.576$. We should therefore reject the null hypothesis if we obtain a z-score $\geqslant 2.576$ or $\leqslant -2.576$. The z-score computed in Table 2.5 is -4.34 which is smaller than the lower tail critical value of -2.576, so we reject the null hypothesis. This means we have reliable evidence of a difference between the two methods. From Table·2.6 we can see that percentage weight-loss tends to be smaller under the first treatment method. We therefore conclude that the second method leads to greater weight-loss after one year's follow-up. In Example 2.7 we shall see how to estimate the size of the effect for these data.

2.3 THE TREATMENT OF TIES

One of the main assumptions of the Wilcoxon Rank-Sum Test is that the response variable is continuous. This means that under 'ideal' measurement conditions, there will be no tied observations. This assumption was used explicitly in constructing the null distribution of S. For example, Table 2.1 shows all possible patterns of results for the case $t_1 = 3, t_2 = 2$ *only* if there are no ties in the response variable. If we allowed ties, other patterns of results would be possible. Therefore, the critical values given in Table A and the normal approximation discussed in the previous section will be accurate only if there are no tied observations. In practice, these ideal conditions will not always be met. Ties occur sometimes as a result of accidentally poor measurement and sometimes by design. Several suggestions for handling ties have been made. We shall discuss only the most frequently used method, which is satisfactory in most cases and which has the advantage of providing a way of generalizing the Rank-Sum Test to situations for which it was not originally intended, as we shall see in Example 2.5 and Section 2.5 below. For a discussion of the other methods of handling ties, see Bradley (1968, Sections 3.2–3.4). The method of handling ties that we shall adopt is very simple. It involves replacing the tied observations by the midrank or average rank they would have received had they not been tied and then following the standard procedure for the Rank-Sum Test described above. It is generally referred to as the midrank method.

The Midrank Method

Suppose that in our simplified example of section 2.1 the scores of the five children had been those given below.

Method A	Method B
50	70
70	100
70	

The first stage in carrying out the Rank-Sum Test is to assign ranks to the scores. In our example, it is clear that the smallest score, 50, should have rank 1 and the largest score, 100, should have rank 5, but it is not clear how the three scores of 70 should be ranked. With the present technique they are given the same rank. The most natural way to do this is to assign to each score of 70 the mean of the ranks they would have obtained had they not been tied, which in this case would be $(2 + 3 + 4)/3 = 3$. The five children in the experiment are then assigned the *midranks* 1, 3, 3, 3, and 5. (One reason for using midranks, rather than some other common score such as the lowest of the ranks they would have received – 2 in this case – is that the midrank technique keeps the sum of all the ranks the same in the tied situation as in the untied situation. For example, $1 + 3 + 3 + 3 + 5$ is the same as $1 + 2 + 3 + 4 + 5$.)

With this procedure the rank-sum R for the B scores will be $3 + 5 = 8$ and S will therefore be $2R - t_2(n + 1) = 16 - 12 = 4$. Unfortunately, the null distribution of S shown in Table 2.2 is no longer appropriate, since that was derived assuming no

Table 2.7. The 10 patterns of results and associated values of R and S when $t_1 = 3$, $t_2 = 2$ and when the middle three scores are tied

	Midrank of response variable						
	1	3	3	3	5	R	S
1.	A	A	A	B	B	8	4
2.	A	A	B	A	B	8	4
3.	A	B	A	A	B	8	4
4.	A	A	B	B	A	6	0
5.	A	B	A	B	A	6	0
6.	B	A	A	A	B	6	0
7.	A	B	B	A	A	6	0
8.	B	A	A	B	A	4	–4
9.	B	A	B	A	A	4	–4
10.	B	B	A	A	A	4	–4

Table 2.8. Null distribution of S for the case $t_1 = 3$, $t_2 = 2$, with the middle three scores tied

S	−4	0	4
Probability	0.3	0.4	0.3

ties. When there are ties, we need to work out the null distribution in a different way. To do this, we use the same logic as we used to construct Table 2.2. If the null hypothesis is true, then we may assume that the assignment of children to teaching methods in no way affects the midrank reading scores they would obtain. In this case, the midrank scores associated with Method B are determined simply by the random assignment of two children to be taught by that method. There are still the same 10 possible ways of assigning children to teaching methods, and they are still equally likely, but this time the values of R and S associated with them will be different. The calculations are given in Table 2.7, which shows the possible patterns of results and the values of R and S based on the midrank scores. The associated null distribution of S is given in Table 2.8. This null distribution has been obtained in the same way as in the untied case. Thus, the 0.3 probability of getting an S of 4 occurs because 3 of the 10 equally likely patterns of results shown in Table 2.7 are associated with an S of 4. With the null distribution shown here, we can see that 4 is no longer the critical value for a one-tailed test with a significance level of 0.2, as it was in the untied case. In fact, the null distribution has changed so much that it is no longer possible to find a critical value corresponding to an α of 0.2. Thus, had we attempted to use the null distribution appropriate to the untied case with an α of 0.2, we should have drawn an incorrect conclusion. So, when using the midrank technique, Table A may be misleading.

This means that we should have to compute a new null distribution for each use of the Rank-Sum Test with ties, since a different null distribution is appropriate for different numbers of ties. For some particular combinations of sample sizes and ties, tables of the null distribution have been constructed, as we shall see in Section 2.5. However, it would not be worthwhile constructing tables for all combinations, since the tables would have to be exceedingly large to cover even small sample sizes.

Fortunately, the problem introduced by ties can be solved quite satisfactorily in an approximate way, which saves having to go through the tedious procedure of calculating an exact null distribution anew for each situation. As we shall see below, the normal approximation discussed in Section 2.2 can be modified to take account of ties and this will give accurate results for most practical purposes.

It is worth pointing out that, despite our example, Table A may still be useful in providing an approximate test when there are few ties. The null distribution of S derived in Table 2.8 is very different from the null distribution in the untied case (Table 2.2) mainly because the ties in our example are so extensive, with 3/5 or 60% of all the scores being tied. As a very rough general rule, if no more than ¼ of all the scores are tied, the critical values given in Table A will be reasonably accurate. In fact, in most cases, using Table A when there are ties will tend to give a slightly conservative test, in the sense that you will be less likely to reject the null hypothesis using Table A than you would had you bothered to calculate the exact null distribution that takes account of ties. So if you reject the null hypothesis using Table A when there are relatively few ties you can usually be confident that this is the right decision.

To summarize, it is recommended that when ties occur in the response variable, Table A should be used to provide approximate (conservative) critical values of S when no more than ¼ of all the scores are involved in ties. When ties are more extensive, the normal approximation given below should be used.

Other Methods of Computing S when there are Ties

Before looking at the normal approximation we shall first see how the direct method of computing S needs to be modified when there are ties. We shall also discuss a third method of computing S that is based on the direct method.

Computing S directly

Only a slight modification of this method is required when there are ties in the response variable. As in the untied case, we take one of the A scores and count how many B scores are larger; this gives p, the positive contribution of the A score to S. We also count how many of the B scores are smaller; this gives q, the negative contribution of the A score to S. When there is a B score exactly equal to the A score, this is ignored in both counts. Apart from this, we proceed as for the untied case, calculating P, the sum of the p's for each A score, and Q, the sum of the q's. S is then given by $P - Q$. This is illustrated for our example in Table 2.9, which gives $S = 4$, the same result as obtained using midranks above.

Table 2.9. Computing S directly when there are ties

Method A			Method B	
Score	p	q	Score	
50	2	0	70	
70	1	0	100	
70	1	0		$S = P - Q$
	$P = 4$	$Q = 0$		$= 4$

Computing S from an ordered contingency table

When there are extensive ties, both the midrank method and the direct method of computing S are tedious. However, a slight variation of the direct method makes the calculations much easier. This method involves representing the data in the form of an *ordered contingency table*. A *contingency table* is a table in which the levels of the explanatory variable form the rows while the levels of the response

Table 2.10. Data in the form of an ordered contingency table

		Reading score			
		50	70	100	t_i
Teaching method	A	1	2		3
	B		1	1	2
	u_i	1	3	1	$5 = n$

variable form the columns. The cells of the table show the number of observations scoring each of the possible combinations of scores. A contingency table is *ordered* if the levels are written down in increasing or decreasing order.

For our example, the levels of the response variable are the scores 50, 70, and 100; the levels of the explanatory variable are simply the two group labels, A and B. The response variable is ordinal, so it makes sense to write down the levels of this variable in increasing order, i.e. 50, 70, and 100. Since we only have two groups, the explanatory variable can be thought of as either categorical (the two categories being the labels A and B) or ordinal.

Being able to think of the explanatory variable as ordinal may seem surprising, but it is quite straightforward. We are attempting to see whether there is a difference between the A group and the B group. The only differences we are interested in as far as the Rank-Sum Test is concerned occur when the A scores are larger than the B scores or when the B scores are larger than the A scores. In the former case we can think of the group labels being ordered with A representing large scores and B representing the small scores; in the latter case, the label A represents small scores and B represents large scores. In the same way, any variable with only 2 levels may be thought of as either categorical or ordinal. We shall exploit this duality over and over again in the following chapters, so it is well worth remembering.

The ordered contingency table for our example is shown in Table 2.10. The 1 in the cell $(A, 50)$ corresponding to a 'score' of A on the explanatory variable and a score of 50 on the response variable shows that one child in the A group scored 50 on the reading test. The blank in the cell $(A, 100)$ shows that none of the children in the A group scored 100. The totals given in the margins of the table show the number of scores on each variable tied at a particular value. Thus, the row totals, labelled t_i, show that there were 3 scores tied at the value A and 2 tied at the value B on the explanatory variable. In other words, there were 3 children in group A and 2 in group B. The column marginal totals, labelled u_i, indicate that one of the children scored 50, three scored 70 and one scored 100. If there were no ties in the reading scores, all the u's would be one. The sum of the marginal totals is always n, the total number of children used in the experiment.

Once the data are represented in the form of an ordered contingency table, S may be computed quite straightforwardly as follows. We take each non-zero cell in turn and find the sum of all the frequencies to its south-east (i.e. below and to the right). In other words, we find the number of observations that have higher scores on both variables. This is just the p score associated with the cell, as in the direct method. In a similar way, we compute the q score associated with the cell by finding the sum of all the frequencies to its south-west (i.e. below and to the left). For the $(A, 50)$ cell in Table 2.9, p is 2 and q is 0; for the $(A, 70)$ cell, p is 1 and q is 0. We don't need to bother with the bottom row of the table, since the p and q scores associated with these cells are necessarily zero. We now find P and Q, the sum of the p's and the sum of the q's. P is given by first multiplying the frequency shown in each cell by the p score for that cell and then summing across cells. Q is given similarly. For our example, we have

$$P = 1 \times 2 + 2 \times 1 = 4$$
$$\text{and } Q = 1 \times 0 + 2 \times 0 = 0$$

As in the direct method, $S = P - Q$, so, for the example,

$$\begin{aligned} S &= P - Q \\ &= 4 - 0 \\ &= 4, \end{aligned}$$

which is exactly the same as the value we obtained using the midrank technique. The two methods will always give the same result. When there are extensive ties, assigning midranks may take a long time. Representing the data in the form of an ordered contingency table and computing S as shown allows us to bypass the calculation of midranks and tends to be much quicker. Further illustrations of the method are given in Examples 2.4 and 2.5. Even when there are no ties in the response variable, the ordered contingency table method of calculating S will give the same result as the other methods given in Section 2.1, but these tend to be quicker in the untied case.

Normal Approximation to S

When there are ties in the response variable, the technique of midranks reduces the number of possible values S can take, as may be seen by comparing Tables 2.1 and 2.7. It hence also reduces the variance of the possible values S can take, so that the expression for the variance given by formula 2.1 for the untied case will be larger than it should be. In the tied case, the variance of S is given by the expression

$$\text{Variance} = \frac{t_1 t_2 (n^3 - \Sigma u_i^3)}{3n(n-1)} \tag{2.2}$$

For our example, $\Sigma u_i^3 = u_1^3 + u_2^3 + u_3^3 = 1^3 + 3^3 + 1^3 = 1 + 27 + 1 = 29$, and $n^3 = 5^3 = 125$

$$\begin{aligned} \therefore \text{Variance} &= \frac{3 \times 2 \times (125 - 29)}{3 \times 5 \times 4} \\ &= 9.6 \end{aligned}$$

For our particular example, we can check the validity of this result by computing the variance directly from Table 2.7 using the method given in Section 1.1.

The mean value of S will always be 0, even when there are ties in the response variable. Thus, a normal approximation to the exact null distribution will be given using the new expression for the variance. So, for our example, the probability of getting an S of 4 or more may be approximated by computing

$$z = \frac{S - \text{MEAN}}{\text{S.D.}}$$

$$= \frac{4 - 0}{\sqrt{9.6}}$$

$$= 1.29$$

Table B(i) then tells us that prob $(z \geqslant 1.29) = 0.0985$. From the exact null distribution computed above for this case, we know that prob $(S \geqslant 4) = 0.3$, so the normal approximation is not very good for our example. This is not surprising, since there are so few observations in our experiment. As before, the normal approximation will improve as sample sizes increase.

The approximation can be improved by using a continuity correction in the tied case as well as in the untied case. However, the appropriate continuity correction is slightly more complicated. A continuity correction of 1 was appropriate in the untied case, since 1 is half the interval between consecutive S values. In our example, Table 2.7 shows that the interval between consecutive S values is 4, so the appropriate continuity correction will be 2. Using this value of 2, we can then make a more accurate stab at an approximation to prob $(S \geqslant 4)$ as follows. Since $S = 4, S_c = 4 - 2 = 2$, so

$$z = \frac{S_c - \text{MEAN}}{\text{S.D.}}$$

$$= \frac{2 - 0}{\sqrt{9.6}}$$

$$= 0.65$$

From Table B, prob $(z \geqslant 0.65) = 0.2578$, which is much closer to the exact probability of 0.3 than the uncorrected value.

In general, the appropriate continuity correction will be given by

$$\frac{2n - u_1 - u_k}{2(k - 1)}, \tag{2.3}$$

where k is the number of distinct values on the response variable. In our example k is 3, since there are the three possible values 50, 70, and 100 on the response variable; $u_1 = 1$, since the smallest of these values, 50, was scored by only one child; and $u_k = u_3 = 1$, since the largest value, 100, was also scored by one child.

Substituting these in the formula gives

$$\frac{2 \times 5 - 1 - 1}{2 \times (3 - 1)} = 2,$$

which is the right correction for our example. For other patterns of ties in the response variable, this continuity correction will not be exactly correct but it will still tend to improve the approximation. This point is discussed in greater detail by Kendall (1970, section 4.12).

As before, the continuity correction should be subtracted from a positive value of S, but added to a negative value of S.

The normal approximation will be somewhat less accurate in the tied case than in the untied case. This is because the null distribution in the untied case takes longer to achieve the bell shape necessary for the normal approximation to work well. It will tend to be reasonably accurate as long as none of the proportions u_i/n is close to one, indicating that one score on the response variable dominates almost totally.

It is worth noting that calculating the variance of S when there are ties using formula 2.2 always results in a lower value than calculating the variance using formula 2.1, which doesn't take account of the ties. Formula 2.1 is easier to compute, so it may be preferable to use it in calculating the z-score. The resulting z-score will always be smaller than it should be, thereby giving a more conservative test. So using formula 2.1 instead of formula 2.2 will always make us err on the cautious side. If we can reject the null hypothesis using formula 2.1, we shall also be able to reject it using the more complicated formula 2.2.

In practice, the more exact formula 2.2 rarely leads to a different decision from formula 2.1, unless the ties are very extensive.

Example 2.3 The Rank-Sum Test with Few Ties

A group of eight smokers is compared with a group of seven non-smokers on a test of anxiety. It is predicted that the smokers should give more evidence of anxiety than the non-smokers. The resulting anxiety scores are shown in Table 2.11, with high scores indicating high anxiety. Do these data support the prediction? Suppose we carry out a one-tailed test with a significance level of 0.05; a one-tailed test is used because of the prediction being tested. We note that there are three tied scores of 52 and no other ties in the response variable. The calculation of S using the direct method is shown alongside the data. With only 3 of the 15 scores involved in ties (less than ¼), we should have a reasonably accurate result using Table A, which gives 30 as the critical value of S for a one-tailed test with $\alpha \doteq 0.05$ and $t_1 = 8$, $t_2 = 7$. Our prediction is that non-smokers should score less on the anxiety test than smokers, so from the way we have recorded the data in Table 2.11 we expect a negative value of S. We therefore need to use a lower tail critical value, i.e. $S = -30$. Our obtained S of -46 is smaller than this, so we reject the null hypothesis that there is no

Table 2.11. Hypothetical data and calculation of S for Example 2.3

Smokers			Non-smokers
Score	p	q	Score
28	2	5	23
52	0	6	32
60	0	7	52
52	0	6	19
53	0	7	17
43	1	6	25
49	1	6	27
64	0	7	

$P = 4 \qquad Q = 50$

$S = P - Q = -46$

difference between the two groups of people. In other words, our prediction that smokers score higher on the anxiety test than the non-smokers is supported.

Example 2.4 The Rank-Sum Test with More than a Quarter of the Scores Involved in Ties

Part of Rotter's (1966) social learning theory has to do with the degree to which people see themselves as being internally or externally controlled. Externally controlled people see what happens to them as being dependent mainly on chance, fate or powerful others, or as being unpredictable because of the great complexities around them. Internally controlled people believe that what happens to them is under their own control. Rotter developed the Internal–External Locus of Control Scale (*I/E* Scale) as an attempt to measure this. Low scores on the *I/E* Scale reflect a general belief in internal control; high scores reflect a general belief in external control.

As part of an unpublished study, Helen Buckley (1978) compared the *I/E* scores of 20 smokers who did not want to stop smoking and 20 smokers who did want to stop. Her results are shown below. The data are independent and it seems reasonable to ask whether people who

Not wanting to stop	13, 18, 11, 17, 8, 10, 10, 16, 14, 15, 15, 10, 11, 10, 10, 13, 10, 13, 16, 10
Wanting to stop	8, 5, 10, 9, 8, 8, 9, 10, 6, 11, 14, 15, 18, 8, 9, 16, 9, 9, 5, 15

Table 2.12. Data for Example 2.4 in the form of an ordered contingency table (From Buckley, 1978)

	I/E score												
	5	6	8	9	10	11	13	14	15	16	17	18	t_i
Wanting to stop	2	1	4	5	2	1		1	2	1		1	20
Not wanting to stop			1		7	2	3	1	2	2	1	1	20
u_i	2	1	5	5	9	3	3	2	4	3	1	2	$40 = n$

want to give up smoking tend to be more or less internally controlled than those who don't. Most of the scores are involved in ties, so it will be more convenient to calculate S using the ordered contingency table method. Table 2.12 shows the data in the form of an ordered contingency table. We first note that both sample sizes, t_1 and t_2, are reasonably large and that none of the proportions u_i/n is close to one, the largest being 9/40, which means that the normal approximation should give a reasonably accurate result. Using a two-tailed test with significance level of 0.05, Table B(ii) shows the critical values of z to be -19.6 and 1.96.

From Table 2.12, we now obtain P, Q and S as follows.

$$
\begin{aligned}
P &= 2 \times (1 + 7 + 2 + 3 + 1 + 2 + 2 + 1 + 1) \\
&\quad + 1 \times (1 + 7 + 2 + 3 + 1 + 2 + 2 + 1 + 1) \\
&\quad + 4 \times (7 + 2 + 3 + 1 + 2 + 2 + 1 + 1) \\
&\quad + 5 \times (7 + 2 + 3 + 1 + 2 + 2 + 1 + 1) \\
&\quad + 2 \times (2 + 3 + 1 + 2 + 2 + 1 + 1) \\
&\quad + 1 \times (3 + 1 + 2 + 2 + 1 + 1) \\
&\quad + 1 \times (2 + 2 + 1 + 1) \\
&\quad + 2 \times (2 + 1 + 1) + 1 \times (1 + 1) + 1 \times 0 \\
&= 40 + 20 + 76 + 95 + 24 + 10 + 6 + 8 + 2 + 0 \\
&= 281
\end{aligned}
$$

$$
\begin{aligned}
Q &= 2 \times 0 + 1 \times 0 + 4 \times 0 + 5 \times 1 + 2 \times 1 + 1 \times (1 + 7) \\
&\quad + 1 \times (1 + 7 + 2 + 3) + 2 \times (1 + 7 + 2 + 3 + 1) \\
&\quad + 1 \times (1 + 7 + 2 + 3 + 1 + 2) \\
&\quad + 1 \times (1 + 7 + 2 + 3 + 1 + 2 + 2 + 1) \\
&= 0 + 0 + 0 + 5 + 2 + 8 + 13 + 28 + 16 + 19 \\
&= 91
\end{aligned}
$$

$$S = P - Q = 281 - 91 = 190$$

There are $k = 12$ distinct scores on the response variable, so the continuity correction will be

$$\frac{2n - u_1 - u_k}{2(k-1)} = \frac{80 - 2 - 2}{2 \times 11} = 3.45$$

Since S is positive, this is subtracted to give $S_c = 190 - 3.45 = 186.55$. To calculate the variance of S using formula 2.2, we first need

$$\Sigma u_i^3 = 2^3 + 1^3 + 5^3 + 5^3 + 9^3 + 3^3 + 3^3 + 2^3 + 4^3 + 3^3 + 1^3 + 2^3$$
$$= 1150$$

The variance is then given by

$$\text{Variance} = \frac{t_1 t_2 (n^3 - \Sigma u_i^3)}{3n(n-1)} = \frac{20 \times 20 \times (64000 - 1150)}{3 \times 40 \times 39}$$
$$= 5371.795$$

The z-score will therefore be

$$z = \frac{S_c - \text{Mean}}{\text{S.D.}} = \frac{186.55 - 0}{\sqrt{5371.795}} = 2.55$$

which is larger than the upper tail critical value of 1.96, so we reject the null hypothesis that there is no difference between the two groups. From Table 2.12, it is clear that the people who wanted to stop smoking tend to have lower scores, associated with a greater belief in internal control. (The gain in accuracy as a result of using formula 2.2 for calculating the variance is not great in this case. If we used formula 2.1 instead, the z-score would be 2.52 which differs only slightly from 2.55.)

Example 2.5 The Rank-Sum Test with Extensive Ties

This example shows how the Rank-Sum Test may be used with data that are not obviously suited to it. Students graduating with an honours degree in Britain usually have their degree results classified into one of four classes: first class (I), upper second class (II:i), lower second class (II:ii) and third class (III). The final results for two consecutive years of a degree course are shown in Table 2.13 which presents the number of students obtaining each of the four degree classes. Could these data be used as evidence that one year's students are better than the other? The data here have been presented already in the form of an ordered contingency table. The explanatory variable is year of the course with the two levels 'First' and 'Second', while the response variable is degree class. This is an ordinal variable, since class I is higher than class II:i and so on. Thus, we have a two-sample situation with an ordinal response variable, so the Rank-Sum Test is applicable. In this case, it is not clear

Table 2.13. Final degree results for two consecutive years (Hypothetical data for Example 2.5)

	Degree class				
	I	II:i	II:ii	III	t_i
First year	1	18	30	2	51
Second year	0	17	27	5	49
u_i	1	35	57	7	$100 = n$

why the two samples are being compared. If we want to see whether anyone could use these data to suggest that standards were changing from one year to the next, we might want a very sensitive or powerful test. In such a situation, we should use a relatively large significance level, such as 0.10. Exact tables are not available for this situation, so we use the normal approximation to the Rank-Sum Test. We can be quite confident that the resulting approximation will be accurate, since our two sample sizes are large, with $t_1 = 51$ and $t_2 = 49$, and the largest of the proportions u_i/n is 57/100, which is not close to 1. Using a two-tailed test with $\alpha = 0.10$, Table B(ii) provides critical values of z of -1.645 and 1.645. Since the data are presented in an ordered contingency table, S can be computed directly as follows.

$$P = 1 \times (17 + 27 + 5) + 18 \times (27 + 5) + 30 \times 5 + 2 \times 0$$
$$= 49 + 576 + 150 + 0$$
$$= 775$$

$$Q = 1 \times 0 + 18 \times 0 + 30 \times (0 + 17) + 2 \times (0 + 17 + 27)$$
$$= 0 + 0 + 510 + 88$$
$$= 598$$

$$S = P - Q = 775 - 598 = 177$$

The continuity correction will be

$$\frac{2n - u_1 - u_k}{2(k-1)} = \frac{200 - 1 - 7}{2 \times 3} = 32.$$

Therefore, $S_c = 177 - 32 = 145$

Since the ties are so extensive in this case, it is wise to use formula 2.2 to compute the variance of S, for which we first need

$$\Sigma u_i^3 = 1^3 + 35^3 + 57^3 + 7^3 = 228412$$

$$\text{Variance} = \frac{t_1 t_2 (n^3 - \Sigma u_i^3)}{3n(n-1)} = \frac{51 \times 49 \times (1000000 - 228412)}{3 \times 100 \times 99}$$
$$= 64922.505$$

The z-score for our data will therefore be

$$z = \frac{S_c - \text{MEAN}}{\text{S.D.}} = \frac{145 - 0}{\sqrt{64922.505}} = 0.57$$

This is smaller than the upper tail critical value of 1.645, so we conclude that there is no reliable evidence of a difference between the degree results for the two years of students.

2.4 ESTIMATORS ASSOCIATED WITH THE RANK-SUM TEST

Having carried out the Rank-Sum Test and obtained a significant result, all we are able to say is that there is a reliable difference between the two samples. A test of significance does not tell us anything about the size of effect. Our discussion of power in Section 1.8 shows that we can obtain a statistically significant result even when there is a minute effect if we collect enough data. In most studies we wish to go beyond merely demonstrating that there is an effect to estimating the size of the effect. In our simplified example comparing two methods of teaching reading, demonstrating that Method B is better than Method A is a useful step, but we should like to know by how much it is better. This would be crucial if we are considering replacing Method A by Method B; it would only be worth doing so if the difference between the two is large.

In this section we discuss two different methods of estimating the size of the effect demonstrated by a significant Rank-Sum Test. The two methods will be introduced within the context of our simplified example.

When calculating an estimate, it is generally useful to assess how accurate the estimate is likely to be. To be able to do this, the standard error of the estimate is required (see section 1.10). A full discussion of standard errors is beyond the scope of this book, but the references cited below give further information for those interested. For our purposes, the estimators we discuss should be thought of as providing the best guess for the size of the effect; because they are guesses, they may not be strictly accurate.

The Hodges–Lehmann Estimator

Suppose Method B really is superior to Method A and we are prepared to assume that the main difference between the B scores and the A scores is one of location. If this is so, then children taught by Method B will have a constant amount, say d (for difference), added to the scores they would have obtained under Method A. The first technique we shall discuss, which was suggested by Hodges and Lehmann, provides an estimate of d. We shall illustrate it with the data shown in Table 2.3, our original example with no ties.

The simplest estimate is obtained by arbitrarily selecting one of the A scores, say 70, and one of the B scores, say 100, and finding the difference $B - A$, which is 30 in this case. Each such selection of an A and a B score provides an estimate of d,

Table 2.14. Calculations for the Hodges–Lehmann estimator

		B scores ($t_2 = 2$)	
		80	100
A	50	30	50
scores	70	10	30
($t_1 = 3$)	90	−10	10

and there are 3 x 2 = 6 different selections. The 6 estimates in this case are

$$80 - 70 = 10, \quad 80 - 90 = -10, \quad 80 - 50 = 30,$$

$$100 - 70 = 30, \quad 100 - 90 = 10, \quad 100 - 50 = 50.$$

The Hodges–Lehmann estimate is just the median of these 6 differences. Now, the median of a set of scores is just the one in the middle if there is an odd number of scores, or the average of the two middle scores if there is an even number of scores. So in this case the median $(10 + 30)/2 = 20$.

In general, there will be $t_1 t_2$ differences to calculate, and the Hodges–Lehmann estimate is the median of these. To tidy up the calculations, it is usually easier to represent the differences in the body of a table as shown in Table 2.14. Here, the *B* scores are written in increasing order to form the columns, while the *A* scores written in increasing order from the rows. The differences $B - A$ are written in the cells of the table. The resulting table looks like an ordered contingency table but it is not, since the numbers in the body of the table are difference scores and not frequencies. The table is useful for finding the median difference score, since the difference scores increase as you go from the bottom to the top and as you go from left to right. This means that in most cases the middle scores will lie on or near the main diagonal of such a table, since approximately half the scores lie to the right and above the diagonal, so it is not necessary to calculate all the difference scores, as we shall see in Example 2.6.

If we do calculate all the difference scores, this provides a check on our calculation of S, since the number of positive difference scores is P and the number of negative difference scores is Q. From Table 2.14, $P = 5$ and $Q = 1$, so S must be 4 for this example.

The resulting estimate of 20 for our example shows that our best bet for the effect of Method *B* is that it improves on Method *A* by increasing a child's score on the reading test by 20 points. An interesting property of the Hodges–Lehmann estimator is that it gives the best estimate of the amount that must be subtracted from each of the *B* scores for the effect to be entirely removed if a Rank-Sum Test is carried out on the resulting scores. Thus, if 20 is subtracted from each of the *B* scores, the modified table of results would be as follows.

Method *A*	Method *B*
70	60
90	80
50	

Carrying out a Rank-Sum Test on the modified table gives $S = 0$, indicating no effect.

For the Hodges–Lehmann estimator to be useful, the resulting estimate should be easily interpretable. In our example, an experimenter familiar with the reading test will probably find the estimate useful. However, suppose we had carried out the study without using the reading test and had merely ranked the children in terms of reading ability with the following results.

Method A	Method B
2	3
4	5
1	

The Hodges–Lehmann estimate for the size of the effect here would be 1.5. This means that being taught by Method B increases a child's rank by 1.5. Such a statement may not be so easy to interpret for an experimenter familiar with the area. In general, the Hodges–Lehmann estimator will be useful if the scale of the response variable has some substantive meaning to the investigator.

When there are ties in the response variable, the Hodges–Lehmann estimator may still be useful and is calculated in exactly the same way, as we shall see in Example 2.8. Frequently, however, extensive ties may mean that the estimate obtained is difficult to interpret (see Example 2.9).

For a further discussion of the Hodges–Lehmann estimator, including information about its properties when there are ties, and about its standard error, see Lehmann (1975, Section 2.5).

Somers' Delta

In cases where the Hodges–Lehmann estimator is not easy to interpret, a different approach to estimation that does not depend on the scale of the response variable may be useful. Suppose we select two children at random, one having been taught by Method A and one by Method B. What is the probability of the child taught by Method B having a higher reading score than the one taught by Method A? In general, this is just $P/(t_1 t_2)$. For our example, this gives 5/6 or 0.83. This is most easily seen to be correct from the table of differences given in Table 2.14. Five of the six differences are positive, so the probability of selecting a B child who scores higher than an A child is just 5/6. The resulting probability is readily interpretable and has been used as an estimator (see, for example, Bradley, 1968, p. 114, or Hollander and Wolfe, 1973, p. 77). However, for our purposes, it is more convenient to go one stage further and use as an estimator how much more probable it is to select a B child who scores higher than an A child than it is to select a B child who scores lower than an A child. The probability of selecting a B child who scores lower than an A child is $Q/(t_1 t_2)$, 1/6 or 0.17 in our case, so the resulting estimate is

$$\delta = \frac{P}{t_1 t_2} - \frac{Q}{t_1 t_2} = \frac{S}{t_1 t_2} \tag{2.4}$$

This estimator was suggested by Somers (1962) and we shall label it δ, the Greek letter delta. For our example, $\delta = 0.83 - 0.17 = 0.66$. Delta has the same value and the same interpretation, no matter whether the data are reading scores or rankings, so it is more generally useful than the Hodges–Lehmann estimator.

Whether or not there are ties, delta always lies between -1 and $+1$, a value of $+1$ reflecting the certainty of a B child scoring higher than an A child and a value of -1 reflecting the certainty of a B child scoring lower than an A child. Values of delta close to zero suggest no effect at all since they indicate that we are as likely to select a B child who scores higher than an A child as to select a B child who scores lower than an A child. Estimators such as this are frequently referred to as *measures of association*.

We discuss delta in a more general context in Chapter 5. For information about the standard error of delta see Goodman and Kruskal (1972). In Chapter 5, we shall also discuss Goodman and Kruskal's gamma and Kendall's tau b, two measures of association similar to delta, which may also be used in the Rank-Sum context.

Example 2.6 Estimating the Size of the Effect for Example 2.1

For the data of Example 2.1, the Rank-Sum Test indicated that subjects in Group 1 solved the test problem reliably faster than subjects in Group 2. The response variable in that example was the number of seconds taken to solve the test problem. Since time taken to solve a problem is a familiar measure that is readily interpretable, the Hodges–Lehmann estimator will provide useful information in this case. In Table 2.15 only the difference scores on or near the main diagonal are shown. There are $t_1 t_2 = 25$ difference scores, so the median will be the 13th smallest. As a first guess, suppose 40 is the median. Because of the way the table has been constructed, all the scores below the line drawn through the table will be less than 40 and we don't have to calculate them to verify this. There are eleven scores smaller than 40. Similarly there are twelve scores larger than 40. This implies that the two scores of 40 will be the 12th and 13th smallest scores, so our guess was correct

Table 2.15. Calculation of the Hodges–Lehmann estimate for the data from Example 2.1

		Group 2 ($t_2 = 5$)				
		91	94	105	120	130
Group 1 ($t_1 = 5$)	20					
	40	51	54			
	65		29	40	55	
	90				30	40
	100					30

in this case and the median is 40. Had the guess not been correct, the information gained could still be used to find the median. Had we chosen 30 as our initial guess, we should find that the two scores of 30 in the table are the 10th and 11th smallest scores, so two scores of 40 must be the 12th and 13th smallest.

40 is therefore the Hodges–Lehmann estimate of the treatment effect. So we can say that the effect of being given training problems similar to the test problem (Group 1) is to improve solution times by 40 seconds relative to the performance of Group 2.

Since the Hodges–Lehmann estimate is readily interpretable in this case, it would seem sensible to prefer it here. However, it may also be interesting to compute Somers' delta, since it provides different information. From the calculation in Table 2.5, we have $S = 21$, $t_1 = 5$ and $t_2 = 5$ for these data, so from formula 2.4,

$$\delta = \frac{21}{25} = 0.84$$

This indicates a large effect, suggesting that if we randomly selected one person from Group 1 and one from Group 2, it is 84% more likely that the Group 2 person takes longer than that the Group 1 person takes longer.

In this case, both estimators lead us to conclude that there is a large difference between the two samples.

Example 2.7 Estimating the Size of the Effect for Example 2.2

The Hodges–Lehmann estimator is not so readily interpretable for the data from Example 2.2, which compared two methods of weight reduction, but it still provides useful information. The data were percentage weight-losses, a scale that is not easy to interpret for many people. A further argument against the Hodges–Lehmann estimator is that with $t_1 = 28$ people in one group and $t_2 = 24$ people in the other, it would take a long time to find the estimate of d. There are $28 \times 24 = 672$ difference scores, so the estimate will be half-way between the 336th and 337th smallest of these, since there is an even number of scores. Even with the short-cut method used in Example 2.6, these scores will take a long time to find (although, if you have access to a computer, it is easy to write a program to find the estimate). The estimate turns out to be 2.27 in this case; the calculations are left as an exercise! Thus, the effect of the 2nd method of weight reduction is to increase percentage weight-loss by 2.27% relative to the first method.

Somers' delta may be more informative and is certainly easier to calculate for these data. In Table 2.6 we found S to be -474, so delta will be

$$\delta = \frac{S}{t_1 t_2} = \frac{-474}{28 \times 24} = -0.71$$

The negative S in this example indicates that method 2 leads to higher percentage weight-losses than method 1. The high negative δ indicates quite a large effect, suggesting that if we randomly selected one person who had used Method 1 and one who had used Method 2, it is 71% more likely that the Method 2 person will have a greater weight-loss than that the Method 1 person will have a greater weight-loss.

Example 2.8 Estimating the Size of the Effect for Example 2.4

For Helen Buckley's study of the relation between locus of control and desire to give up smoking, which we discussed in Example 2.4, the Hodges–Lehmann estimator provides a useful index of the difference between those who want to give up smoking and those who don't, since Rotter's *I/E* Scale is fairly widely used. The only difficulty here is that, with $t_1 = 20$ and $t_2 = 20$, 400 difference scores will need to be considered. However, in this case, since the *I/E* scale is scored in integers (whole numbers) and since there are so many ties, the calculations are simple. The table for computing the difference scores together with those difference scores on or near the main diagonal are given in Table 2.16. From the scores calculated, it looks as though the median difference score will be 2. Now, there are $t_1 t_2 = 400$ difference scores, so the median will be halfway between the 200th and the 201st smallest score. Each of the scores below the line will necessarily be smaller than 2 and there are 165 of these. There are 47 scores equal to 2, so 165 + 47 = 212 of the scores are smaller than 3. This means that both the 200th and the 201st smallest score will be 2, so the median difference score is 2, which is therefore the required estimate. Thus, we can conclude that, on average, those wanting to give up smoking score about 2 points less on the *I/E* scale than those not wanting to give up.

In Example 2.4, we found S to be 190 for these data, so delta will be

$$\delta = \frac{S}{t_1 t_2} = \frac{190}{400} = 0.475$$

This value is not as large as those obtained for the previous two examples, but it still indicates a reasonable effect.

Example 2.9 Estimating the Size of the Effect for Example 2.5

For the data of Example 2.5 shown in Table 2.13, the Hodges–Lehmann estimator will not be particularly useful. Apart from being tedious to calculate, the interpretation of an obtained estimate would

Table 2.16. Calculation of the Hodges–Lehmann estimate for the data from Example 2.4

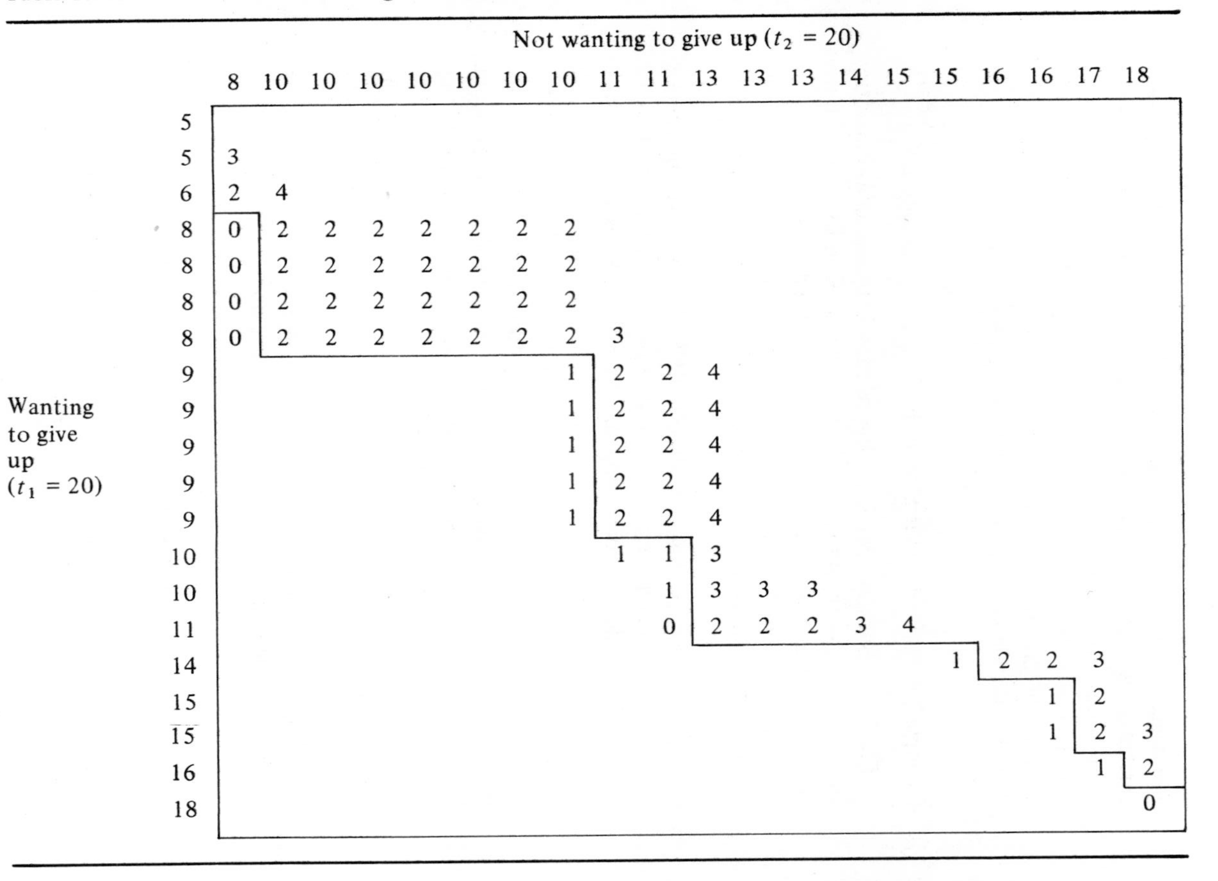

Wanting to give up ($t_1 = 20$)	Not wanting to give up ($t_2 = 20$)																			
	8	10	10	10	10	10	10	10	11	11	13	13	13	14	15	15	16	16	17	18
5																				
5	3																			
6	2	4																		
8	0	2	2	2	2	2	2	2												
8	0	2	2	2	2	2	2	2												
8	0	2	2	2	2	2	2	2												
8	0	2	2	2	2	2	2	2	3											
9								1	2	2	4									
9								1	2	2	4									
9								1	2	2	4									
9								1	2	2	4									
9								1	2	2	4									
10									1	1	3									
10										1	3	3	3							
11										0	2	2	2	3	4					
14																1	2	2	3	
15																		1	2	
15																		1	2	3
16																			1	2
18																				0

not be at all clear for such data. To say, for example, that one year's students differ from those of another year by having degree results that are about one-third of a class higher would not mean very much to most people. For such data, Somers' delta is much more informative. For the data used in Example 2.5, we should expect to obtain a relatively small value of delta, since the sample sizes were quite large and a non-significant result for the Rank-Sum Test was obtained. Delta is given by

$$\delta = \frac{S}{t_1 t_2} = \frac{177}{51 \times 49} = 0.071$$

which is sufficiently small to indicate a negligible effect, confirming the conclusions of the Rank-Sum Test. The low value of δ means that if we selected two students at random, one from each year, the probability that the student from the first year obtains a better degree than the student from the second year is not much different from the probability that the student from the first year obtains a worse degree than the other one.

2.5 THE FISHER EXACT TEST – TWO CATEGORY RESPONSE VARIABLE

We have noted above that exact tables for the Rank-Sum Test when there are extensive ties in the response variable are not generally available. A notable exception is when the ties become so extensive that the response variable has only two levels. If we used an ordered contingency table to record the data resulting from such a situation, we should obtain a 2 x 2 table. The version of the Rank-Sum Test thus obtained is so commonly used as to deserve a name of its own. It is generally known as the Fisher Exact Test, after Ronald Fisher, who first devised the test. It should always be remembered that, as is the case with the Rank-Sum Test, the Fisher Exact Test requires that the data be independent.

Simplified Example

In our example comparing two methods of teaching reading, suppose we had recorded simply whether each child had passed or failed the reading test. Then, with $t_1 = 3$ children taught by Method A and $t_2 = 2$ children taught by Method B, we might have obtained the following results, where the response variable has just the two levels P and F for pass and fail. This way of recording the results, which

Method *A*	Method *B*
F	F
P	P
F	

was natural for the Rank-Sum Test without ties, is rather wasteful when there are only two levels of the response variable. In this case, it is far more economical to record the data in the form of a 2 x 2 contingency table, as shown below.

		Result		
		F	P	t_i
Teaching method	A	2	1	3
	B	1	1	2
	u_i	3	2	$5 = n$

Test Statistic – *S*

Since the Fisher Exact Test is just the Rank-Sum Test with extensive ties, we have already seen in section 2.3 that S will be the test statistic. As before, we can compute S in a number of different ways. The first method, which involves calculating midranks and computing a rank-sum for the B scores is shown below.

Method A		Method B	
Score	Rank	Score	Rank
F	2	F	2
P	4.5	P	4.5
F	2		$R = 6.5$

$$S = 2R - t_2(n + 1) = 2 \times 6.5 - 2 \times 6 = 13 - 12 = 1.$$

Since this is not the best method of displaying the results, it is generally simpler to obtain S using the ordered contingency table method. From the 2 x 2 contingency table shown above, P, Q and S are computed as

$$P = 2 \times 1 + 1 \times 0 = 2$$
$$Q = 2 \times 0 + 1 \times 1 = 1$$
$$S = P - Q = 1,$$

as before.

Table 2.17. A generic 2 x 2 contingency table

a	b	t_1
c	d	t_2
u_1	u_2	n

It is helpful to capture what we have just done by means of a formula that will be applicable to all 2 x 2 contingency tables. Such tables will have the form shown in Table 2.17, where *a, b, c,* and *d* refer to the number of observations in each cell of the table, the t_i refer to the number of observations tied at each level of the explanatory variable, and the u_i refer to the number of observations tied at each level of the response variable. With this general form, our method of computing S will then be given by

$$P = ad$$

$$Q = bc$$

$$S = ad - bc$$

For our example $a = 2$, $b = 1$, $c = 1$, and $d = 1$, so $S = 2 \times 1 - 1 \times 1 = 1$, as before.

Null Distribution of S

We have already seen in Section 2.3 how to compute the null distribution of S when there are extensive ties. However, it will not hurt to have another example of this, applicable to 2 x 2 contingency tables, in view of the importance of this particular version of the test. If the null hypothesis is true, we assume that the assignment of children to teaching methods in no way affects whether they pass or fail. In this case, the number of children passing under Method B is determined simply by the random assignment of two children to be taught by that method. With $t_1 = 3$ and $t_2 = 2$, we know from our previous examples that there are ten possible ways of assigning children to teaching methods. If three children fail ($u_1 = 3$) and two pass ($u_2 = 2$), the ten possible patterns of results together with associated values of R and S (calculated using the midrank technique) will be those shown in Table 2.18. Under the null hypothesis, each of these ten patterns of results is equally likely to be obtained, so the null distribution of S will be as shown in Table 2.19.

Table 2.18. The 10 patterns of results and associated values of R and S for the case $t_1 = 3, t_2 = 2, u_1 = 3, u_2 = 2$

	Midrank of response variable						
	2	2	2	4.5	4.5	R	S
1.	*A*	*A*	*A*	*B*	*B*	9	6
2.	*A*	*A*	*B*	*A*	*B*	6.5	1
3.	*A*	*B*	*A*	*A*	*B*	6.5	1
4.	*A*	*A*	*B*	*B*	*A*	6.5	1
5.	*A*	*B*	*A*	*B*	*A*	6.5	1
6.	*B*	*A*	*A*	*A*	*B*	6.5	1
7.	*A*	*B*	*B*	*A*	*A*	4	–4
8.	*B*	*A*	*A*	*B*	*A*	6.5	1
9.	*B*	*A*	*B*	*A*	*A*	4	–4
10.	*B*	*B*	*A*	*A*	*A*	4	–4

Table 2.19. Null distribution of S for the Fisher Exact Test with $t_1 = 3$, $t_2 = 2$, $u_1 = 3$, $u_2 = 2$

S	-4	1	6
Probability	0.3	0.6	0.1

If we had predicted that Method B should be more effective than Method A and we were not interested in detecting extreme results going in the opposite direction, a one-tailed test is appropriate. From the way we calculated S for our example, large positive values are in line with this prediction, so we require an upper tail test. If we wished to use a significance level as low as 0.05, we can see from Table 2.19 that there is no relevant upper tail critical value of S. This merely reflects the fact that with only 5 children, any of the possible results are likely to be obtained by chance even if there is no effect. To be able to use one of the standard significance levels, we should need to collect more data. If we were prepared to use a significance level as high as 0.1, then Table 2.19 shows that the relevant upper tail critical value is 6, since $\text{prob}(S \geqslant 6) = 0.1$. S was 1 for our example data, which is smaller than this critical value, so even with such a high significance level we cannot reject the null hypothesis of no difference between the two methods.

If we had predicted that Method A should be more effective than Method B, a lower tail test would be appropriate, since high negative values of S are more in line with Method A being better. This time, even with a significance level as high as 0.1, there is no relevant critical value of S. From Table 2.19, it is clear that the null distribution of S is not symmetrical, as was the case for the Rank-Sum Test without ties (see, for example, Table 2.2). This means that in many cases the relevant critical value for a lower tail test will be different in magnitude from that for an upper tail test.

If we were interested in detecting differences between the methods in either direction, then a two-tailed test would be appropriate. Despite the asymmetry of the null distribution, two-tailed tests are easily constructed following the method outlined in Section 1.9. We first note that the statistic S reflects the magnitude of the difference between the two samples. The asymmetry means that it is just not possible to get a result as extreme in the negative direction as in the positive direction. This is most clearly seen in Table 2.18, where pattern 1 shows that it is possible to have *all* the B children passing and *all* the A children passing. There are no patterns indicating such an extreme difference in the other direction, simply because only two of the five children pass and the A group in this case must contain three children.

For a two-tailed test, we wish to reject the null hypothesis when there is evidence of a large difference in either direction. Therefore, to find two-tailed critical values, we use that value of S for which the probability of obtaining an S larger than or equal to it *or* smaller than or equal to $-S$ is the same as our required significance level. Thus, for our example, with a significance level of 0.1, 6 will be the required value, since prob $(S \geqslant 6)$ + prob $(S \leqslant -6) = 0.1$. The two-tailed critical values will then be -6 and 6, and we should reject the null hypothesis *either* if our obtained S is less than or equal to -6 *or* if it is greater than or equal to 6. With a significance level as high as 0.4, the critical values will be -4 and 4, since prob $(S \geqslant 4)$ + prob $(S \leqslant -4) = 0.1 + 0.3 = 0.4$.

Table of the Null Distribution of *S* for the Fisher Exact Test (Appendix Table C)

A table of critical values of the null distribution of S is provided in Table C of the Appendix. This is used in the same way as Table A for the Rank-Sum Test without ties. It has been constructed as described above. There is a separate entry for each combination of sample sizes (t_1 and t_2) and ties (u_1 and u_2); t_1 is always the larger of the two sizes, so that $t_1 \geqslant t_2$; u_1 always refers to that level of the response variable with the most extensive ties, so that $u_1 \geqslant u_2$. Both one- and two-tailed critical values are given for the three most commonly used significance levels, $\alpha = 0.05$, $\alpha = 0.01$, and $\alpha = 0.001$. Because of the asymmetry of the distribution, a separate entry is given for the upper and the lower tail in the one-tailed case.

To illustrate its use, suppose we had used larger sample sizes of 7 and 5 in our experiment and had obtained the following results:

	F	P	t_i
A	5	2	7
B	1	4	5
u_i	6	6	$12 = n$

In this case, $t_1 = 7$, $t_2 = 5$, $u_1 = 6$ and $u_2 = 6$, so with a one-tailed test using an α of 0.05, Table C tells us that the upper tail critical value of S is 30. Our obtained value of S is $5 \times 4 - 2 \times 1 = 18$, which is smaller than this critical value, so with these data we could not reject the null hypothesis. The number 30 is also the upper tail critical value in this case for a two-tailed test using an α of 0.05; here we should reject the null hypothesis if we obtained an $S \geqslant 30$ or $\leqslant -30$.

Since the number of combinations of sample sizes and ties is very large even for the 2×2 situation, Table C does not cater for all possibilities. Had we obtained instead the following results with $t_1 = 6$, $t_2 = 6$, $u_1 = 7$ and $u_2 = 5$, we find no entry in Table C.

	F	P	t_i
A	5	1	6
B	2	4	6
u_i	7	5	$12 = n$

However, we *can* use Table C in such a case, by noting that the Fisher Exact Test is neutral with respect to which variable is labelled explanatory and which is labelled response. Exactly the same results will be obtained, although they may mean different things in terms of our experiment. This means that we can get the correct critical value for this situation by reversing the labels, setting $t_1 = 7, t_2 = 5, u_1 = 6$ and $u_2 = 6$ and using the same part of the table as before to give a critical value of 30 for an α of 0.05. Table C has been constructed only for the cases where $t_1 \geqslant u_1$. Where that does not hold, as in this example, the table can be used by reversing which variable is labelled with t's and which with u's.

The Normal Approximation to S

Since the Fisher Exact Test is just the Rank-Sum Test with extensive ties, we can immediately use the normal approximation for the tied case given in Section 2.3. However, since the ties are so extensive that there are only two levels of the response variable, we can cut down the amount of work necessary by noting that the expressions for the variance and the continuity correction given in Section 2.3 can be written in a simpler form. The variance is now given by the formula

$$\text{Variance} = \frac{t_1 t_2 u_1 u_2}{n-1} \tag{2.5}$$

while the continuity correction becomes $n/2$. For our simple example with $t_1 = 3$, $t_2 = 2$, $u_1 = 3$ and $u_2 = 2$, the variance will then be $3 \times 2 \times 3 \times 2/4 = 9$ and the continuity correction will be $5/2 = 2.5$. We can check that these calculations are correct by computing the variance of the possible S values directly from Table 2.18 and also noting that the interval between consecutive S values is 5, which means that a continuity correction of 5/2 is in fact appropriate. As with all uses of S, the mean of the possible S values will be 0 in this case.

Thus, when the data obtained fall outside the scope of Table C, a normal approximation to the null distribution of the Fisher Exact Test will be given by computing a z-score as follows and referring it to Table B.

$$z = \frac{S_c - \text{Mean}}{\text{S.D.}}$$

where

$$S_c = \begin{cases} S - n/2, \text{ if } S \text{ is positive} \\ S + n/2, \text{ if } S \text{ is negative} \end{cases}$$

$$\text{Mean} = 0$$

and

$$\text{S.D.} = \sqrt{\frac{t_1 t_2 u_1 u_2}{n-1}}$$

To see how this approximation fares with our example, we can compare the exact probability of getting an S of 6 or larger, which we know from the null distribution constructed above to be 0.1, with the approximate value given by Table B. In this case, with $S = 6$, we have $S_c = 3.5$ and

$$z = \frac{3.5 - 0}{\sqrt{9}} = 1.17$$

From Table B(i), we find prob ($z \geqslant 1.17$) = 0.121, which is surprisingly close to the exact value of 0.1, in view of the small sample sizes used in the example.

As before, the normal approximation improves with increasing sample sizes.

The Independence Assumption

As noted above, the Fisher Exact Test, like the Wilcoxon Rank-Sum Test, assumes that the data have been collected and recorded in an independent manner. This assumption is so frequently (unknowingly) violated in practice that it is worth discussing further. Lack of independence frequently occurs when several data items are obtained from a single individual. If *all* the data apply to one person there is no problem – the null hypothesis and research hypothesis relate to that individual only and are not generalizable. Even in his case, however, we must assume that there is some sort of independence between the observations obtained from that individual if we want to use the Fisher Exact Test. We shall see an example of this use of the test in Example 2.11 below.

On the other hand, the situation gets really messy if one individual gives some but not all of the data to be analysed. A simple example will illustrate this. Suppose we ask six men and six women to solve five difficult problems. We record for each person the number of problems correctly solved. So far so good. We now unthinkingly cast the results in the form of a 2 x 2 contingency table, as shown below. We are interested in whether men and women differ in their ability to solve these

	Correct	Incorrect	
Men	5	25	30
Women	25	5	30
	30	30	60

problems. On the surface, the table suggests that women are better than men at these problems, and they may well be, but we cannot test whether this is the case using the Fisher Exact Test. The contingency table contains dependent data. Each man and each woman may well be contributing to both categories of the response variable and is certainly contributing more than once to one of the cells. By representing these data in the form of a 2 x 2 table, we have lost all information about variability between subjects in the male and female groups. The 5 in the first cell may represent only one good man's results, which means that all the other men each failed to solve all five problems. Alternatively, it may result from five men each solving one problem. With the data recorded in this form, we have no way of knowing which alternative is correct.

If, on the other hand, we had kept track of the number of problems correctly solved by each person, we could record this information in a table like the following one.

Men	3	1	0	1	0	0
Women	5	4	5	5	3	3

In this table, the data *are* independent. Each person contributes only once, so we know that the 3 in the male group represents the fact that the first man solved 3 of the 5 problems. With the data in this form, we are now able to use the Rank-Sum Test (with ties) to test whether the women are better than the men at solving these problems. If we prefer to record the data in the form of an ordered contingency table, the appropriate table will be the following one, which contains independent data and from which the other representation of the data can be precisely reconstructed.

	Number of problems solved				
	0	1	3	4	5
Men	3	2	1		
Women			2	1	3

Further Comments

The Fisher Exact Test is crucially important for two main reasons. The first is that it is applicable to a commonly occurring research situation, namely that in which independent data are recorded in a 2 x 2 contingency table. The second is that it is possible to regard it as a special case of a large number of other tests. Different ways of thinking about the Fisher Exact Test provide different ways of generalizing it and thereby provide tests applicable to a large number of research situations. The reason for this is that, in a 2 x 2 contingency table, both the explanatory variable and the response variable take only two possible values. As we noted when discussing contingency tables in Section 2.3, any variable with only two levels may be regarded either as categorical or as ordinal. Thus, the Rank-Sum Test is only one way of generalizing the Fisher Exact Test, in this case the response variable being regarded as an ordinal variable. Some of the other ways of generalizing the test are described in Chapters 4, 5, and 8.

In discussing the Fisher Exact Test we have assumed so far that two separate samples of observations have been collected. In an experimental study such as our reading example, this is the only way of collecting the data. One sample of children is randomly assigned to be taught by Method A and a second sample is randomly assigned to be taught by Method B. In such cases, we have control over the sample sizes, t_1 and t_2, and it is usual to attempt to make them equal.

Suppose, however, that we were doing a correlational study to investigate whether there is an association between smoking and lung cancer. In such a correlational study, there are a number of different ways of collecting the data. One way, which is similar to the method used in experimental studies, is to select t_1 smokers and t_2 non-smokers and decide for each person whether or not there is evidence of lung cancer. Here again we can control the sample sizes and we should usually want them to be approximately equal. A rather different way of collecting the data would be to take a *single* sample of n people and cross-classify them according to whether or not they smoked and according to whether or not they had lung cancer. Here we only have control over n, the total number of people in the study, and we are not able to control t_1 and t_2. Such differences in the method of collecting data are known as differences in sampling method. For the present example, both sampling methods lead to data that may be represented in the form of a 2 x 2 contingency table and the Fisher Exact Test is applicable in both cases. The examples given in this chapter all make use of the first sampling method. For an example of the second sampling method, see Example 5.6. For a fuller discussion of sampling methods in the context of 2 x 2 contingency tables, see Fleiss (1973).

For a further discussion of the Fisher Exact Test from a different perspective, see Bradley (1968, Section 8.2), in which a straightforward method of computing the exact null distribution is presented.

Example 2.10 The Fisher Exact Test

A clinical psychologist has developed a test of cognitive complexity. The test classifies each person as cognitively complex or cognitively simple. It is claimed that, if the test is valid, it should differentiate between obsessional neurotic patients and non-obsessional patients, with the obsessionals being more likely to be classified as cognitively simple. The results of a validation study are shown in the table below, which gives the number of obsessionals and non-obsessionals classified as cognitively complex or cognitively simple. Do these results suggest that the test is valid? These data are independent, since each of the 25 people contributes once to only one of the cells. To use Table C we note that the largest marginal total is 15, so we set $t_1 = 15$, $t_2 = 10$, $u_1 = 13$ and $u_2 = 12$. With these values and a two-tailed test with $\alpha = 0.05$, Table C shows that the critical values of S are -70 and 70. S is computed from the data as $1 \times 4 - 11 \times 9 = -95$ which is more extreme than the lower tail critical value of -70, so we reject the null hypothesis of no difference between the groups. Because of the way we

Table 2.20. Hypothetical data for Example 2.10

	Complex	Simple	
Obsessionals	1	11	12
Non-obsessionals	9	4	13
	10	15	25

set up the contingency table, if the test is valid, we should obtain a negative value of S. Therefore, this result does provide reliable evidence in favour of the validity of this test of congitive complexity: the obsessionals were more often classified as cognitively simple than the non-obsessionals.

Example 2.11 The Fisher Exact Test with Data from a Single Individual

A man who claims to possess extra-sensory perception was asked to guess the colour of each of 10 cards, knowing that 5 were red and 5 were black. The results are given below. Was he guessing? To apply the Fisher Exact Test to this example, we need to be careful that the independence assumption has not been violated. In this case *all* the data come from a single individual, so we shall only be able to draw conclusions applicable to this individual, which is what we want here. The crucial aspect of independence in this case turns on how the experiment was conducted. Suppose the man was presented with the 10 cards one at a time and had to say 'red' or 'black' to each. If the card was turned over after each trial, then the man would have some knowledge of what the later cards will be – for example, once 5 red cards have been shown, the rest must be black. In this case, the trials and hence the data recorded in the contingency table will not be independent, so that the Fisher Exact Test is not appropriate. If, on the other hand, he is given no knowledge of results until after the session, then the Fisher Exact Test will provide useful information. Even in this case, it is almost certain that his performance on consecutive trials will not be independent. But this time, we have no knowledge of the possible sources of dependency. Carrying out the Fisher Exact Test then gives us a test of a particular sort of dependency, i.e. that in which the guessed colours are determined by the actual colours, among all the other sorts of dependency that are possible.

In this latter case, we can therefore apply the Fisher Exact Test, with $t_1 = 5$, $t_2 = 5$, $u_1 = 5$ and $u_2 = 5$. If we use a one-tailed test with $\alpha = 0.05$, the upper tail critical value of S is given in Table C as 25. The value of S computed from the data is $4 \times 4 - 1 \times 1 = 15$, which is smaller than this critical value, so we cannot reject the null hypothesis

Table 2.21. Hypothetical data for Example 2.11

		Guessed colour		
		Red	Black	
Actual colour	Red	4	1	5
	Black	1	4	5
		5	5	10

that the man was guessing, even though he makes only 2 mistakes in the 10 trials.

We have used a one-tailed test since we are interested in whether the man does significantly better than chance. In studies like this, there is frequently some interest in identifying a person who does significantly worse than chance. Thus, we might argue that a two-tailed test would be more appropriate. With this example, our conclusion with a two-tailed test would be the same.

Example 2.12 The Fisher Exact Test with Large Samples

In an experiment on the effects of different instructions on recognition memory, two groups of 30 people read a long passage. They are later required to say whether a particular sentence appeared in the passage, saying 'same' if they thought the sentence appeared in exactly the same form or 'different' otherwise. Before reading the passage, the first group are told that they will later be required to remember the detailed construction of the sentences in the passage, while the second group are told simply that their comprehension of the passage will be tested. The number of people in each group saying same (S) and different (D) is recorded in Table 2.22. Do the two groups differ in the proportion of same judgements? We first note that the data are independent; each person contributes once only to a single cell of the table. To apply the Fisher Exact Test here we need to use the normal approximation, since no matter which way we label the marginal totals, we shall be outside the range of Table C.

Suppose we wish to use a two-tailed test with a significance level of 0.05. Then Table B(ii) gives −1.96 and 1.96 as the lower and upper tail critical values of z. To compare these with our data, we compute S to be $25 \times 15 - 5 \times 15 = 300$. $S_c = S - n/2 = 300 - 30 = 270$. The variance is then $t_1 t_2 u_1 u_2/(n-1)$ or $30 \times 30 \times 40 \times 20/59 = 12203.390$, so the resulting z-score is

$$z = \frac{S_c - \text{Mean}}{\text{S.D.}}$$

$$= \frac{270 - 0}{\sqrt{12203.390}} = 2.44$$

Table 2.22. Hypothetical data for Example 2.12

		S	D	
Instructions	Memory	25	5	30
	Comprehension	15	15	30
		40	20	60

This value exceeds the upper tail critical value, so we reject the null hypothesis and conclude that our two instruction conditions differ in the proportion of same judgements obtained. Inspection of the table of results then shows that instructions to memorize lead to a greater proportion of same judgements than do instructions to comprehend.

2.6 ESTIMATORS ASSOCIATED WITH THE FISHER EXACT TEST

There are several different ways of estimating the size of the effect when the data are in the form of a 2 x 2 contingency table. Of the two discussed in Section 2.4, only Somers' delta is useful here. This is the only one we shall discuss in this section and we shall see it has a particularly simple interpretation in 2 x 2 tables. In Chapter 5, we shall see that Goodman and Kruskal's gamma and Kendall's tau *b* are also particularly useful measures of association for 2 x 2 tables.

Somer's Delta

Suppose, as in our original simplified example in Section 2.5, that one of the three children taught by Method *A* passed and one of the two children taught by Method *B* passed. In this case, $S = 1$, $t_1 = 3$ and $t_2 = 2$, so, from formula 2.4, Somers' delta will be

$$\delta = \frac{S}{t_1 t_2} = \frac{1}{3 \times 2} = \frac{1}{6} \text{ or } 0.167$$

This may be interpreted, as before, as saying that, if two children are selected at random, one from the *A* group and one from the *B* group, it is about 17% more likly that the *A* child does better than the *B* child than the other way round.

In this case, delta may equivalently be viewed as estimating the difference in the proportion of children passing (or failing) under the two methods. Since ½ of the children passed under Method *B* and 1/3 under Method *A*, the difference is just 1/3 – ½ = –1/6. Alternatively, the difference in the proportion of children failing will be 2/3 – ½ = 1/6. These two calculations have the same magnitude (but different signs), since they are estimating the same thing from different points of view. Calculating the difference in proportions passing (or failing) will always give the same result as calculating delta, as here.

Thus, *for 2 x 2 tables only*, Somers' delta may be interpreted as estimating the difference in proportion of subjects in each group at one of the two levels of the response variable. When the data are represented in the form of an ordered contingency table labelled as in Table 2.17, δ may then be calculated either using formula 2.4 or, equivalently, as

$$\delta = \frac{a}{t_1} - \frac{c}{t_2} \tag{2.6}$$

For information about the standard error of δ when used for 2 x 2 tables, see Hodges and Lehmann (1970, p. 251).

Example 2.13 Estimating the Difference in Proportions for Example 2.10

For the data shown in Table 2.20, the Fisher Exact Test indicated a reliable difference between obsessional neurotic patients and non-obsessional patients on the test of cognitive complexity. Using formula 2.6, the estimate of the difference in the proportion of people classified as complex in the two groups is

$$\delta = \frac{a}{t_1} - \frac{c}{t_2} = \frac{1}{12} - \frac{9}{13} = -0.609$$

Since we have already found S to be −95 for these data, we can get the same answer using formula 2.4:

$$\frac{S}{t_1 t_2} = \frac{-95}{12 \times 13} = -0.609.$$

This suggest that approximately 61% fewer obsessionals than non-obsessionals will be classified as complex using this test.

Example 2.14 Estimating the Difference in Proportions for Example 2.12

Using formula 2.6 with the data shown in Table 2.22, our estimate of the degree to which the proportion of 'same' judgements is larger under memory instructions than under comprehension instructions is

$$\delta = \frac{a}{t_1} - \frac{c}{t_2} = \frac{25}{30} - \frac{15}{30} = 0.333$$

Thus, there are approximately 33% more 'same' judgements under memory instructions than under comprehension instructions.

2.7 SUMMARY OF SUGGESTED PROCEDURE

This section and similar ones at the end of each subsequent chapter summarize the main points discussed in the chapter. Once the contents of the chapter have been understood, it may be used as a quick way of finding the calculations appropriate for each test. Relevant formulae are repeated here and suggestions for using the tests are summarized.

General Points

1. Do your data consist of two independent groups? If not, look elsewhere (see the table at the front of the book for suggestions).
2. Is the response variable ordinal? If so, try the Rank-Sum Test.

3. Does the response variable have two categories? If so, try the the Fisher Exact Test.
4. Is the response variable categorical with more than two categories? If so, look in Chapter 8.

Rank-Sum Test

1. Do you wish to test whether the scores of one group tend to be higher than those of the other? If not, see the references at the end of Section 2.1.
2. Find t_1, the number of scores in the larger group, and t_2, the number in the smaller group, and $n = t_1 + t_2$. Select a significance level, α, and decide whether a one- or a two-tailed test is required.
3. Are more than a quarter of the scores on the response variable involved in ties? If so, go to 8.
4. Calculate S by either method a method b:
   (*a*) *Direct method*. Focus on one group and, for each score in that group, calculate p, the number of scores in the other group strictly larger, and q, the number of scores in the other group strictly smaller. Find P, the sum of the p's, and Q, the sum of the q's. Find $S = P - Q$.
   (*b*) *Rank-sum method*. Rank all the scores; if there are ties, use midranks. Find R, the sum of the ranks in the smaller group. Find $S = 2R - t_2(n + 1)$.
5. Are t_1 and t_2 both less than 26? If not, go to 7.
6. From Table A, find the relevant critical value(s) of S and make decision as specified at the top of Table A.
   Go to 9.

7. *Normal approximation*.

$$\text{Compute Variance of } S = \frac{t_1 t_2 (n + 1)}{3} \qquad (2.1)$$

$$\text{Compute } S_c = \begin{cases} S - 1, \text{ if } S \text{ positive} \\ S + 1, \text{ if } S \text{ negative} \end{cases}$$

$$\text{Compute } z = \frac{S_c}{\text{S.D.}}, \text{ where S.D.} = \sqrt{\text{Variance}}$$

   From Table B(ii), find critical value(s) of z and make decision. If t_2 is less than 4 the approximation may not be accurate. If there are ties and the obtained z is close to the critical value, use the more accurate approximation given in 8(b).
   Go to 9.

8. *Extensive ties*
   (a) Represent the data in the form of an ordered contingency table with marginal totals t_i giving the number of scores in each group and u_i giving the number of scores tied at a particular value on the response variable. Check that the largest proportion u_i/n is not close to unity; if it is, the normal approximation in 8(b) may not be accurate. Check also that the sample sizes

t_i are not too small; for small t_i the approximation may not be accurate. Compute S as shown in Example 2.5.

(b) Normal approximation.

$$\text{Variance} = \frac{t_1 t_2 (n^3 - \Sigma u_i^3)}{3n(n-1)} \tag{2.2}$$

Continuity correction = $[2n - u_1 - u_k]/[2(k-1)]$, where k is the number of distinct scores on response variable. Compute $z = S_c/\text{S.D.}$, where S.D. = $\sqrt{\text{Variance}}$, and compare with critical value(s) given in Table B(ii) to make decision.

9. *Estimating the size of the effect*. Use one or both of the following estimators.
   (a) *Hodges-Lehmann estimator*. Useful only if the scores on the response variable are on an easily interpretable scale. See Example 2.6 for the necessary calculations.
   (b) *Somers' delta*. To estimate how much more likely it is to select a person from the first sample who scores higher than a person from the second sample than the other way round, calculate

$$\delta = \frac{S}{t_1 t_2} \tag{2.4}$$

Fisher Exact Test

1. Represent data in the form of a 2 x 2 contingency table. Label the marginal totals so that $t_1 \geqslant t_2$, $u_1 \geqslant u_2$ and $t_1 \geqslant u_1$. Compute $S = ad - bc$ (see Table 2.17). Select the significance level, α, and decide whether a one- or a two- tailed test is required. Is $t_1 > 18$? If so, go to 3.
2. From Table C, find the relevant critical value(s) of S and make decision as specified at the top of Table C.
   Go to 4.
3. *Normal approximation*

   $$\text{Compute Variance of } S = \frac{t_1 t_2 u_1 u_2}{n-1} \tag{2.5}$$

   Continuity correction = $n/2$
   Compute $z = S_c/\text{S.D.}$, where S.D. = $\sqrt{\text{Variance}}$, and compare with critical value(s) given in Table B(ii) to make decision.
4. *Estimating the size of the effect*. To estimate the difference in proportions, make sure the contingency table has rows representing levels of the explanatory variable; if not, transpose it so that it does.

   Compute

   $$\delta = \frac{a}{t_1} - \frac{c}{t_2} \tag{2.6}$$

   or, equivalently,

   $$\delta = \frac{S}{t_1 t_2} \tag{2.4}$$

   For other relevant estimators, see Chapter 5.

2.8 EXERCISES

Section 2.1

1. 10 men and 8 women each complete a questionnaire reflecting distortion of body image. Do the data shown below support the prediction that women have a more distorted body image than men? Large scores imply greater distortion.

Men	10	20	19	6	7	18	23	12	25	21
Women	22	17	24	14	26	30	29	28		

2. As part of a study of personality differences among psychologists, one group of six psychologists working on decision-making was compared with a second group of six working on learning theory in terms of amount of prevarication. Accordingly, time taken in minutes to make a simple decision was recorded for each person. What conclusions may be drawn?

Decision-makers	15	7	5	10	11	9
Learning theorists	4	8	6	2	1	3

3. Compute S for the previous exercises using the other method and verify that both methods give the same result. Does it make any difference to the rank-sum method if we rank the scores from high to low rather than from low to high before calculating R?
4. (Optional) Calculate the null distribution of S for the case $t_1 = 3$, $t_2 = 3$ and compare your obtained distribution with the critical values given in Table A. (There are 20 possible patterns of results that need to be considered.)

Section 2.2

5. To test the effects of different instructions on simple reaction times, 24 people are randomly assigned to one of two groups of 12. One group is instructed to respond as quickly as possible (Speed instructions), while the other group is instructed to respond as accurately as possible (Accuracy instructions). Their reaction times are shown below. (a) Do the two groups differ? (b) Suppose you don't have access to Table A and have to use the normal approximation. If you set α at 0.01, is the normal approximation accurate in this case?

Speed instructions	172	146	165	170	139	183	160	167	122	175	125	189
Accuracy instructions	202	187	217	194	185	173	197	180	161	196	178	177

Section 2.3

6. Test the prediction made in Exercise 1, first with the data shown in (*a*) and then with the data shown in (*b*).

(*a*)	Men	10	20	20	6	7	18	23	12	25	21
	Women	20	17	24	14	26	30	29	28		
(*b*)	Men	10	15	15	20	22	20	15	15	15	15
	Women	22	22	22	15	20	20	20	22		

7. Another sample of 20 men and 20 women is given a different test of body image; this test yields the three classifications Grossly Distorted (GD), Slightly Distorted (SD) and Not Distorted (ND). Do the data below support the predicted difference between men and women?

	GD	SD	ND
Men	1	12	7
Women	2	15	3

Section 2.4

8. Estimate the size of the effect for the data in each of Exercises 1, 2, 5, 6 and 7.

Section 2.5

9. Another sample of 10 men and 11 women is given the test of Exercise 7. This time nobody scored GD. Test the prediction with the data below.

	SD	ND
Men	2	8
Women	6	5

10. How good is the normal approximation for the data of Exercise 9?
11. A person takes part in a study of the 'feeling-of-knowing' phenomenon. The definitions of 40 words are presented and after each definition the person classifies it in terms of the degree to which the word defined comes to mind, using the following 3-point scale:

A. I know the word and can retrieve it;
B. I have some 'feeling-of-knowing' without immediately being able to retrieve it;
C. I have no knowledge of the word defined.

Following this phase of the study, the person attempts to recognize the 40 target words from a list of 80 alternatives. Our interest is such a study might centre on whether words classified into category *B* are more likely to be recognized than those in category *C* (ignoring those in category *A*). Test this prediction with the data below.

		Recognized	Not recognized
Category	*B*	10	4
	C	5	11

Section 2.6

12. Estimate the size of the effect for the data in Exercises 9 and 11.
13. Which of the examples in this chapter are experimental studies and which are correlational studies?

CHAPTER 3

If they be two, they are two so
As stiff twin compasses are two.

John Donne, *Valediction: Forbidding Mourning*

Tests for One Sample or Two Related Samples

The tests to be introduced in this chapter are applicable either when one-sample data are collected (see Examples 1.1 and 1.2) or when the data consist of two related samples (see Examples 1.7 and 1.8). The response variable is assumed to be either ordinal or categorical with two categories. For the two-sample situation, the tests in this chapter are restricted to the case in which only one observation is collected for each subject under each level of the explanatory variable. The more general case is covered in Chapter 7.

3.1 THE WILCOXON SIGNED-RANK TEST – ORDINAL RESPONSE VARIABLE

The Signed-Rank Test is another frequently used test devised by Frank Wilcoxon. It may be applied equally well to one-sample data or to data from two related samples. In the one-sample situation, it is normally used to test whether the data come from a symmetric population with a specified median (the null hypothesis) or from a symmetric population with a median different from the one specified (the alternative hypothesis). Example 1.1 illustrates such a one-sample situation (see Chapter 1, section 1.6). In the two-sample situation (e.g. Example 1.7), the Signed-Rank Test is sensitive to differences in location between the two samples, and is generally used to test whether the difference between the two scores for each subject comes from a population that is symmetric about a median of zero (the null hypothesis) or from a population with a median different from zero (the alternative hypothesis). The test assumes that the data (in the one-sample situation) or the difference-scores (in the two-sample situation) are continuous ordinal data from a symmetric population. It also assumes that each subject's data are independent of the data from the other subjects.

In describing the test, we shall concentrate on its use in the two-sample situation. The one-sample use is almost identical and will be described briefly at the end of the section.

Advantages and Disadvantages of using Related Samples

The tests discussed in Chapter 2 may be applied to experiments with two independent groups of subjects. Each subject gives one response at only one level of the explanatory variable. Such experimental designs require a large number of subjects. It is also well known that individual subjects vary a great deal on practically everything we are interested in measuring. The independent groups design attempts to get round this problem by assigning subjects randomly to groups. The aim of such random assignment is to spread out the variability between subjects as evenly as possible throughout both levels of the explanatory variable. Thus, in our reading example of Section 2.1, it may be the case that some of the children in our sample of 5 would be better readers than the others no matter which method they were taught by. By assigning the 5 children randomly to the two methods of teaching we are attempting to reduce the probability that the inherently good readers will all be assigned to one of the groups, thereby biasing the results in favour of that group.

In some experimental situations, a related samples design allows us to take more direct account of the variability between subjects. For example, suppose we are interested in whether a new drug (Drug X) tends to reduce reaction time (RT) when compared with a placebo drug (Drug Y). Since we know that people differ widely in their RTs, it is helpful to use a related samples design, in which we measure each person's RT twice, once after receiving Drug X and once after receiving Drug Y. If Drug X does reduce RT, then for each person the Drug X RT should tend to be smaller than the Drug Y RT. If Drug X has no effect on RT, then there should be no systematic difference between the two RTs across all people. This design, while reducing the variability between subjects, carries with it a great danger. To be sure that any systematic difference we observe between the two RTs is due only to the effects of the drugs, we must assume that there is no carryover effect across treatments. So, if all subjects are given Drug X first, we must assume that their RTs to Drug Y are not affected by their previous response to Drug X, either in terms of the drug still being in their systems or in terms of practice at the reaction time response. This assumption is rarely justified, but its effects can be mitigated somewhat by counterbalancing or randomizing the order in which the two drugs are administered. Randomization is the most frequently used and simplest method; it involves deciding randomly for each subject which drug should be administered first. In counterbalancing, half the subjects are given Drug X first followed by Drug Y and the other half receive them in reverse order. Such a procedure makes it possible to test whether there is any carryover or order effect. Some suggestions as to how such tests of order effects may be carried out with counterbalanced designs are made in Section 3.5.

A further way of getting round the difficulty of carryover effects in a related samples design is to use pairs of subjects who are comparable in as many relevant ways as possible. One member of each pair is given Drug X and the other Drug Y. This technique is frequently used in twin studies. The pairs of subjects are generally referred to as *matched pairs*.

Notice that the related samples design would probably not be very helpful in our reading study. Once a child has been taught to read by one method, there will necessarily be a carryover effect if the same child is taught by a second method. Even the techniques of randomizing or counterbalancing will not help here. The option of using matched pairs of subjects is still open to us however, although it would be difficult to decide along what variables we might sensibly match children who are learning to read.

Simplified Example

Suppose we have obtained data from three people in the drug experiment described above. Each person has produced a reaction time response after receiving each drug. Let us assume that for each subject we have randomly decided which drug to administer first as a crude attempt to get round the problem of carryover effects. Let n refer to the number of subjects or number of pairs of observations in the experiment; in our case, $n = 3$. Suppose the data are those shown in Table 3.1, where the reaction times are measured in msec.

In this example the explanatory variable is the drug used, which has the two possible 'scores', Drug X and Drug Y. The response variable consists of the reaction times measured under each drug. Each subject gives one reaction time under each level of the explanatory variable.

For each subject, the difference between the two RTs is calculated; this is shown in the row $X_i - Y_i$. This step is the only difference between the one-sample and the two-sample application of the Signed-Rank Test. By calculating difference scores we have converted a two-sample situation into a one-sample one. It is because of the necessity to calculate difference scores that the Signed-Rank Test and the other tests in this chapter require only one observation per subject under each level of the

Table 3.1. Data and calculation of $W+$ for simplified example

	Subjects			
	1	2	3	$n = 3$
RT for Drug X	236	210	203	
RT for Drug Y	241	216	200	
Difference $X_i - Y_i$	−5	−6	3	
Rank of $\lvert X_i - Y_i \rvert$	2	3	1	
Signed-Rank	−2	−3	+1	$W+ = 1$

explanatory variable in the two-sample case. A more sensible experimental procedure for our example might have been to collect several RTs for each subject under each drug. In this situation, we could of course subtract the average of the RTs under Drug Y from the average under Drug X to obtain a single difference score for each subject. This might well be a sensible procedure in some cases, but more often than not we should not be making full use of the data supplied by each subject. The tests described in Chapter 7 attempt to remedy this is some extent, and we should be wise to use the tests described there rather than the tests of the present chapter in such cases.

Test Statistic – *W*+

Suppose that the two drugs have no differential effect. As long as we can assume that there is no carryover effect that might bias the results, there should be no systematic difference between the X and the Y scores for each subject. If we had a perfect measuring device and could completely get rid of variability in responding and were certain that there was no carryover effect, then the difference scores should all be zero. However, since we are bound to get within-subject variability with RT data, it is reasonable to assume that a positive difference score is as likely to be obtained as a negative one for each subject. In addition, we might also be prepared to assume that the magnitude of any positive difference scores should be about the same as the magnitude of the negative difference scores. This is the null hypothesis of the Signed-Rank Test and is all that was meant by the more formal statement earlier in the section that under the null hypothesis the difference score for each subject comes from a population that is symmetric about a median of zero. It is further assumed that the difference scores are continuous, so that no difference scores of exactly equal magnitude should occur and no zero difference scores should occur.

On the other hand, suppose that Drug X really does lead to faster RTs than Drug Y. This is the alternative hypothesis. In this case, we should expect more negative difference scores than positive ones. In addition, if we do get any positive difference scores, we might reasonably expect them to be small in magnitude relative to the negative difference scores.

The test statistic based on this argument is very simple to compute. We shall label it $W+$. The sequence of calculations is shown in Table 3.1 along with the data. Having worked out a difference score for each subject in row $X_i - Y_i$, in the next row we rank order the difference scores from low to high, *ignoring the signs.* In our case the difference scores are –5, –6, and +3. The smallest of these numbers is –6, but if we ignore the signs, the smallest number is 3. So our scores get ranks of 2, 3 and 1, respectively. In the final row of the table, the ranks are remarried with the signs of the original difference scores to give –2, –3, and +1. The statistic $W+$ is then simply the sum of all the positive ranks. For our example, there is only one positive rank; this has value 1, so $W+ = 1$.

It is easy to see that $W+$ is capturing what we want from the situation. If it is small, there should be few positive difference scores of small magnitude, so our alternative hypothesis is quite likely to be correct. The smaller $W+$ becomes, the less confidence we should have in the null hypothesis.

Null Distribution of $W+$

We now have to work out the null distribution of $W+$, so that we may decide how small an obtained $W+$ needs to be before we can be confident that it was very unlikely to have occurred under the null hypothesis. This will involve deciding on the set of all possible outcomes that could have occurred in the experiment.

We first note that, if the null hypothesis is true, since each subject's difference score is assumed to come from a population that is symmetric about zero, it is as likely to have a positive sign associated with it as a negative one. This is saying in effect that the two RTs obtained from subject 1, for example, represent our best estimates of that subject's RTs, but it is an accident that the smaller RT happened to be associated with Drug X. If we repeated the experiment with that subject, we are just as likely to get a difference score with a magnitude of 5, but this time the subject may well have a faster reaction to Drug Y, leading to a positive difference score.

This means that the rank ordering of the difference scores will always stay the same, since this depends only on their magnitudes and not on their signs. To find the null distribution, then, all we need do is to calculate $W+$ for all the possible ways of assigning + and – to the ranked difference scores. It would help to know how many ways there are of doing this. In our example, there are 8 ways. There are two ways of giving Subject 1's difference score a sign: it gets either a + or a –. For each of these two ways, there are a further two ways of giving a sign to Subject 2's result, which makes $2 \times 2 = 4$ so far. For each of these four ways, there are two ways of giving a sign to Subject 3's result, making $4 \times 2 = 8$ in all. This means that there are 8 possible patterns of results that we need to investigate when $n = 3$. In general, for n subjects, we need to look at 2^n possible patterns of results – note that $2^3 = 8$. The possible patterns for our case are shown in Table 3.2 together with $W+$ computed for each. The results actually obtained for our example data are shown as pattern 7 here. Now, under the null hypothesis, each of these 8 patterns is equally likely to be obtained, so we can straightforwardly work out the null distribution of $W+$ in the usual way. Thus, a $W+$ of 6 is associated with only 1 of the 8 patterns, so the probability that $W+ = 6$ is $\frac{1}{8}$. A $W+$ of 3 is associated with 2 of the 8 patterns and so has a probability of $\frac{1}{4}$. The complete null distribution is shown in the final columns of Table 3.2.

Table 3.2 shows that $W+$ has large values when the positive signs are associated with higher ranks, i.e. with large difference scores. Compare rows 6 and 7, for example. In both rows, there is only one positive difference score, but in row 7 it has a smaller rank (i.e. is associated with a smaller magnitude) than in row 6. $W+$ is correspondingly higher for row 6 than for row 7, which matches our requirement that when there is only one positive difference score, a very small magnitude will be more in line with our suspected alternative hypothesis than will a large one. Thus, if our alternative hypothesis (which predicts mainly negative difference scores) is

Table 3.2. The 8 possible patterns of results when $n = 3$ and the resulting null distribution of $W+$ or $W-$

	Rank					
	1	2	3	$W+$	$W-$	prob
1.	+	+	+	6	0	$\frac{1}{8} = 0.125$
2.	–	+	+	5	1	$\frac{1}{8} = 0.125$
3.	+	–	+	4	2	$\frac{1}{8} = 0.125$
4.	+	+	–	3	3	$\frac{1}{4} = 0.250$
5.	–	–	+	3	3	
6.	–	+	–	2	4	$\frac{1}{8} = 0.125$
7.	+	–	–	1	5	$\frac{1}{8} = 0.125$
8.	–	–	–	0	6	$\frac{1}{8} = 0.125$

correct, then the patterns at the bottom of Table 3.2 are more likely to occur than the other patterns.

Following our previous practice, we can now choose a decision rule to enable us to draw a conclusion from a given set of data. For this example, we are only interested in testing whether Drug X *decreases* RT, so we require a one-tailed test. Our prediction corresponds to a desire to detect extremely small values of $W+$, so we want a lower tail test. If we use a sensible significance level such as 0.05, we find from Table 3.2 that we should never be able to reject the null hypothesis with such a small n, since all 8 patterns of results are quite likely to be obtained. To be able to reject the null hypothesis for our obtained data with $W+ = 1$, we should need to use a significance level as high as 0.25, since prob $(W+ \leqslant 1) = 0.25$; this would be an unacceptably high significance level for most purposes. Thus, our obtained data lead us to conclude that there is no reliable evidence of a difference between the two drugs in the direction predicted. However, to obtain a proper test that would allow us to use a sensible significance level, we should really increase our sample size, n.

If we wanted instead to do an upper tail test, i.e. if we were only interested in testing whether Drug X *increases* RT, then we should make use of the upper part of Table 3.2. In this case, we should reject the null hypothesis only if extremely large values of $W+$ were obtained. Alternatively, we can make use of the complementary statistic $W-$. This is simply the sum of the ranks associated with a negative difference score. For the data in Table 3.1, $W- = 2 + 3 = 5$. If $W+$ is large, then $W-$ is small, and *vice versa.* Values of $W-$ are shown in Table 3.2 for all possible patterns of results with $n = 3$. So, to do an upper tail test, we note that there should be fewer negative difference scores and $W-$ should be correspondingly small. We can seen from Table 3.2 that the distributions of $W+$ or $W-$ are symmetric about a mean of 3, so that, for example, the probability of getting a $W+$ of 1 or less is exactly the same as the probability of getting a $W-$ of 1 or less. This is true for all values of n.

Computing $W-$ as well as $W+$ makes it easier to see what happens in a two-tailed test. If we make no prediction about whether Drug X increases or decreases RT, we should need a two-tailed test. In this case, we should reject the null hypothesis if we obtained very low *or* very high values of $W+$. Equivalently, we should reject the null hypothesis *either* if $W+$ were low *or* if $W-$ were low. Thus, for a two-tailed test with a significance level of 0.25, we should reject the null hypothesis if either $W+ = 0$ or $W- = 0$. As in the one-tailed case, there are no relevant critical values for sensibly small significance levels when $n = 3$, so we should never be able to reject the null hypothesis in this case.

Table of the Null Distribution of $W+$ (Appendix Table D)

The null distribution of $W+$ will be different for different sample sizes, n. To save time in carrying out the test, Appendix Table D contains lower tail critical values of the null distribution of $W+$ for all values of n up to 50, for the most commonly used significance levels. As with the Rank-Sum Test, since $W+$ is a discrete variable the null distribution may not contain a value of $W+$ that is exactly appropriate for a given significance level. Where this is the case, Table D gives that value of $W+$ with the largest probability less than the given α.

To illustrate the use of Table D, suppose our sample size had been 8 and not 3. If we wished to do a lower tail test with $\alpha = 0.05$, then the table tells us that the critical value of $W+$ is 5. Therefore, with $\alpha = 0.05$, we should reject the null hypothesis if our obtained $W+$ is 5 or less.

To carry out an upper tail test, compute $W-$ instead of $W+$ and use the table exactly as described above. Thus, with $\alpha = 0.05$, we should reject the null hypothesis in this case if our obtained $W-$ is 5 or less.

To do a two-tailed test, compute both $W+$ and $W-$ and refer the smaller of the two values to Table D. With $n = 8$ and $\alpha = 0.05$, Table D tells us that the two-tailed critical value is 3. We should therefore reject the null hypothesis if either our obtained $W+$ or our obtained $W-$ is 3 or less.

The Treatment of Ties

Our calculation of the null distribution of $W+$ was based on the assumption that the difference scores were continuously distributed. This implies that there should be no ties in the difference scores and also that there should be no difference scores exactly equal to zero. Otherwise, calculations such as those shown in Table 3.2 of the set of all possible patterns of outcomes will be inaccurate. We therefore need methods of handling ties when they occur in practice.

Ties in the difference scores

When there are ties in the difference scores, we use the midrank technique described in Section 2.3. Any difference scores tied at a particular value receive the average of the ranks they would have obtained had they not been tied. This is

Table 3.3. Calculation of $W+$ when there are tied difference scores, using the midrank technique

	Subjects			
	1	2	3	
RT for Drug X	236	210	203	
RT for Drug Y	241	216	198	
Difference $X_i - Y_i$	−5	−6	+5	
Midrank of $\mid X_i - Y_i \mid$	1.5	3	1.5	
Signed-Rank	−1.5	−3	+1.5	$W+ = 1.5$

illustrated with the data shown in Table 3.3. Ties in the difference scores mean that the critical values given in Table D will no longer be accurate, since they were obtained assuming no ties. To obtain accurate critical values, we should need to calculate a new null distribution appropriate for data with ties.

As long as there are not too many ties, however, Table D will give a reasonably good approximation. As a very rough general rule, Table D should not be used when more than a quarter of the difference scores are involved in ties.

When more than a quarter of the scores are involved in ties, the normal approximation given below, corrected for ties, will generally be adequate.

Zero difference scores

If there are ties in any subject's data that lead to zero difference scores, this will also affect the null distribution of $W+$. An example of such a situation is shown in Table 3.4. The most straightforward way of handling ties of this sort is to discard them and to use the standard null distribution of $W+$ with n reduced accordingly. For the data in Table 3.4 there is only one zero difference score, so we refer the obtained $W+$ of 0 to Table D with $n = 2$.

This method is reasonable as long as the proportion of zero difference scores is not too large. A large proportion of zeros would normally lead us to suspect that there is little difference between the two drugs and carrying out the Signed-Rank Test on the remaining difference scores may not be particularly informative.

Table 3.4. Calculation of $W+$ with zero difference scores

	Subjects			
	1	2	3	
RT for Drug X	236	210	200	
RT for Drug Y	241	216	200	
Difference $X_i - Y_i$	−5	−6	0	
Rank of $\mid X_i - Y_i \mid$	1	2	x	
Signed-Rank	−1	−2	x	$W+ = 0, n = 2$

Normal Approximation to $W+$

As with the Rank-Sum Test, the normal distribution may be used to provide a good approximation to the null distribution of $W+$ when the sample size is large. In this case, the normal approximation will generally be very good when n is 20 or larger. To use the normal approximation we need to know both the mean and the variance of the possible values that $W+$ can take for any given sample size. These are given by

$$\text{Mean} = n(n + 1)/4 \tag{3.1}$$

$$\text{Variance} = n(n + 1)/(2n + 1)/24 \tag{3.2}$$

To show that these formulae work, for the case $n = 3$ with no ties we know from Table 3.2 that the possible values of $W+$ are 0, 1, 2, 3, 3, 4, 5, and 6. Using the methods of Section 1.1 it is easy to calculate the mean and variance of these 8 numbers as 3 and 3.5, which are exactly the values given by the formulae above, since $n(n + 1)/4 = 3 \times 4/4 = 3$ and $n(n + 1)(2n + 1)/24 = 3 \times 4 \times 7/24 = 3.5$.

Since we know that $W+$ takes only discrete values, the normal approximation is usually improved by making use of a continuity correction when there are no ties in the difference scores. For $W+$, the appropriate continuity correction is ½, since, as we know for the case $n = 3$, the spacing between consecutive possible values of $W+$ is always 1. The continuity correction should be subtracted from values of $W+$ that are larger than the mean, $n(n + 1)/4$, and added to values of $W+$ that are smaller than the mean.

To illustrate its use in the untied case, suppose we had carried out our experiment with a sample size of 40 and had obtained a $W+$ of 286. The mean of the possible values that $W+$ could have taken is $n(n + 1)/4 = 40 \times 41/4 = 410$. Since our obtained $W+$ is smaller than this, the continuity correction of ½ must be added to it, which gives 286.5. The variance of $W+$ is given by $n(n + 1)(2n + 1)/24 = 40 \times 41 \times 81/24 = 5535$, so the standard deviation is $\sqrt{5535}$. Therefore, our obtained value of $W+$ is converted into a z-score as follows:

$$\begin{aligned} z &= \frac{W+ - \text{Mean}}{\text{S.D.}} \\ &= \frac{286.5 - 410}{\sqrt{5535}} \\ &= -1.660 \end{aligned}$$

From Table B(ii), we find that the lower tail critical value of z for a one-tailed test with $\alpha = 0.05$ is -1.645, which is close to our obtained value. To compare this with the exact probability, Table D tells us that for $n = 40$ and a one-tailed test with $\alpha = 0.05$, our obtained $W+$ of 287 is exactly equal to the critical value, so the approximation agrees well with the exact tables. As usual, of course, Table D should be used for those cases for which $n < 51$, but the normal approximation will be entirely adequate for all cases for which Table D does not apply.

Ties in the difference scores

When there are ties in the difference scores, we need to modify the normal approximation slightly. As with the Rank-Sum Test, ties have the effect of reducing the variance of possible values that *W*+ can take, although the mean will stay the same. To modify the variance we need to know the number of distinct difference scores (ignoring signs) together with the number of scores tied at each value. The most straightforward way of computing this can be illustrated using the example in Table 3.3 in which there are three difference scores, –5, –6, and +5. Ignoring the signs, there are two distinct values here, so the information we require can be recorded as shown below. The row t_i records the extent of the ties. If there were

Magnitude of difference score	5	6
No. of scores tied at that value, t_i	2	1

no ties at all this row would contain all ones. The required expression for the variance in the case of ties is then given by

$$\text{Variance} = \frac{n(n+1)(2n+1)}{24} - \frac{1}{48}\Sigma t_i(t_i - 1)(t_i + 1) \qquad (3.3)$$

For our example, we have

$$\Sigma\, t_i(t_i \quad 1)(t_i + 1) = 2 \times 1 \times 3 + 1 \times 0 \times 2 = 6,$$

so the variance will be

$$\text{Variance} = \frac{3 \times 4 \times 7}{24} - \frac{6}{48} = 3.5 - 0.125 = 3.375$$

It is worth noting that when there are no ties in the difference scores, the above expression reduces to the expression given by formula 3.2 for the untied case.

As we noted for the Rank-Sum Test, unless the proportion of ties is extremely large, the variance of *W*+ calculated using formula 3.3 will not be very different from that given by formula 3.2, ignoring the ties. In addition, using formula 3.3 will always give a smaller value for the variance when there are ties than using formula 3.2. So if the simpler formula 3.2 is used when there are ties, a conservative test will be obtained.

The use of the normal approximation when there are ties will be illustrated in Example 3.2. As in the untied case, the normal approximation will generally be good if the sample size is 20 or larger. A correction for continuity of ½ generally improves the approximation, even though the spacing between consecutive possible values of *W*+ becomes uneven when there are ties.

The Signed-Rank Test with One-Sample Data

Suppose we have reason to believe that the time taken to get served in a particular restaurant is on average 15 minutes. To test this we might ask a number of people to go to the restaurant and to record their waiting times. We can use the Signed-Rank Test to test whether the median waiting time was 15 minutes, as long as the recorded waiting times were independent (so that, for example, the people did not go to the restaurant together). From each person's waiting time we subtract the predicted median time of 15 minutes. If we are prepared to assume that the distribution of waiting times from which our sample is drawn is symmetric (so that, for example, our chances of waiting 10 minutes longer than the actual median time are the same as our chances of waiting 10 minutes shorter), then we can treat the obtained scores as difference scores and apply the Signed-Rank Test. If the true median is 15 minutes (the null hypothesis), then a positive difference score is as likely to be obtained as a negative one. If the median is not 15 minutes (the alternative hypothesis), difference scores of one sign are likely to predominate in our sample.

This use of the test will be illustrated in Example 3.3.

Further Comments

In some applications, the Signed-Rank Test may be misleading, since it assumes that the difference scores are comparable. For example, in many tests of ability or achievement, differences in the middle of the range of possible scores may be less important than differences at the extremes. If a person is given an IQ test twice, a change from 70 to 75 may well indicate greater improvement than a change from 100 to 105; these changes have the same magnitude and so the difference scores of 5 will be given the same rank when computing $W+$. If considerations such as this are important in a particular application, the Sign Test described in Section 3.2 should be used in preference to the Signed-Rank Test.

For a fuller discussion of the appropriate use of the Signed-Rank Test, see Bradley (1968, Chapter 5), where there is a good account of the use of this test with reaction time data. Bradley also discusses other methods of handling ties in Chapter 3, as does Lehmann (1975, Sections 3.2 and 3.5B).

Example 3.1 The Wilcoxon Signed-Rank Test – Two-Sample Case

In a study of the physiological effects of hypnotic suggestion, the emotions of fear and happiness were requested from each of ten subjects during hypnosis. The emotion requested first was decided randomly for each subject. Table 3.5 gives the resulting measurements of skin potential in millivolts, together with the calculations necessary to compute $W+$ and $W-$. With these data, it seems reasonable to assume that, if there is no difference between the two emotions, each of the difference scores comes from a population that is symmetric about zero. With this assumption we are justified in carrying out a Signed-Rank Test on these data. Suppose we decide to use a two-tailed test with an α of 0.05. Then from Table D we find that the smaller of $W+$ and $W-$ should be less than or equal to the critical value of 8 when

Table 3.5. Hypothetical data for Example 3.1

Subject	1	2	3	4	5	6	7	8	9	10
X: Fear	57.6	10.5	23.1	23.6	11.9	54.6	21.0	20.3	22.1	21.3
Y: Happiness	53.6	9.7	22.7	19.6	13.8	47.1	13.6	23.6	18.6	17.1
$X_i - Y_i$	4.0	0.8	0.4	4.0	−1.9	7.5	7.4	−3.3	3.5	4.2
Rank of $\mid X_i - Y_i \mid$	6.5	2	1	6.5	3	10	9	4	5	8
Signed-Rank	+6.5	+2	+1	+6.5	−3	+10	+9	−4	+5	+8

$n = 10$. Since only two of the ten difference scores are involved in ties, a test using Table D should be reasonably accurate. From the computations shown in the table of results it is clear that $W-$ will be much smaller than $W+$, so we need not compute $W+$. $W-$ will be $3 + 4 = 7$. Since this is smaller than the critical value, we conclude that the data provide evidence that the two emotions requested have different physiological effects at the 0.05 significance level. From the data it is clear that requesting the emotion of fear under hypnosis leads to a greater evoked response than does requesting the emotion of happiness. We shall see in Example 3.7 how to estimate the size of the effect demonstrated.

Example 3.2 The Wilcoxon Signed-Rank Test with Extensive Ties

In a study investigating whether active and passive sentences are processed differently, 25 people were asked to read a passage containing an equal proportion of active and passive sentences and then to recall the passage. The number of active and passive sentences correctly recalled by each subject is given in Table 3.6, together with the calculations necessary to compute $W+$ and $W-$. The null hypothesis associated with the Signed-Rank Test, that the difference scores come from a population that is symmetric about zero, seems sensible for this type of data. Suppose we decide to use a two-tailed test with $\alpha = 0.05$. We note that there is a large proportion of tied difference scores, so we shall have to use the normal approximation to $W+$, corrected for ties. There is one zero difference score (subject 11's), so we drop this and base our test on the remaining 24 subjects. With $n = 24$, the normal approximation is likely to be quite accurate. From Table B(ii), the critical values of z can be found to be -1.96 and 1.96 for a two-tailed test with $\alpha = 0.05$, so our obtained z-score will need to be *either* larger than or equal to 1.96 *or* smaller than or equal to -1.96. To compute the z-score from our data, we note that it doesn't matter whether we first compute $W+$ or $W-$, since the resulting z-scores will have the same magnitude but will merely differ in sign. For our example, therefore, it is easier to compute $W-$ as there are only a few negative difference scores. $W-$ is given by $2.5 + 2.5 + 6.5 + 16.0 = 27.5$. The mean of $W-$

Table 3.6. Hypothetical data for Example 3.2

Subject	Active	Passive	$A_i - P_i$	Rank of $\lvert A_i - P_i \rvert$	Signed-Rank
1	9	10	−1	2.5	−2.5
2	7	4	3	11.5	11.5
3	9	3	6	22	22
4	8	2	6	22	22
5	7	8	−1	2.5	−2.5
6	8	1	7	24	24
7	10	9	1	2.5	2.5
8	10	5	5	19	19
9	12	7	5	19	19
10	6	3	3	11.5	11.5
11	7	7	0	x	x
12	9	6	3	11.5	11.5
13	8	5	3	11.5	11.5
14	6	4	2	6.5	6.5
15	10	9	1	2.5	2.5
16	11	9	2	6.5	6.5
17	7	5	2	6.5	6.5
18	5	1	4	16	16
19	7	4	3	11.5	11.5
20	7	4	3	11.5	11.5
21	8	4	4	16	16
22	9	11	−2	6.5	−6.5
23	8	12	−4	16	−16
24	8	3	5	19	19
25	10	4	6	22	22

(or, equivalently, of $W+$) is

$$\text{Mean} = n(n+1)/4 = 24 \times 25/4 = 150$$

To compute the variance of $W-$, we first need to note the number and extent of the ties in the difference scores, which is done below.

Magnitude of difference scores	1	2	3	4	5	6	7
No. of scores tied at that value, t_i	4	4	6	3	3	3	1

Thus, we have

$$\Sigma t_i(t_i - 1)(t_i + 1) = 4 \times 3 \times 5 + 4 \times 3 \times 5 + 6 \times 5 \times 7 + 3 \times 2 \times 4$$
$$+ 3 \times 2 \times 4 + 3 \times 2 \times 4 + 1 \times 0 \times 2 = 402$$

Using formula 3.3, the variance of $W-$ is given by

$$\text{Variance} = \frac{n(n+1)(2n+1)}{24} - \frac{1}{48}\Sigma t_i(t_i - 1)(t_i + 1)$$

$$= \frac{24 \times 25 \times 49}{24} - \frac{402}{48} = 1225 - 8.375 = 1216.625$$

Since our obtained $W-$ of 27.5 is smaller than the mean of 150, the continuity correction of ½ is added, so the z-score is calculated as follows

$$z = \frac{W- - \text{Mean}}{\text{S.D.}} = \frac{28 - 150}{\sqrt{1216.625}} = -3.50$$

Our obtained z-score is much smaller than the lower tail critical value of -1.96, so we conclude that there is a reliable difference between the recall of active and passive sentences from this passage at the 0.05 level. The data suggest that the active sentences are easier to recall than the passive sentences. (Had we not bothered with the correction for ties and calculated the variance using formula 3.2 instead, the resulting z-score would be -3.49, so in this case the correction makes little difference.)

Example 3.3 Using the Signed-Rank Test with One-Sample Data

The Golden Section is the number that results from the calculation of $(\sqrt{5} - 1)/2$. This rather unlikely number, which is usually referred to as ϕ, the Greek letter phi, has a habit of cropping up all over the place. It can be seen that $\phi = 0.618$, approximately. It has been postulated by Benjafield and Adams-Webber (1976) and Benjafield and Green (1978) that the proportion of positive adjectives used by people to describe others is exactly ϕ. They argue that this allows the negative adjectives, which they believe to be more important when describing acquaintances, to stand out as 'figure' against a larger positive 'ground'. To test this, Veronica Chilton and I asked 58 people, 32 women and 26 men, to complete a repertory grid in which they described their acquaintances in a standardized format using constructs of their own choosing. They were then asked to say which of their constructs they considered to be of an evaluative nature. Our test of the Golden Section hypothesis concentrated on these evaluative constructs. For each person, we calculated the proportion of times the positive pole of a construct was used to describe an acquaintance. The data for the 32 women are shown in the second column of Table 3.7. We wish to test whether these data are consistent with the prediction that, on average, this proportion is ϕ. In other words, could the data have been sampled from a population whose median value is ϕ?

We can use the Signed-Rank Test to test this, and other similar, predictions as follows. If we subtract ϕ from each person's score, using the Signed-Rank Test on the resulting scores, instead of on difference scores as in the two-sample case, allows us to test the null hypothesis that these scores come from a population that is symmetrical about ϕ, which is what we want. Apart from the initial stage, the procedure is identical to that in the two-sample case. The calculation of $W+$ and $W-$ is shown in Table 3.7.

Table 3.7. Data and calculation of $W+$ and $W-$ for the 32 women in Chilton and Leach's study

Subject	Proportion of positive descriptions, p_i	Difference $p_i - 0.618$	Rank of $\mid p_i - 0.618 \mid$	Signed-Rank
1	0.438	−0.180	30	−30
2	0.500	−0.118	29	−29
3	0.550	−0.068	26	−26
4	0.551	−0.067	25	−25
5	0.556	−0.062	23	−23
6	0.560	−0.058	21	−21
7	0.575	−0.043	15	−15
8	0.583	−0.035	13	−13
9	0.593	−0.025	11	−11
10	0.600	−0.018	9	− 9
11	0.600	−0.018	9	− 9
12	0.600	−0.018	9	− 9
13	0.611	−0.007	4.5	− 4.5
14	0.617	−0.001	1.5	− 1.5
15	0.617	−0.001	1.5	− 1.5
16	0.625	0.007	4.5	4.5
17	0.625	0.007	4.5	4.5
18	0.625	0.007	4.5	4.5
19	0.631	0.013	7	7
20	0.646	0.028	12	12
21	0.655	0.037	14	14
22	0.667	0.049	18	18
23	0.667	0.049	18	18
24	0.667	0.049	18	18
25	0.667	0.049	18	18
26	0.667	0.049	18	18
27	0.679	0.061	22	22
28	0.683	0.065	24	24
29	0.722	0.104	27.5	27.5
30	0.722	0.104	27.5	27.5
31	0.819	0.201	31	31
32	0.833	0.215	32	32

$W- = 227.5$
$W+ = 300.5$

For this example, we wish to test whether the data are consistent with a null hypothesis in which we have a vested interest. For this reason, we should be wise to use a large significance level, to give us a greater chance of rejecting the null hypothesis and thereby a more powerful test. Suppose we choose $\alpha = 0.20$. We shall use a two-tailed test, since we are interested in detecting departures from ϕ in either direction. Since more than a quarter of the difference scores in the third column of Table 3.7 are involved in ties, we shall use the normal approximation, which should be reasonably accurate in this case with $n = 32$. From Table B(ii) we find the relevant critical values of z to be -1.282 and 1.282.

To calculate z for our data, we need the mean and variance of $W+$.

Using formula 3.1, we have

$$\text{Mean} = \frac{n(n+1)}{4} = \frac{32 \times 33}{4} = 264$$

For the variance, we first need to compute the number and extent of the ties in order to find $\Sigma\, t_i(t_i - 1)(t_i + 1)$. This is done below.

Magnitude of difference scores	0.001	0.007	0.013	0.018	0.025	0.028	0.035	0.037	0.043	0.049	
No. of scores tied at that value, t_i	2	4	1	3	1	1	1	1	1	5	
$t_i(t_i - 1)(t_i + 1)$	6	60	0	24	0	0	0	0	0	120	
Magnitude of difference scores	0.058	0.061	0.062	0.065	0.067	0.068	0.104	0.118	0.180	0.201	0.215
No. of scores tied at that value, t_i	1	1	1	1	1	1	2	1	1	1	1
$t_i(t_i - 1)(t_i + 1)$	0	0	0	0	0	0	6	0	0	0	0

We can then easily calculate $\Sigma\, t_i(t_i - 1)(t_i + 1) = 6 + 60 + 24 + 120 + 6 = 216$. Using formula 3.3, the variance is then given by

$$\begin{aligned}\text{Variance} &= \frac{n(n+1)(2n+1)}{24} - \frac{1}{48}\Sigma\, t_i(t_i - 1)(t_i + 1)\\ &= \frac{32 \times 33 \times 65}{24} - \frac{216}{48}\\ &= 2860 - 4.5\\ &= 2855.5\end{aligned}$$

From our obtained $W+$ of 300.5, with a continuity correction of ½, z is then given by

$$z = \frac{300 - 264}{\sqrt{2855.5}} = 0.674$$

This is well within the bounds given by our very conservative significance level, so we conclude that the data are consistent with the golden section hypothesis. (As in the previous example, the correction for ties makes little difference here to the resulting z-score, which is 0.673 without the correction.) To supplement this conclusion, we shall estimate the proportion of positive descriptions for these data in Example 3.8 to see how close the best estimate is to ϕ. The data for the men in this study do not so clearly support the hypothesis; they are given in Exercise 3.2.

3.2 THE SIGN TEST – ORDINAL RESPONSE VARIABLE

The Sign Test is an appealingly simple test which is applicable in the same situations as the Wilcoxon Signed-Rank Test. Thus, it can be used to test whether two related samples differ in location or whether a single sample comes from a population with a specified median. The main difference between the Sign Test and the Signed-Rank Test is that the former does not make use of the magnitude of the difference scores but simply notes their signs – hence the name. For this reason, the Sign Test is also applicable in situations where it is known only whether the difference scores are positive or negative and the magnitudes are not available (see Example 3.6).

In situations where the magnitudes of the difference scores are available, the Signed-Rank Test is generally preferable to the Sign Test, since it makes more use of the data, unless there is reason to question the assumption that the difference scores come from a symmetric population or the assumption that the difference scores are comparable and hence orderable. However, in many cases the Sign Test provides a quick and easy alternative to the Signed-Rank Test, even though it is easy to find situations where the two tests lead to different conclusions (see Example 3.4 and Exercises 3.5 and 3.6). In fact, it can easily be shown that the Sign Test is a special case of the Signed-Rank Test when all the difference scores are tied at the same magnitude (see Exercise 3.8). Like the Signed-Rank Test, the Sign Test assumes that each subject's data are independent of the data from other subjects.

Test Statistic, $N+$, and its Null Distribution

Consider again the simplified example of Section 3.1, where reaction times were obtained from each of 3 people under two drugs, and we wished to test whether the RTs under Drug X tended to be faster than those under Drug Y. The difference scores for the 3 people were -5, -6, and $+3$. The test statistic for the Sign Test is simply the number of positive difference scores, labelled $N+$. In this case, $N+ = 1$. Equivalently, as was the case with the Signed-Rank Test, we could use $N-$, the number of negative difference scores, as our test statistic. This very simple test statistic is easily seen to give us what we require. If Drug X does lead to faster RTs than Drug Y, then the majority of the difference scores should be negative, so $N+$ should be small.

The null distribution of $N+$ (or $N-$) is computed in the same way as that of $W+$. Using the same logic as in the discussion of $W+$'s null distribution, it is easily seen that there are 2^n possible patterns of results, each of which is equally likely to have occurred under the null hypothesis that a positive difference score was as likely to be obtained by each person as a negative one. The 8 patterns of results for our example, where $n = 3$, together with the resulting null distribution of $N+$ (and $N-$) are shown in Table 3.8.

Using a one-tailed test, we should need to use a significance level as large as 0.50 before we could reject the null hypothesis with our data for which $N+ = 1$, since prob $(N+ \leqslant 1) = \frac{3}{8} + \frac{1}{8} = 0.50$. For these same data we should have been able to reject the null hypothesis with an α of 0.25 had we used the Signed-Rank Test (c.f. Table 3.2). This example illustrates the greater sensitivity of the Signed-Rank Test, which makes use of the fact that the single positive difference score in our example was the one with smallest magnitude; the Sign Test ignores this.

Table 3.8. The 8 possible patterns of results when $n = 3$ and the resulting null distribution of $N+$ or $N-$

	Person 1	2	3	$N+$	$N-$	prob
1.	+	+	+	3	0	$\frac{1}{8} = 0.125$
2.	–	+	+	2	1	
3.	+	–	+	2	1	$\frac{3}{8} = 0.375$
4.	+	+	–	2	1	
5.	–	–	+	1	2	
6.	–	+	–	1	2	$\frac{3}{8} = 0.375$
7.	+	–	–	1	2	
8.	–	–	–	0	3	$\frac{1}{8} = 0.125$

Had we wished to carry out a two-tailed test, we proceed as we did with the Signed-Rank Test. Thus we should reject the null hypothesis if we obtain *either* a very low value of $N+$ *or* a very low value of $N-$. For example, with $\alpha = 0.25$, we can see from Table 3.8 that the critical value for $n = 3$ would be 0, since prob $(N+ \leqslant 0)$ + prob $(N- \leqslant 0) = \frac{1}{8} + \frac{1}{8} = 0.25$, so we should reject the null hypothesis if we obtained either an $N+$ of 0 or an $N-$ of 0.

Of course, with such a small sample size, we should not be able to use a sensibly small significance level. To be able to draw any reasonable conclusions we should, as usual, need to use a much larger sample size.

Table of the Null Distribution of $N+$ (Appendix Table E)

To save having to calculate the null distribution of $N+$ anew for each sample size, n, Appendix Table E provides critical values of the null distribution of $N+$ for all values of n up to 50 associated with the most commonly used significance levels. As with our previous tables, this table gives that value of $N+$ which has the largest probability less than or equal to the given α.

To illustrate the use of Table E, suppose our sample size had been 11. If we wished to do a lower tail test with $\alpha = 0.05$, then the table gives the critical value of $N+$ as 2. Therefore, with $\alpha = 0.05$, we should reject the null hypothesis if we obtained 2 or fewer positive difference scores.

To carry out an upper tail test, compute $N-$ instead of $N+$ and use the table exactly as described above. Thus, with $\alpha = 0.05$, we should reject the null hypothesis if we obtained 2 or fewer negative difference scores.

To do a two-tailed test, compute both $N+$ and $N-$ and refer the smaller of these to Table E. Thus, with $n = 11$ and $\alpha = 0.05$, Table E gives a two-tailed critical value of 1. We should therefore reject the null hypothesis *either* if we obtained 1 or fewer positive difference scores *or* if we obtained 1 or fewer negatives.

The Treatment of Zero Difference Scores

Ties in the difference scores have no effect on the null distribution of $N+$, since the magnitudes of the difference scores are ignored. However, zero difference scores do have an effect. As with the Signed-Rank Test, as long as the proportion of zeros is not too large, the recommended procedure is to drop them from the data and reduce n accordingly. Of course, when reporting the data, it is necessary to state that this has been done.

Normal Approximation to $N+$

The normal distribution gives a good approximation to $N+$ with large sample sizes. To make use of it, we need to know the mean and variance of the possible values $N+$ can take for a given sample size. These are given by

$$\text{Mean} = n/2 \tag{3.4}$$

$$\text{Variance} = n/4 \tag{3.5}$$

To show that these formulae work, they give the values of 1.5 and 0.75 for the case $n = 3$, and these are easily seen to be the mean and variance of the possible values of $N+$ shown in Table 3.8.

$N+$ takes only discrete values, so the normal approximation will generally be improved by using a continuity correction of ½, since the spacing between consecutive possible values of $N+$ is 1. The continuity correction should be subtracted from values of $N+$ larger than the mean, $n/2$, and added to values smaller than the mean.

To illustrate its use, suppose we had carried out our experiment with a sample size of 30 and obtained 10 positive difference scores, so that $N+$ is 10. The mean of the possible values $N+$ could take is then $n/2 = 15$ and the variance is $n/4 = 7.5$. Since our obtained $N+$ is smaller than the mean, we add the continuity correction to give 10.5. Therefore,

$$z = \frac{N+ - \text{Mean}}{\text{S.D.}}$$

$$= \frac{10.5 - 15}{\sqrt{7.5}} = -1.643$$

This is close to the lower tail critical value of -1.645 for a one-tailed test with $\alpha = 0.05$ given in Table B(ii). To compare this with the exact probability, Table E tells us that, for $n = 30$, 10 is the critical value for a one-tailed test with $\alpha = 0.05$, so the approximation agrees very well with the exact table.

Further Comments

The Sign Test, like the Signed-Rank Test, may be used with one-sample data. An illustration of this use is provided in Example 3.5.

For a fuller discussion of the Sign Test and a detailed comparison with the Signed-Rank Test, see Lehmann (1975, Chapters 3 and 4).

Example 3.4 The Two-Sample Sign Test

To illustrate the use of the Sign Test with two related samples, we shall reanalyse the data from Example 3.1 shown in Table 3.5. For these data, we have $n = 10$. Eight of the difference scores are positive and two are negative, so that $N+ = 8$ and $N- = 2$. Using a two-tailed test with $\alpha = 0.05$, Table E tells us that the smaller of $N+$ and $N-$ should be less than or equal to 1 before we can reject the null hypothesis. Since both $N+$ and $N-$ are larger than 1, we cannot reject the null hypothesis using the Sign Test with these data. We conclude that there is no differential effect on skin potential from requesting the emotions of fear and happiness under hypnosis.

Note that when we originally analysed these data using the Signed-Rank Test, we were able to reject the null hypothesis. This is because the two negative difference scores obtained by subjects 5 and 8 were of relatively small magnitude. Which test to believe turns on how much importance we wish to attach to the magnitudes of the difference scores.

In this example, there seems little reason to ignore the additional information, so the Signed-Rank Test probably wins out.

Example 3.5 The One-Sample Sign Test

The Sign Test may be used in exactly the same way as the Signed-Rank Test to test whether the median of the population from which one-sample data have been obtained is a particular specified value. This will be illustrated by reanalysing the 32 subjects' data from Example 3.3 using a Sign Test.

The Sign Test simply involves counting $N+$, the number of subjects for whom the proportion of positive adjectives is larger than the predicted value of 0.618, and $N-$, the number of subjects for whom the proportion is less than 0.618. For the data shown in Table 3.7, $N+ = 17$ and $N- = 15$. We note that there are no subjects whose data exactly agree with the predicted value; if there were these would constitute zeros and they would be dropped from the analysis.

Choosing a two-tailed test with $\alpha = 0.20$ for the reasons given in Example 3.3, Table E gives a critical value of 11 when $n = 32$. Either $N+$ or $N-$ would need to be less than or equal to 11 before we should reject the null hypothesis that the median is 0.618. Since our values are both larger than 11, we conclude again that there are no grounds for rejecting the golden section hypothesis with these data.

Example 3.6 The Sign Test with Large Samples

To illustrate the use of the normal approximation, we shall use data from a study by Dr. John Arbuthnott, Physitian in Ordinary to Her

Majesty, reported in 1710 in a paper entitled 'An Argument for Divine Providence, taken from the constant Regularity observ'd in the Births of both Sexes'. This paper contains what is apparently the earliest use of the Sign Test. Arbuthnott noted that in each of the 82 years from 1629 to 1710 more males than females were christened in London.

If the probability of a male being born were the same as the probability of a female being born, then we should expect the difference between the total number of male and female births in any year to be positive as often as it is negative. This is the null hypothesis we can test using the Sign Test. We have $n = 82$, the number of years and $N+ = 82$, since Arbuthnott noted 82 positive differences. We have to use the normal approximation, since Table E does not go as far as $n = 82$. (It is worth noting, however, that Equation 3.6 given in Section 3.4 provides an exact method of calculating the probability of these results occurring by chance.)

The mean and variance of the possible values $N+$ can take are $n/2 = 41$ and $n/4 = 20.5$. Since the obtained $N+$ is larger than the mean, we subtract the continuity correction of ½ before computing the z-score. We then obtain

$$z = \frac{N+ - n/2}{\sqrt{n/4}} = \frac{81.5 - 41}{\sqrt{20.5}} = 8.94$$

With a two-tailed α as low as 0.0002 we find from Table B(ii) that our obtained value of z should be larger than or equal to 3.719 before we can reject the null hypothesis. Our value is much larger than this, so even with such a ridiculously small significance level, we must reject the null hypothesis and conclude that males were more likely to be born than females. Note that we cannot estimate from this test the extent of the difference between male and female births. To be able to do this, we should need to have access to the total numbers of male and female births in each year, as we shall see in Section 3.3.

Arbuthnott was not content simply to reject the null hypothesis. He wished to explain it by noting 'that the external Accidents to which Males are subject (who must seek their Food with danger) do make great havock of them, and that this loss exceeds far that of the other Sex, occasioned by Diseases incident to it, as Experience convinces us. To repair that Loss, provident Nature, by the Disposal of its wise Creator, brings forth more Males than Females; and that in almost a constant proportion.' This process produces an 'exact Ballance ... between the Numbers of Men and Women; for by this means it is provided, that the Species may never fail, nor perish, since every Male may have its Female, and of a proportionable Age.'

His final conclusion is worth repeating as an object lesson in going beyond one's data. 'From hence it follows, that Polygamy is contrary to the Law of Nature and Justice, and to the Propogation of Human

Race; for where Males and Females are in equal number, if one Man takes Twenty Wives, Nineteen Men must live in Celibacy, which is repugnant to the Design of Nature; nor is it probable that Twenty Women will be so well impregnated by one Man as by Twenty'.

3.3 ESTIMATORS ASSOCIATED WITH THE SIGN TEST AND THE SIGNED-RANK TEST

Having demonstrated a significant effect using either the Sign Test or the Signed-Rank Test, it is generally useful to estimate the size of the effect. The two estimators presented below allow us to do this, and both are applicable to either one-sample or two-sample data.

To be able to carry out the Sign Test or the Signed-Rank Test, each subject (or matched pair) may be thought of as providing us with a single score – in the one-sample case this is the original response score; in the two-sample case it is a difference score. The score for a particular subject comes from a population with a median of, say, d. Although other subjects' data may come from different populations of potential scores, we assume in carrying out the tests that each population has the same median of d. In the one-sample case, the tests attempt to discover whether this common median has a particular specified value. In the two-sample case, the tests attempt to discover whether $d = 0$, which indicates no difference in location between the two-samples. The estimators in this section provide an estimate of d. The estimate produced is the value of d that, when subtracted from each subject's score, totally removes the effect as tested by one of the two tests. Since the Sign Test and the Signed-Rank Test concentrate on different aspects of the data, the Signed-Rank Test emphasizing the magnitude of the scores and assuming that each score comes from a symmetric population, the value of d necessary to remove the effect may depend on which of the two tests is used to demonstrate the effect. For this reason, two estimators are presented below. The first and simplest is more appropriate when the data have been analysed using the Sign Test, while the second is more appropriate when the data have been analysed using the Signed-Rank Test.

Both estimators assume that we know the magnitude of each of the scores, so we should not be able to use them to estimate the size of the effect for the data of Example 3.6, where we know only the sign of each difference score.

Using the Sample Median to Estimate the Population Median

The estimator associated with the Sign Test is just the sample median. For our simplified example, the three difference scores from Table 3.1, written in increasing order, are –6, –5, and 3, so the median is –5, the one in the middle. –5 is therefore our best estimate of the difference between the two drug conditions; Drug X leads to reaction times that are on average 5 msec faster than those under Drug Y. For these data, $N+ = 1$ and $N- = 2$, indicating a very small effect. If we subtract our estimate from each of the obtained difference scores, we get –1, 0 and

8, for which $N+ = 1$ and $N- = 1$; subtracting −5 has completely removed the effect, with $N+$ exactly equal to $N-$.

This estimator is particularly useful since it is very easy to calculate, even with a large sample size. If there are any zero difference scores, these must be included in the data when the median is calculated.

The Hodges–Lehmann Estimator for the Signed-Rank Test

The estimator associated with the Signed-Rank Test, another estimator suggested by Hodges and Lehmann, is more laborious to calculate, since it makes more use of the numerical information in the data. For our simplified example, each of the original difference scores, −6, −5, and 3, provides a crude estimate of the size of the effect. If we consider pairs of these scores, the average of each possible pair also provides an estimate of the size of the effect. These averages will be $(-6 - 5)/2 = -5.5$, $(-6 + 3)/2 = -1.5$, and $(-5 + 3)/2 = -1$.

Considering the difference scores by themselves and in pairs therefore gives us the six estimates, −6, −5.5, −5, −1.5, −1, and 3. The Hodges–Lehmann estimate is the median of these six, which is halfway between the 3rd and the 4th smallest score, −3.25 in our case. This is different from the estimate of −5 obtained by considering only the median of the difference scores, since it is putting more weight on the magnitudes of the difference scores. Had the positive difference been 10 and not 3, the median would still be −5, but the Hodges–Lehmann estimate would be changed from −3.25 to −1.5.

The Hodges–Lehmann estimator provides the value of d that, when subtracted from each of the difference scores, totally removes the effect as assessed by the Signed-Rank Test. To see this, we note that $W+ = 1$ and $W- = 5$ for the original data (see Table 3.1). Subtracting our estimated effect of −3.25 (or, equivalently adding +3.25) from each of the difference scores gives −2.75, −1.75 and 6.25, for which $W+ = 3$ and $W- = 3$, indicating absolutely no effect.

As with the previous estimator, if there are any zero difference scores, these must be included in the calculation of the Hodges–Lehmann estimate.

If there are n difference scores, there will be a total of $n(n + 1)/2$ scores to consider in calculating the estimate (n was 3 for our example and $3 \times 4/2 = 6$ scores were used in calculating the estimate). When n is large the number of scores to consider makes this estimator very tedious to calculate (unless you have a computer program to help you). However, the necessary calculations can be simplified somewhat by the following procedure. Write the difference scores in increasing order as both the columns and the rows of a table, as in Table 3.9. For those cells of the table on or above the main diagonal, compute the sum of the relevant row and column scores. The entries on the main diagonal, underlined in Table 3.9, will be twice the original difference scores. The entries in the rest of the table are twice the average of the pairs of difference scores. The table therefore contains all the necessary scores (multiplied by two), so the Hodges–Lehmann estimate is just the median of these scores divided by two. In fact, it is not necessary to calculate all the scores, once you note that the scores in the table increase as you move from

Table 3.9. Calculating the Hodges–Lehmann estimate

	−6	−5	3
−6	−12	−11	−3
−5		−10	−2
3			6

left to right and from top to bottom. As a result, the median score will normally be on or near the diagonal in the table going from SW to NE. The use of this property to reduce the number of calculations is illustrated in Example 3.7.

If we do calculate all the scores in the table, this provides a useful check on our calculations for the Signed-Rank Test, since $W+$ is just the number of positive scores in the table and $W-$ is the number of negative scores, as long as there are no ties or zero difference scores. For the example in Table 3.9, $W+ = 1$ and $W- = 5$, which agrees with our original calculations in Table 3.1.

To choose which estimator to use in any particular case, the best guide is to use the same criteria as we used to choose between the Sign Test and the Signed-Rank Test. If the magnitude of the difference scores provides important information, then the Hodges–Lehmann estimator will be the most appropriate. On the other hand, the sample median will be the better of the two estimators either if the difference scores cannot be assumed to come from symmetrical populations or if they are not comparable and orderable.

In most cases, it is useful to compute both estimates, since any marked discrepancy between the values obtained frequently throws light on the data.

For further discussion of these and other estimators for one-sample or two related samples see Lehmann (1975, Section 4.4) and Hollander and Wolfe (1973, Sections 3.2 and 3.5). These references also contain information about the standard errors of the estimators.

Example 3.7 Estimating the Size of the Effect for Example 3.1

In Example 3.1 we showed that the Signed-Rank Test indicated a reliable difference in skin potential for the data in Table 3.5 when the emotions of fear and happiness were requested (although the Sign Test did not agree with this). In Example 3.4 we argued that the Signed-Rank Test was probably more appropriate for these data than the Sign Test, since the magnitudes of the difference scores convey useful information in this case. The Hodges–Lehmann estimator will therefore be the best bet for these data, but we shall also calculate the sample median for comparison.

There are $n = 10$ difference scores in Table 3.5, so the median will be

Table 3.10. Calculating the Hodges–Lehmann estimate for the data in Table 3.5

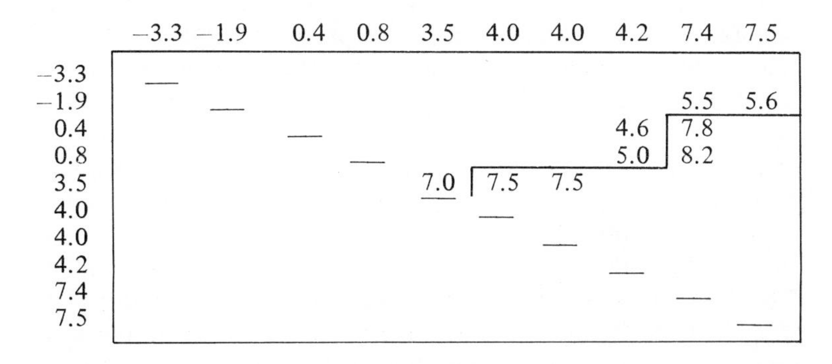

	−3.3	−1.9	0.4	0.8	3.5	4.0	4.0	4.2	7.4	7.5
−3.3	—									
−1.9		—							5.5	5.6
0.4			—					4.6	7.8	
0.8				—				5.0	8.2	
3.5					7.0	7.5	7.5			
4.0						—				
4.0							—			
4.2								—		
7.4									—	
7.5										—

halfway between the 5th and the 6th smallest score, i.e. ½(3.5 + 4.0) = 3.75.

To find the Hodges–Lehmann estimate, we first write the difference scores in order as the columns and the rows of a table as in Table 3.10. Since $n = 10$, there are $n(n + 1)/2 = 10 \times 11/5 = 55$ cells on or above the main diagonal of this table and we need to find the median of the 55 numbers obtained by entering in these cells the sum of the corresponding row and column entries. The median will therefore be the 28th smallest such score. This score will lie on or near the SW–NE diagonal of the table; some of these diagonal scores have been recorded in the table. The easiest way to find the median score is to start with an educated guess and then modify it if necessary. We start with a guess of 7.5, which is twice the sample median of 3.75 previously calculated. The line shown in Table 3.10 has all the cells above it and to the left with entries less than our guess of 7.5. Counting the relevant cells on or above the main diagonal, we find that there are 31 cells with entries smaller than 7.5. We want the 28th smallest entry, so our guess was too high. It is easy to see from Table 3.10 that, in decreasing order, the scores below 7.5 are 7.0, 5.6, 5.5, 5.0, etc., so the 28th smallest score is 5.0. This is twice the required estimate, so the Hodges–Lehmann estimate for these data is 2.5.

Referring back to the data in Table 3.5, this means that our best estimate for the size of the effect is that requesting the emotion of happiness rather than fear reduces the skin potential on average by 2.5 millivolts.

Using the sample median of 3.75 as the estimate indicates a larger effect. The reason for this is that the sample median is not using as much of the numerical information in the data as the Hodges–Lehmann estimator. Since there is no reason to ignore this extra information, the Hodges–Lehmann estimator is to be preferred in this case.

Example 3.8 Estimating the Size of the Effect for Example 3.3

In Example 3.3 we analysed the data in Table 3.7 using the Signed-Rank Test and concluded that there were no grounds for rejecting the golden section hypothesis with these data. The same conclusion was reached using the Sign Test when the data were reanalysed in Example 3.5. In this case, the Signed-Rank Test might be the more appropriate test to use, since the magnitude of the scores gives useful information. On the other hand, since the data are proportions, the symmetry assumption required by the Signed-Rank Test might not be met. If each person's score is a sample from a population with a median of $\phi = 0.618$ (our null hypothesis) then we might expect this population not to be symmetrical since there is more room to obtain a lower score than ϕ in such a population than a higher one, i.e. there are more potential scores from 0 to 0.618 than there are from 0.618 to 1. To be able to judge whether this is in fact so, we should need to know more about this particular situation than we do at present. On balance, the Signed-Rank Test seems reasonable for these data, but we should be wise to supplement any conclusions drawn by using the Sign Test. Thus, it will be helpful to use both of our estimators for these data.

Since there are 32 scores in the data shown in Table 3.7, the sample median will be halfway between the 16th and 17th smallest score; these are both 0.625, so the sample median is also 0.625.

The Hodges–Lehmann estimate is much more tedious to calculate for these data. With $n = 32$, we shall need to find the median of $n(n + 1)/2 = 32 \times 33/2 = 528$ numbers; the median will therefore be halfway between the 264th and 265th smallest score obtained by comparing the original scores individually and in pairs. I shall not present the details of the calculations, which of course can be simplified as in the previous example, but leave them as an exercise for the reader in need of spiritual uplift. The Hodges–Lehmann estimate is 0.627 for these data, which is quite close to the estimate obtained using the sample median.

If the golden section hypothesis is correct, the true proportion of positive descriptions should be exactly ϕ or 0.618. Our obtained estimates are both quite close to this and give useful confirming support to our original tests carried out in Examples 3.3 and 3.5.

3.4 THE BINOMIAL TEST – TWO CATEGORY RESPONSE VARIABLE

The Sign Test of Section 3.2 is usually thought of as a special case of the Binomial Test used with ordinal data. The Binomial Test is applicable to either a one-sample or a two-sample situation when the response variable consists of two categories only, such as success or failure, male or female, and so on. The name Binomial Test reflects the fact that two response categories are being considered. The Sign Test focuses only on whether a difference score is positive or negative and so may be viewed as converting the original ordinal difference scores into two categories + and −.

The type of null hypothesis tested by the Sign Test and the Signed-Rank Test involves assuming that, for each subject, a positive difference score is as likely to occur as a negative one. We may, however, be interested in testing a more general type of null hypothesis, under which the probability of a positive is not equal to the probability of a negative, as illustrated by the simplified example below. The Binomial Test gives us a way of testing this type of null hypothesis when we have two categories in the response variable.

Since the Binomial Test is most frequently used in one-sample situations, our discussion below will focus on these. The use of the test with two-sample data is fairly obvious and will be illustrated in Example 3.11. The test assumes that the data obtained from each subject are independent of the data from other subjects.

Simplified Example

Suppose that an opinion research survey carried out in Canada showed that only 30% of the people who saw Richard Fleischer's film *Mandingo* liked it. In the hope that the British might be more appreciative of a good movie, we decide to test a British audience's views of the film. On the night we see the film, there are only three other people in the audience. They are sitting sufficiently far apart for us to be able to make the assumption that they have not come together and so might not be expected to influence each other's opinions of the film. Thus the data we obtain may reasonably be assumed independent. On questioning after the film, two of the three said they liked the film, while the third disliked it. We wish to test whether the data from this meagre audience are consistent with the Canadian data (the null hypothesis) or whether this audience were more favourably disposed towards the film (the alternative hypothesis).

Test Statistic, B, and its Null Distribution

Each person in our example says either 'Like' or 'Dislike', so we have two categories of response. The test statistic for the Binomial Test is simply the number of people who liked the film, in our case 2, which we label B. As long as we keep track of the sample size n (3 in our case), this gives us all the information we need about the data, since, once we know B and n, we can immediately see that the number of people disliking the film is $n - B$ or 3–2 in our case. Instead of taking B as the number liking the film, we could equivalently call B the number disliking the film. It does not matter which we choose, as long as we remember what B refers to. For our example, we shall keep B as the number liking the film.

From our data, we can see that 2/3 of our audience liked the film, which is more in line with our alternative hypothesis. However, we need to see how likely we should be to obtain such a result under the null hypothesis before brashly concluding that our British audience is more refined than Canadian audiences.

To calculate the null distribution of B, we first note that, since each person

Table 3.11. The 8 possible patterns of results when $n = 3$ and the resulting null distribution of B when $p = 0.3$, $q = 0.7$

	Person					
	1	2	3	B	prob	
1.	L	L	L	3	$(0.3)^3$	= 0.027
2.	D	L	L	2		
3.	L	D	L	2	$3 \times (0.3)^2 \times (0.7)$	= 0.189
4.	L	L	D	2		
5.	D	D	L	1		
6.	D	L	D	1	$3 \times (0.3) \times (0.7)^2$	= 0.441
7.	L	D	D	1		
8.	D	D	D	0	$(0.7)^3$	= 0.343

could say either 'Like' or 'Dislike', there are 2^n possible patterns of results, as was the case with the Signed-Rank and Sign Tests. The 8 possibilities for $n = 3$ are listed in Table 3.11, together with B calculated for each pattern. Thus, pattern 2 represents the situation where Person 1 disliked the film while the other two liked it, so that $B = 2$ in this case. We can see that our data must have been associated with either pattern 2 or pattern 3 or pattern 4. In carrying out the test, it does not matter that we have not kept track of which person said what, since these three patterns of results are all equivalent as far as the test statistic B is concerned, each resulting in $B = 2$.

We now need to take into account the actual null hypothesis we wish to test. This is that 30% of the people should like the film. Put a slightly different way, this means that the probability of a person liking the film is 0.3 and the probability of that person disliking the film is 0.7. To save space, let us label the probability of a person liking the film p and the probability of a person disliking the film q. Thus, $p = 0.3$ and $q = 0.7$. We can now quite straightforwardly compute the probabilities associated with each value of B. Pattern 1 is the only one with $B = 3$; this has each person liking the film. Since the 3 people's judgements are assumed independent, the probability of all 3 people liking the film is $0.3 \times 0.3 \times 0.3 = (0.3)^3 = 0.027$ by the simple multiplication law of probability given in Section 1.2. Thus, prob $(B = 3) = 0.027$. To obtain prob $(B = 2)$, we note that there are three patterns of results with $B = 2$; each of these has 2 L's and 1 D, so each has a probability of $p^2q = (0.3)^2 \times (0.7)$. Since there are three patterns like this, prob$(B = 2)$ is given by $3 \times (0.3)^2 \times (0.7) = 0.189$. Similarly, prob$(B = 1)$ is given by $3 \times p \times q^2 = 3 \times (0.3) \times (0.7)^2 = 0.441$ and prob$(B = 0)$ is given by $q^3 = (0.7)^3 = 0.343$. These results are all shown on the right of Table 3.11 and they give the complete null distribution of B when $p = 0.3$, $q = 0.7$ for a sample size of 3.

It is worth inspecting this null distribution to see what it tells us. The largest probability, 0.441, is associated with $B = 1$. This means that if the true proportion of people liking the film really is 30%, then in a sample of three, the most likely result is that 1 person will like the film and 2 will dislike it. Also, we are rather unlikely to find a sample of three people all of whom liked the film, since prob$(B = 3)$ is only 0.027.

We can easily use this null distribution to test the hypothesis for our sample data, for which $B = 2$. Table 3.11 tells us that the probability of getting a B of 2 or larger when $n = 3$ is $0.189 + 0.027 = 0.216$. Thus, we should only be willing to reject the null hypothesis with these data if we were using a one-tailed test with a significance level of at least 0.216, which is too large for most purposes. So we must unfortunately conclude that this sample of 3 provides no reliable evidence that a British audience appreciates Richard Fleischer's work more than Canadian audiences. Using a standard significance level such as 0.05, Table 3.11 tells us that the upper tail critical value of B is 3, so we should only be able to reject the null hypothesis if all three people in the audience had liked the film.

Using an upper tail test allows us to test the prediction that the British audience like the film more than Canadian audiences, i.e. $p > 0.3$. Had we wished to test the prediction that the British audience like the film less than Canadian audiences, i.e. $p < 0.3$, we should need a lower tail test, since small values of B are more in line with this alternative hypothesis. With $\alpha = 0.05$, no relevant critical value is available when $n = 3$, as can be seen in Table 3.11. This is because the null distribution of B is asymmetrical; if p is 0.3, we are very likely to obtain small values of B and rather unlikely to obtain large values. So, to be able to identify effects at the lower tail test with a standard significance level we need a larger size than 3.

The null distribution for the Binomial Test will always be asymmetrical except when $p = 0.5$. (In this latter case the distribution is identical to that of the Sign Test.) In all cases, the mean of the possible values that B can take is given by np, which is $3 \times 0.3 = 0.9$ for our example. To find critical values for a two-tailed test we use values of B equidistant from the mean in either direction, following the procedure outlined in Section 1.9. Because of the asymmetry of the distribution, we may end up with only one critical value, since its partner may be outside the range of possible values B can take. To illustrate, suppose we want to find the two-tailed critical values of B associated with an α of 0.05. Let us start with $B = 3$ as a possible contender for the upper tail value. This value is at a distance of $3 - 0.9 = 2.1$ from the mean, so the lower tail value will need to be 2.1 below the mean, i.e. $0.9 - 2.1 = -1.2$, which is outside the range of possible values: we can never have -1.2 people liking the film. Now, from Table 3.11, $\text{prob}(B \geqslant 3) = 0.027$ and, obviously, $\text{prob}(B \leqslant -1.2) = 0$, since these values cannot occur, so the associated two-tailed probability is $0.027 + 0 = 0.027$, which is lower than our required α. To see if we can get closer to α with a different choice, let us try $B = 2$ as the upper tail value. In this case, since the upper tail value is 1.1 above the mean, the lower tail value will need to be $0.9 - 1.1 = -0.2$, which is again outside the range of possible values. The associated two-tailed probability will be $\text{prob}(B \geqslant 2) + \text{prob}(B \leqslant -0.2) = 0.189 + 0.027 + 0 = 0.216$. This is larger than our required α, so we have gone too far. In this case, then, with $\alpha = 0.05$, the critical values of B for a two-tailed test will be 3 and -1.2, so we reject the null hypothesis *only* when $B = 3$.

When the sample size n is large it will generally be possible to obtain both an upper and a lower tail critical value of a two-tailed test.

Simplifying the Calculations of the Null Distribution of B

When p and q are equal to 0.5, it is possible to use Appendix Table E to find critical values of the null distribution of B. However, this table is not appropriate when p and q differ from 0.5. When n is smaller than 26, tables of the null distribution of B are available for different values of p and q (see, for example, Mosteller, Rourke and Thomas, 1970, Table IV). When such tables are not available, it will be necessary to calculate part of the null distribution from first principles. This is not as tedious as it might seem, since there is a very simple formula that can be used to aid the calculations.

In Table 3.11, it can be seen that the probability of any particular value of B is made up of two components, first the number of patterns leading to that value of B and second the probability of any one of them occurring. So, prob(B = 2) is given by multiplying 3 (the number of patterns with $B = 2$) by p^2q (the probability of any one of them). In general, using the factorial notation introduced in Section 1.12, the number of patterns associated with a particular value of B, say r, is given by

$$\frac{n!}{(n-r)!r!}$$

To see that this works, in our case we have $n = 3$ and $r = 2$, so the number of patterns with $B = 2$ will be

$$\frac{3!}{1!2!} = \frac{3 \times 2 \times 1}{1 \times 2 \times 1} = 3$$

which we know to be correct. The probability of any one of the patterns will be p^rq^{n-r}, since when $B = r$ there will be r people who liked the film, each with a probability of p, and $n - r$ people who disliked it, each with a probability of q. So the probability of getting r people out of n who liked the film is given by

$$\text{prob}(B = r) = \frac{n!}{(n-r)!r!}\, p^rq^{n-r} \tag{3.6}$$

Using this formula for our example with $n = 3, r = 2, p = 0.3$ and $q = 0.7$, we obtain

$$\text{prob}(B = 2) = \frac{3!}{1!2!}\,(0.3)^2(0.7)^1$$
$$= 3 \times (0.3)^2 \times (0.7) = 0.189,$$

which agrees with the value in Table 3.11. We shall illustrate the use of this formula in Example 3.9.

Normal Approximation to B

When the sample size, n, is fairly large and p is not close to 0 or 1, it is possible to use the normal distribution to approximate the null distribution of B. As a rough rule of thumb, the normal approximation in this case will be accurate if both np and nq are 5 or larger. The mean and variance of the possible values that B can take are given by

$$\text{Mean} = np \tag{3.7}$$

$$\text{Variance} = npq \tag{3.8}$$

As with the Sign Test, a continuity correction of ½ usually improves the approximation. The use of the normal approximation is illustrated in Example 3.10.

The Binomial Test with Two-sample Data

Suppose we carry out a small-scale survey of voting behaviour in two elections. We take a sample of 100 people who have voted either Conservative or Labour in the two elections and find that 30 people voted Conservative both times, 40 voted Labour both times, 5 voted Labour in the first election and Conservative in the second, while 25 voted Conservative in the first election and Labour in the second. In such studies we are not usually interested in those people who vote for the same party both times. We normally wish to compare those changing from L to C with those changing from C to L. For example, we might want to test whether an equal number change from L to C as change from C to L; or we might want to test the prediction that four times as many change from C to L as change from L to C. We can use the Binomial Test for either of these, by setting n equal to the number of people changing in either direction, 30 in our case, B equal to the number changing from L to C, 5, and p equal to the predicted proportion changing from L to C. To test whether as many people change from L to C as change from C to L, we set $p = 0.5$ and use Table E to find the relevant critical value of B. With $\alpha = 0.05$, the critical value for a two-tailed test with $n = 30$ is 9; since our value of B is smaller than this, we reject the null hypothesis and conclude that fewer people change from L to C than change from C to L. To test the prediction that four times as many people change from C to L as change from L to C, we set $p = 0.2, q = 0.8$ and use formula 3.6 or the normal approximation with continuity correction. Using the normal approximation, which is likely to be accurate in this case since both $np = 6$ and $nq = 24$ are larger than 5, we have Mean = np = 6 and Variance = npq = 4.8, so

$$z = \frac{5.5 - 6}{\sqrt{4.8}} = -0.23,$$

which is nowhere near any of the standard critical values given in Table B(ii). In this case, therefore, we cannot reject the null hypothesis; we conclude that these data are consistent with the prediction.

This version of the Binomial Test is frequently used to study the pattern of disagreement between two judges or interviewers. For example, if the candidates for a job are seen by two interviewers and 20 of them are accepted by interviewer A but not by interviewer B while 10 are accepted by B but not by A, the Binomial Test may be used to test whether A is more likely to accept one of these candidates than B (see Exercise 3.11).

When $p = 0.5$, this use of the Binomial Test is generally referred to as the McNemar Test. A further illustration of the McNemar Test is given in Example 3.11.

Estimating the Size of the Effect

To estimate the size of the effect following a Binomial Test, the most frequently used estimator is the proportion of the sample responding in one direction. This is the best estimate of the proportion of the population responding in that direction. In our original example, with 2 of the 3 people in the audience liking *Mandingo*, our best bet of the proportion of people in Britain liking the film is 2/3. The use of this estimator is illustrated in Example 3.9.

Further Comments

For a more detailed account of the binomial distribution and its uses, see Mosteller, Rourke and Thomas (1970). For more on the McNemar Test, see Bradley (1968, Section 7.7.5). In some cases, rather than assessing *disagreement* between interviewers, we may wish to assess *agreement*. One way of doing this is discussed in Section 8.4.

Example 3.9. The One-Sample Binomial Test

In cases of high blood-pressure, a particular drug is effective in 60% of patients. A modification of the drug is claimed to be more effective. It is tested on ten volunteers with high blood pressure and nine of them show substantial improvement. Do these data support the claim?

Suppose we set $\alpha = 0.05$. We want a one-tailed test in this case, since we should not be interested in the modified drug if it were significantly worse than the original. The null hypothesis is that the modification is no different from the original, so we set $p = 0.6$ and $q = 0.4$. With this null hypothesis, we require the probability of 9 or more successes when $n = 10$. Remembering that the result of raising any number to the power zero is 1, this is given by

$$
\begin{aligned}
\text{prob}(B \geqslant 9) &= \text{prob}(B = 9) + \text{prob}(B = 10) \\
&= \frac{n!}{(n-9)!9!} p^9 q^1 + \frac{n!}{(n-10)!10!} p^{10} q^0 \\
&= \frac{10!}{1!9!} (0.6)^9 (0.4)^1 + \frac{10!}{0!10!} (0.6)^{10} (0.4)^0 \\
&= 10 \times (0.6)^9 \times 0.4 + 1 \times (0.6)^{10} \\
&= 0.040 + 0.006 \\
&= 0.046
\end{aligned}
$$

(The 0! here may worry some readers, since it doesn't fit in with the usual meaning of the factorial notation; when 0! occurs, it is always defined to be equal to 1.) Thus, the probability of 9 or more successes out of 10 is only 0.046, which is smaller than the significance level of 0.05, so we reject the null hypothesis and conclude that his sample of volunteers provide evidence that the modification is an improvement over the original, as claimed.

Our best estimate of the proportion of patients for whom the modified drug is likely to be effective is 9/10 or 0.9.

Example 3.10 The Binomial Test with Large Samples

A hundred students answer a 5-alternative multiple-choice question as part of an examination. Twenty-nine of them give the correct answer. Is this better than would be expected by chance if none of them knew the answer?

Since the question has 5 alternatives, only one of which is correct, the probability of giving a correct answer by chance is $1/5 = 0.2$ and the probability of getting it wrong is $4/5 = 0.8$. We can therefore set $p = 0.2$, $q = 0.8$, $n = 100$ and $B = 29 - ½ = 28.5$ and use the normal approximation to the Binomial Test. The z-score is then given by

$$z = \frac{B - \text{Mean}}{\text{S.D.}} = \frac{B - np}{\sqrt{npq}}$$

$$= \frac{28.5 - 100 \times 0.2}{\sqrt{100 \times 0.2 \times 0.8}} = \frac{28.5 - 20}{\sqrt{16}} = 2.125$$

Since we want to discover whether the observed number is better than would be expected by chance, we require a one-tailed test. Suppose we use a significance level of 0.05. Then Table B(ii) gives 1.645 as the upper tail critical value of z. Our obtained z is larger than this, so we reject the null hypothesis and conclude that these students were doing better than might be expected by chance.

Example 3.11 The McNemar Test

The most frequent application of the Binomial Test in the two-sample situation occurs when $p = 0.5$; it is usually known as the McNemar Test.

To illustrate its use, suppose we wish to test whether two questions in an examination are of equal difficulty. 80 students take the examination; 20 of them fail both questions while 25 of them pass both questions. Of the remainder, 12 pass equation 1 but fail question 2, while 23 pass question 2 but fail question 1. The McNemar Test ignores those 45 students who did the same on both questions and focuses on the remaining 35 who passed on only one question. If the two questions are of equal difficulty (the null hypothesis), then such a person is as likely to have passed only on question 1 as to have passed only on question 2. If the two questions are not of equal difficulty (the alternative hypothesis), then such a person is more likely to have passed on one rather than the other question. We can test this by setting $n = 35$, the number of people passing on only one question, $p = 0.5$, the probability of it being question 1, and $q = 0.5$, the probability of it being question 2. We require a two-tailed test. Suppose we set $\alpha = 0.05$. Then from Table E we find the critical value to be 11 when $n = 35$, since the Sign Test and the Binomial Test are identical when $p = 0.5$. Our obtained value of B would need to be smaller than or equal to 11 before we could reject the null hypothesis. Since we have observed 12 people passing only question 1 and 23 passing question 2, B will be either 12 or 23. Neither of these is smaller than the critical value, so we have no grounds for rejecting the null hypothesis using a two-tailed test with a significance level of 0.05. We therefore conclude that the two questions seem to be of equal difficulty for these students.

3.5 TESTING FOR ORDER EFFECTS WITH TWO RELATED SAMPLES

We noted in Section 3.1 that when more than one observation is collected from a single individual it is frequently difficult to ensure there is no carryover or order effect such as practice or boredom from one observation to the next. The two-sample tests discussed so far in this chapter have attempted to get round this problem by counterbalancing or randomizing the order of presentation of the two treatments to each person. This procedure is not entirely satisfactory, however, since it is rarely possible to rule out completely the possibility that order effects were responsible for any difference or lack of difference in the two samples. The techniques illustrated in the present section provide a way of doing this, in that they make it possible to test for both order effects and treatment effects simultaneously in the two-sample situation. They should be used whenever an order effect is suspected. In many cases, it is the treatment effect that is of interest, with the possibility of an order effect being a nuisance factor. This is illustrated by the study in Example 3.13. In some situations, however, it is the order effect itself that is of interest, with the possibility of treatment differences being the nuisance factor, as illustrated by the study in Example 3.12. Both techniques presented in this section are applicable in either situation. They are both fairly obvious applications of the tests presented already in Chapter 2. The only new ideas involved are the ways in which the same set of data may be viewed from two different perspectives to emphasize different aspects of it.

Ideally, in situations where there is a possibility of an order effect being important, the design of the experiment should involve as nearly as possible the same number of subjects getting the two treatments in the order AB as those getting the treatments in the order *BA*. However, both techniques will work even if order effects were not anticipated but the researcher has kept track of the order in which the treatments were presented to each subject and wishes to test post hoc the possibility of an order effect biasing the results.

The techniques have been presented as tests for order effects. However, they are not limited to this and may be used in certain circumstances to test for other possible types of bias in a matched-pairs design. For example, they may be used in twin studies, where there may be differences between first and second born. In a standard matched-pairs design, even though an attempt has been made to equate the members of each pair on relevant variables, it may be possible to obtain external predictions that one member of each pair might do better than the other. Such a situation is illustrated in Exercise 3.14.

Example 3.12 The Gart Test for Order Effects – Two Category Response Variable

This test, devised by John Gart (1969), applies the Fisher Exact Test (Section 2.5) twice to the same set of data, once in a way that tests for an order effect and once in a way that tests for a treatment effect.

It will be illustrated by an example from social psychology where several investigators have attempted to discover whether order effects are important when forming impressions of others. Luchins (1958), for example, presented two conflicting descriptions of an imaginary person named Jim. One of the descriptions (the E block) showed Jim behaving in an extraverted manner while the other (the I block) showed him to be introverted. Half the subjects read the descriptions in the order IE and the other half in the order EI. Luchins found that, when subjects completed a questionnaire about their impressions of Jim after the first block is presented and again after the second block, their final impression tended to predominantly influenced by the last block read. Believing this finding to be the result of misleading instructions, I attempted to replicate it (Leach, 1974), using instructions emphasizing that both blocks of information referred to the same person and that subjects should attempt to form a composite impression of Jim based on all the information they had about him. Thirteen subjects read the two descriptions of Jim, seven in IE order and six in EI order. As part of the questionnaire, they wrote a brief characterization of Jim. The characterization written after the second block was scored as showing the predominant influence of the I block or as showing the predominant influence of the E block or as being equally based on both. Four of the subjects wrote characterizations based equally on both blocks. For the purpose of this analysis, these subjects give no information, so Gart's test concentrates on the remaining 9 subjects.

Testing for an order effect with treatment as a nuisance factor

The results for the nine subjects who showed a predominant influence of one block or the other are shown in Table 3.12(a) With the results recorded in this way, if the final block read had predominant influence, this would be shown by cells b and c containing large frequencies and cells a and d containing small frequencies. This is obviously not the case with these data. We can test this using the Fisher Exact Test, since a large negative S will reflect the predominant influence of the first block while a large positive S will reflect the predominant influence of the first block. For these data, $S = 4$. With the given marginal totals and a one-tailed test (since we are testing a prediction from Luchin's work) with $\alpha = 0.05$, Table C indicates that it will not be possible to reject the null hypothesis. In other words, there is no effect of order of presentation of the blocks.

Table 3.12. Data for Example 3.12 (from Leach, 1974)

(a)

		Predominant influence		
		I block	E block	t_i
Order of presentation	IE	4(a)	0(b)	4
	EI	4(c)	1(d)	5
	u_i	8	1	$S = 4$

(b)

		Predominant influence		
		First block	Second block	t_i
Order of presentation	IE	4	0	4
	EI	1	4	5
	u_i	5	4	$S = 16$

Testing for a treatment effect with order as a nuisance factor

Gart's test also allows us to test for treatment effects unconfounded by order of presentation. In this example, a treatment effect would constitute one or other of the blocks having a predominant influence on the characterizations, irrespective of the order in which they were presented. The data above seem to show that the I block is the more salient of the two, with eight of the nine characterizations showing its influence. To test for this, the data are rearranged as shown in Table 3.12(b). If we carry out a Fisher Exact Test on the data in this form, a large positive S will reflect the predominant influence of the I block while a large negative S will reflect the predominant influence of the E block, and so will give us a test of the treatment effect. Since we have no predictions about which block should be more salient, a two-tailed test is required. With $\alpha = 0.05$, Table C gives critical values of -16 and 16. The value of S computed from the data is 16, so we reject the null hypothesis and conclude that there is a treatment effect. In this case the I block is more salient in determining the composite impression.

This combination of tests thus shows that there is no evidence of an order effect but that there is a treatment effect. So the experiment has failed to replicate Luchin's finding, but has suggested that the difference between the two blocks of information, which constitutes a nuisance variable when studying order effects, is more important in this situation. (Further data from this study are presented in Exercise 3.13.)

In situations where interest does not focus on the order effect, it may by tempting to ignore any possibility of an order effect and use the Sign Test or McNemar's test which are applicable to the same type of data. The Sign Test or McNemar's test should only be used if there is no possibility of an order effect biasing the results. Where there is reason to suspect an order effect, Gart's test is preferable.

For a further discussion of the Gart Test, see Everitt (1977, Section 2.6).

Example 3.13 Testing for Order Effects – Ordinal Response Variable

Gart's test may straightforwardly be generalized to situations where the data come in the form of ordinal difference scores rather than the two-category form of Example 3.12. This involves using the Rank-Sum Test (Section 2.1) in the same way that the Fisher Exact Test is used by Gart.

To illustrate, suppose a theory of semantic memory predicts that exemplars of the categories 'fish' and 'birds' should be equally easy to produce. To test this we ask five people to name as many fish as they can in 20 seconds and then to name as many birds as possible in 20 seconds. A further five people do the same task in reverse order. The

Table 3.13. Hypothetical data for Example 3.13

	Subject	1	2	3	4	5
BF order	Birds	23	16	14	15	20
	Fish	20	12	7	10	10
	Subject	6	7	8	9	10
FB order	Birds	16	10	20	21	22
	Fish	10	12	12	22	13

results are recorded in Table 3.13. It seems that more birds were named than fish, but we should be wise to test for any effect of order of presentation before doing an analysis of the treatment effect.

Testing for an order effect with treatment as a nuisance factor

To test for an order effect, difference scores are computed for each subject as shown below. These data are then analysed using a Rank-Sum Test, since we have two independent samples of difference scores. For

BF order	B–F	3	4	7	5	10	$S = -3$
FB order	B–F	6	–2	8	–1	9	

these data, $S = -3$. Using a two-tailed test with $\alpha = 0.05$ and entering Table A with $t_1 = 5$ and $t_2 = 5$, we find the critical values of S to be –21 and 21. Our obtained value is between these critical values, so we cannot reject the null hypothesis. We conclude that there is no evidence of an order effect.

Testing for a treatment effect with order as a nuisance factor

Following the same procedure as with Gart's test we can test for a treatment effect unconfounded by any order effect by computing the difference scores in the order 1st–2nd and carrying out a Rank-Sum Test. The resulting data and analysis are shown below.

BF order	B–F	3	4	7	5	10	$S = 25$
FB order	F–B	–6	2	–8	1	–9	

Using a two-tailed test with $\alpha = 0.05$, the critical values for S are –21 and 21. Our obtained S of 25 is larger than the upper tail value, so we reject the null hypothesis and conclude that there is a treatment effect. In this case it is clear that more birds were named than fish.

As with Gart's test, the difference score data presented here could have been analysed using the Signed-Rank Test of Section 3.1 rather than by the present method. However, the Signed-Rank Test does not allow for order effects to be tested. As before, if there is reason to suspect an order effect, the present combination of tests should be used. Only if there are no grounds for suspecting an order effect should the Signed-Rank Test be used.

For a further discussion of the Order Effects Test, see Lehmann (1975, Section 3.4).

3.6 SUMMARY OF SUGGESTED PROCEDURE

General Points

1. Do you have either one-sample data or two related samples? If not, look elsewhere (see the table at the front of the book for suggestions). For two-sample data, go to 5.

One-sample data

2. If the response variable has two categories, try the Binomial Test.
3. If the response variable is ordinal, go to 8.
4. If the response variable has more than two categories, look in Chapter 8.

Two-sample data

5. Is there the possibility of an order effect influencing the results? If so, try the Gart Test if the response variable has two categories or the Order Effects Test if the response variable is ordinal.
6. If the response variable has two categories and order effects are not involved, try the Binomial Test.
7. If the response variable is ordinal and order effects are not involved, go to 8. If the response variable has more than two categories, try pretending you have one-sample data and look in Chapter 8.
8. In the one-sample case, use the original scores from each subject. In the two-sample case, compute a difference score for each subject or matched pair. In either case, answer the following questions.
   (a) Is it reasonable to assume that the scores for different subjects are comparable in the sense of being orderable?
   (b) Is it reasonable to assume that the score for each subject comes from a symmetrical population?
   (c) Do you want to pay particular attention to the magnitudes of the difference scores?

   If the answer to any of these questions is no, try the Sign Test. Otherwise try the Signed-Rank Test.

Wilcoxon Signed-Rank Test

1. For *one-sample data*, this test may be used to assess whether each subject's score comes from a symmetric population with a predicted median, say M. To do this, subtract M from each score to obtain a difference score and go to 3.
2. For *two-sample data*, this test may be used to assess whether the difference score for each subject comes from a symmetric population with a median of zero; this will generally be true if there is no difference between the populations from which the two raw scores for each subject come.

3. Find n, the number of non-zero difference scores. Select the significance level α and decide whether a one- or a two-tailed test is required.
4. Ignore the signs of the difference scores and rank the non-zero ones, the lowest score getting a rank of 1 and the highest getting a rank of n, using midranks if there are ties.
5. Attach the sign of each non-zero difference score to its rank. Find $W+$, the sum of the positive ranks, and $W-$, the sum of the negative ranks.
6. If $n > 50$ or if more than a quarter of the difference scores are involved in ties, use the normal approximation in 7. Otherwise, compare the obtained values of $W+$ and $W-$ with the relevant critical value given in Table D and complete the test as indicated at the top of Table D. Go to 8.
7. *Normal approximation*

$$\text{Mean} = n(n+1)/4 \tag{3.1}$$

If there are no ties,

$$\text{Variance} = \frac{n(n+1)(2n+1)}{24} \tag{3.2}$$

If there are ties,

$$\text{Variance} = \frac{n(n+1)(2n+1)}{24} - \frac{1}{48}\Sigma t_i(t_i - 1)(t_i + 1) \tag{3.3}$$

where t_i is the number of scores at a particular value.
If $W+ < \text{Mean}$, add continuity correction of ½ to $W+$.
If $W+ > \text{Mean}$, subtract continuity correction of ½ from $W+$.

$$\text{Compute } z = \frac{W+ - \text{Mean}}{\text{S.D.}}, \text{ where}$$

S.D. = $\sqrt{\text{Variance}}$, and compare z with the relevant critical value(s) given in Table B(ii).

8. *To estimate the size of the effect*, compute the Hodges–Lehmann estimate as shown in Example 3.7. Make sure you include any zero difference scores in the calculations.

Sign Test

1. For *one-sample data*, this test may be used to assess whether each subject's score comes from a population with a predicted median, say M. To do this, subtract M from each score to obtain a difference score and go to 3.
2. For *two-sample data*, this test may be used to assess whether the difference score for each subject comes from a population with a median of zero; this will be true if there is no difference between the populations from which the two raw scores for each subject come.
3. Find n, the number of non-zero difference scores. Select the significance level α and decide whether a one- or a two-tailed test is required.
4. Find $N+$, the number of positive difference scores, and $N-$, the number of negative difference scores.

5. If $n > 50$, use the normal approximation in 6. Otherwise, compare the obtained values of $N+$ and $N-$ with the relevant critical value in Table E and complete the test as indicated at the top of Table E. Go to 7.
6. *Normal approximation*

$$\text{Mean} = n/2 \tag{3.4}$$

$$\text{Variance} = n/4 \tag{3.5}$$

   If $N+ <$ Mean, add continuity correction of ½ to $N+$.
   If $N+ >$ Mean, subtract continuity correction of ½ from $N+$.

   Compute $z = \dfrac{N+ - \text{Mean}}{\text{S.D.}}$, where

   S.D. $= \sqrt{\text{Variance}}$, and compare z with the relevant critical value(s) given in Table B(ii).
7. *To estimate the size of the effect*, for the one-sample case compute the median of the raw scores, and for the two-sample case compute the median of the difference scores, making sure you include any zero scores in the calculation.

Binomial Test

1. For *one-sample data*, this test may be used to assess whether the proportion of scores in one of the two response categories is equal to a specified value, p. Go to 3.
2. For *two-sample data*, this test may be used to assess whether, for those subjects (or matched pairs) having different responses on the two occasions, the proportion of subjects with one of the two possible combinations of scores is equal to a specified value, p. When $p = ½$, the test is known as the *McNemar Test*.
3. Find n, the total number of scores for both possible response categories; B, the number in one of the two response categories; p, the predicted proportion in that category; and q $(=1 - p)$, the predicted proportion in the other category.
4. Select significance level α and decide whether a one- or a two-tailed test is required.
5. If $p = ½$ and $n < 51$, use Table E to find the relevant critical value and complete the test as indicated at the top of Table E. Go to 10.
6. If np and nq are both larger than 4, use the normal approximation in 9. Otherwise, if the obtained value of B is r, find the probability of getting this value, using the formula

$$\text{prob}(B = r) = \frac{n!}{(n-r)!r!}\, p^r q^{n-r} \tag{3.6}$$

7. If a one-tailed test is required, compute the probability of getting a value of B equal to or more extreme than the obtained value in the predicted direction, where each of the individual probabilities is given by formula 3.6 (see Example 3.9). If the resulting cumulative probability is less than α, reject the null hypothesis. Go to 10.
8. If a two-tailed test is required, compute the probability of getting a value of B

as far from the mean np as the obtained value or further in either direction. If the resulting cumulative probability is less than α, reject the null hypothesis. Go to 10.

9. *Normal approximation*

$$\text{Mean} \quad = np \tag{3.7}$$

$$\text{Variance} = npq \tag{3.8}$$

If obtained $B < np$, add a continuity correction of ½.
If obtained $B > np$, subtract a continuity correction of ½.

Compute $z = \dfrac{B - np}{\text{S.D.}}$, where

$\text{S.D.} = \sqrt{\text{Variance}}$, and compare z with the relevant critical value given in Table B(ii).

10. *To estimate the size of the effect*, use the sample proportion, as in Example 3.9.

The Gart Test

1. This test may be used in the two-sample situation to test both for an order effect and for a difference between the two treatments. Each subject is given the two treatments, A and B, some in the order AB and some in the order BA. The response is *either* predominant influence of treatment A *or* predominant influence of treatment B. Any subjects for which there is no predominant influence are ignored. This two-category response variable may arise either directly (as in Example 3.12) or indirectly according to whether a difference score computed for each subject is positive or negative.
2. To test for an *order effect*, record the data in a 2 x 2 contingency table as shown below and carry out the Fisher Exact Test.

		Predominant influence	
		A	B
Order of	AB		
presentation	BA		

3. To test for a *treatment effect*, record the data in a 2 x 2 contingency table as shown below and carry out the Fisher Exact Test.

		Predominant influence	
		1st treatment	2nd treatment
Order of	AB		
presentation	BA		

4. See Example 3.12 for details.

The Order Effects Test

1. This test may be used in the two-sample situation to test both for an order effect and for a difference between the two treatments. Each subject is given the two treatments, some in the order AB and some in the order BA. For each subject a difference score $A - B$ is computed. If the difference scores are not comparable across subjects or if you don't want to pay particular attention to the magnitudes of the difference scores, use the Gart Test.
2. To test for an *order effect*, having computed difference scores $A - B$ for all subjects, compare the two groups AB and BA using the Rank-Sum Test.
3. To test for a *treatment effect*, compute difference scores $A - B$ for group AB and $B - A$ for group BA, and compare the two groups using the Rank-Sum Test.
4. See Example 3.13 for details.

3.7 EXERCISES

Section 3.1

1. Suppose we had carried out the drug study outlined in the simplified example and had obtained the following results from 9 subjects. What conclusion would you draw using a two-tailed test with $\alpha = 0.05$?

	Subject								
	1	2	3	4	5	6	7	8	9
RT under Drug X	208	205	202	207	206	204	201	209	227
RT under Drug Y	223	216	211	212	209	205	203	221	211

2. The results for the 26 men in the Chilton and Leach study described in Example 3.3 were as follows: 0.417, 0.458, 0.458, 0.500, 0.517, 0.531, 0.533, 0.542, 0.556, 0.556, 0.560, 0.573, 0.583, 0.590, 0.595, 0.600, 0.625, 0.639, 0.643, 0.643, 0.648, 0.652, 0.653, 0.702, 0.722, 0.786. Test the golden section hypothesis with these data.
3. Using the data in Exercise 1, decide whether it makes a difference if you rank the difference scores from high to low rather than from low to high.
4. (Optional) Compute the exact null distribution of $W+$ for the case $n = 5$ and compare it with the critical values given in Table D.

Section 3.2

5. Analyse the data of Exercise 1 using the Sign Test and comment on the conclusion drawn.
6. Analyse the data of Exercise 2 using the Sign Test.

7. (Optional) Compute the exact null distribution of $N+$ for the case $n = 5$ and compare it with the critical values given in Table E.
8. (Optional) Suppose the data for 3 subjects in the drug study had been those given below. Show that the Sign Test and the Signed-Rank Test are exactly equivalent in this case. This demonstrates that the Sign Test may be viewed as a special case of the Signed-Rank Test.

	Subject		
	1	2	3
RT under Drug X	200	195	209
RT under Drug Y	210	205	199

Section 3.3

9. Estimate the size of the effect using *both* the Hodges–Lehmann estimator *and* the sample median (a) for the data in Exercise 1 and (b) for the data in Exercise 2.

Section 3.4

10. In a 5-alternative multiple choice test in which all questions had to be attempted, Bill had 12 answers correct out of 25. Was he just guessing? Mike had only 2 correct; was he guessing?
11. When interviewing candidates for a job, two interviewers disagree about 30 of the candidates. 20 of them are accepted by interviewer A but not by interviewer B; 10 are accepted by B but not by A. For such candidates, is A more likely to accept than B?
12. Byer and Abrams (1953), quoted in Hollander and Wolfe (1973), wanted to assess whether a group of 50 subjects could discriminate a small difference in bitterness. Each subject tasted from three glasses, randomly presented, two of which contained the same quinine solution and the third a different quinine solution. They were asked to select the odd one out. 25 of the subjects selected correctly and 25 selected incorrectly. Do these results indicate that the group of subjects could discriminate the difference in bitterness? What is the best estimate of the probability of a subject being able to select the odd sample?

Section 3.5

13. In my study described in Example 3.12 (Leach, 1974), a further 12 people read the two descriptions of Jim, 6 in IE order and 6 in EI order. These subjects were given the standard instructions used by Luchins (1958) that didn't stress that the two descriptions referred to the same person. Three of the subjects wrote characterizations following the second description that were

based equally on both descriptions. Of the remaining subjects, 1 in Group IE and 5 in Group EI showed the predominant influence of the I block, while 3 in Group IE and none in Group EI showed the predominant influence of the E block. Test these data for order effect and treatment effect.

14. Twelve pairs of identical twins take part in a study to compare two purportedly equivalent forms of a test of arithmetical ability. One twin from each pair is randomly selected to complete Form *A* and the other completes Form *B*. The investigator later obtains information about which of each pair was born first. Analyse the hypothetical test scores shown below to assess (a) whether there is a difference between the two forms and (b) whether there is a difference between first and second born.

	Twin pair	1	2	3	4	5		
First born	Form *A*	50	63	55	69	56		
gets Form *A*	Form *B*	40	50	49	72	48		
	Twin pair	6	7	8	9	10	11	12
First born	Form *A*	55	50	43	42	48	51	60
gets Form *B*	Form *B*	54	62	50	44	53	65	64

CHAPTER 4

Tests for Several Independent Samples – Categorical Explanatory Variable

The tests discussed in this chapter are applicable when more than two independent samples of data have been collected and when the response variable may be thought of as either ordinal (see Example 1.9) or categorical with two categories (see Example 1.10). The more general categorical case will be discussed in Chapter 8. The tests here provide one way of generalizing the tests discussed in Chapter 2. As with those tests, the most important assumption is that of independence. Each person in the experiment must contribute only one score on the response variable and one score on the explanatory variable, and should not be able to influence the scores of any other person.

4.1 THE KRUSKAL–WALLIS TEST – ORDINAL RESPONSE VARIABLE

The Kruskal–Wallis Test is a direct generalization of the Wilcoxon Rank-Sum Test to three or more independent samples. The test attempts to decide whether the samples of scores come from the same population (the null hypothesis) or from several populations that differ in location (the alternative hypothesis). It assumes that the data are independent and that the scores on the response variable consist of continuous ordinal data.

Simplified Example

Suppose we wish to compare three different weight reduction treatments and we have a sample of four women who wish to lose weight. One of the women undergoes treatment I, two undergo treatment II and one undergoes treatment III. The percentage weight loss for each of the women is shown in Table 4.1. From these data it looks as though treatment III is the most effective and treatment II the least effective with I being somewhere between them. As with our other tests, we wish to find how likely our obtained results are under the null hypothesis that there is no real difference between the three treatments.

To allow us to talk in more general terms about this test, it is convenient to use

Table 4.1. Data for the simplified example

Treatments		
I	II	III
14.2	12.8	17.3
	12.3	

some simple notation. Let n be the total number of women in the study, t_1 be the number undergoing treatment I, t_2 the number undergoing treatment II, and t_3 the number undergoing treatment III. In our case, $n = 4$, $t_1 = 1$, $t_2 = 2$ and $t_3 = 1$.

Test Statistic – *K*

As the first step in producing a test statistic that reflects how large any difference in location between the three samples is, we follow the procedure of the Rank-Sum Test, ranking the data from low to high and computing rank-sums for the three samples. This is done in Table 4.2, where R_i refers to the rank-sum of the ith group, so $R_1 = 3$, $R_2 = 3$ and $R_3 = 4$. Notice that it is not sufficient to calculate the rank-sum of only one group, as we did with the Rank-Sum Test, since this time the fact that we have more than two samples makes things more complicated. Our test statistic will have to take account of what is going on in all three groups to give an adequate picture of the data. Now, since there are different numbers of women in the three groups, the mean rank in each group is more informative than the rank-sum. This is obtained by dividing the rank-sum, R_i, for a given group by the number of women, t_i, in that group and is shown in Table 4.2 for each group.

If the null hypothesis is true, these three average ranks should all be relatively close together, while if the alternative hypothesis is correct the average ranks should differ. Thus, we want our test statistic to reflect how different these average ranks are; in other words, we want a measure of dispersion for the average ranks. The measure used is similar to the variance of the average ranks and is obtained as follows.

Table 4.2. Finding average ranks for the data in Table 4.1

	Treatment		
	I	II	III
	3	2	4
		1	
Rank-sum, R_i	3	3	4
Average rank, R_i/t_i	3	1.5	4

If the three average ranks are all close together, they should also be close to the grand mean of all four ranks, which is $(1 + 2 + 3 + 4)/4 = 2.5$. The more they deviate from this grand mean, the more they will differ amongst themselves. These deviations are $3 - 2.5 = 0.5$, $1.5 - 2.5 = -1.0$ and $4 - 2.5 = 1.5$ for treatments I, II, and III, respectively. We can then get a single number that reflects the dispersion of the average ranks by summing the squares of these deviations, with each squared deviation weighted by the number of women in that sample. This gives

$$\begin{aligned} & 1 \times (0.5)^2 + 2 \times (-1.0)^2 + 1 \times (1.5)^2 \\ &= 0.25 + 2.00 + 2.25 \\ &= 4.50 \end{aligned}$$

The larger this number is, the greater is the difference between the three samples.

We can express what we have done so far in a general formula. First we note that, in general, the mean of n ranks can be obtained simply as $(n + 1)/2$ instead of bothering to add all the ranks together and divide by n as we did above. This can be seen to work for our example where $n = 4$ and $(n + 1)/2 = 5/2 = 2.5$, which is the value we obtained by the laborious method. The general formula for our measure of the dispersion of the average ranks is then

$$\Sigma t_i \left(\frac{R_i}{t_i} - \frac{n+1}{2}\right)^2$$

This just expresses in symbolic form the way in which we arrived at our value 4.50 above.

We could use this measure as a test statistic. However, it is usual to multiply the value we have obtained so far by a constant. The only reason for this is that it simplifies the use of an approximation to the null distribution, as we shall see below. We therefore use as our test statistic the value K given by

$$K = \frac{12}{n(n+1)} \Sigma t_i \left(\frac{R_i}{t_i} - \frac{n+1}{2}\right)^2 \tag{4.1}$$

In our example, we know that the last part of this expression comes to 4.5, so K is given by

$$K = \frac{12}{4 \times 5} \times 4.5 = 2.7$$

K preserves the properties we require of a test statistic in this situation. If the null hypothesis is true, then the average ranks will all be close together and K will be small. If the alternative hypothesis is true, however, the average ranks will differ and K will be large. It is worth remembering that K must always be positive. If you obtain a negative K there's a mistake in your calculations.

Simplifying the calculation of K

Our formula for K in equation 4.1 has the advantage that it shows clearly what we are doing – namely, squaring deviations from the mean. However, it is possible to reduce the formula to a form that is equivalent but involves fewer arithmetical computations. The simplified formula is

$$K = -3(n+1) + \frac{12}{n(n+1)} \Sigma \frac{R_i^2}{t_i}, \qquad (4.2)$$

where R_i is the sum of the ranks in the ith sample, t_i is the number of subjects in the ith sample, and n is the total number of subjects. The calculations for our example can be set out as follows

	Treatment			
	I	II	III	
Rank-sum, R_i	3	3	4	
R_i^2	9	9	16	
Ri^2/t_i	9	4.5	16	$\Sigma \frac{R_i^2}{t_i} = 29.5$

Using our new formula for K, we then get

$$K = -3(4+1) + \frac{12}{4(4+1)} \times 29.5 = -15 + 17.7 = 2.7$$

which agrees with the value obtained by the original method.

As a check on the calculations, the rank-sums R_i will always add to $n(n+1)/2$. For our example $\Sigma R_i = 3 + 3 + 4 = 10$ and $n(n+1)/2 = 4 \times 5/2 = 10$.

Null Distribution of K

As usual, to find how large a value of K must be before we are prepared to reject the null hypothesis, we must investigate all the possible patterns of results that could occur and from these generate the null distribution of K.

The possible patterns that could occur for our example with $t_1 = 1, t_2 = 2$, and $t_3 = 1$ are given by all the permutations of four ranks, such that treatments I and III contain 1 number each while treatment II contains 2 numbers. These are listed in Table 4.3, together with a value of K calculated for each. Notice that some patterns of results are missing from the table; for example, the pattern

I	II	III
1	3	4
	2	

is not there. However, this will have exactly the same value of K as pattern 7, which is identical apart from the order of the two treatment II ranks. For each of the 12 patterns shown in Table 4.3, a further pattern with the same value of K can be

Table 4.3. The 12 distinct patterns of results when $t_1 = 1$, $t_2 = 2$, $t_3 = 1$ and associated values of K. Roman numerals show groups, arabic show ranked scores

1. I	II	III	2. I	II	III	3. I	II	III	4. I	II	III
3	1	4	4	1	3	2	1	4	4	1	2
	2			2			3			3	
	$K = 2.7$			$K = 2.7$			$K = 1.8$			$K = 1.8$	
5. I	**II**	**III**	**6. I**	**II**	**III**	**7. I**	**II**	**III**	**8. I**	**II**	**III**
2	1	3	3	1	2	1	2	4	4	2	1
	4			4			3			3	
	$K = 0.3$			$K = 0.3$			$K = 2.7$			$K = 2.7$	
9. I	**II**	**III**	**10. I**	**II**	**III**	**11. I**	**II**	**III**	**12. I**	**II**	**III**
1	2	3	3	2	1	1	3	2	2	3	1
	4			4			4			4	
	$K = 1.8$			$K = 1.8$			$K = 2.7$			$K = 2.7$	

generated by changing the order of the treatment II ranks. We could have included these in Table 4.3, but there is no need to, since, because they have the same value of K as their partners in the table, the null distribution will be the same whether we include them or not. We can see that the actual set of data we obtained in our example is the partner of pattern 1 and has the same value of K (2.7).

Under the null hypothesis, these distinct patterns of results are all equally likely, so we can generate the null distribution of K for our case by noting that 6 of the 12 patterns have a K of 2.7, 4 of the patterns have $K = 1.8$ and 2 have $K = 0.3$. Thus the null distribution of K for the case $t_1 = 1, t_2 = 2, t_3 = 1$, is

Table 4.4 Null distribution of K for the case $t_1 = 1$, $t_2 = 2$, $t_3 = 1$

K	0.3	1.8	2.7
Probability	2/12	4/12	6/12

Under the alternative hypothesis that the treatments differ in location, large values of K are more likely to occur, as can be seen from Table 4.3. For example, pattern 7 implies that treatment I is the least effective and treatment III is the most effective, while pattern 12 has treatment III least effective with treatment II most effective. On the other hand, patterns 5 and 6, which have the smallest value of K, give treatment II both the lowest and highest scores with treatments I and III getting intermediate scores. These patterns do not suggest location differences between the treatments.

Thus, small values of K tend to favour the null hypothesis while large values favour the alternative hypothesis. It is convenient to think of the Kruskal–Wallis

Test as inherently two-tailed since there is no direct equivalent of a one-tailed test. This is because there are many different types of pattern of result that lead to a large value of K as we saw in the previous paragraph, and the Kruskal–Wallis Test does not differentiate between them in any way.

To return to our example, we can see from the null distribution that a value of K as large as or larger than the one we obtained is very likely to occur with sample sizes as small as we have used, since prob $(K \geqslant 2.7) = 0.5$. Thus, we should need to use a significance level of at least 0.5 before being able to reject the null hypothesis, which is unacceptably large. We therefore conclude that there is no reliable evidence from these data that the three treatments differ in effectiveness. However, we note from the null distribution that with such small sample sizes, we should never be able to reject the null hypothesis for any sensible value of α.

Table of the Null Distribution K (Appendix Table F)

Table F in the Appendix gives critical values of the null distribution of K. It is appropriate when only three samples are being compared and each sample size is less than or equal to 5. When there are more than three samples or when sample sizes are larger than 5, the approximation given in the next section should be used. In Table F there is a separate entry for each combination of sample sizes, t_1, t_2 and t_3; t_1 is always the largest and t_3 is always the smallest of the sample sizes, so that $t_1 \geqslant t_2 \geqslant t_3$. It can, however, be used to obtain critical values in other cases, since the null distribution of K will be the same no matter what order the samples are written in. To see this, consider what would happen to the values of K obtained in Table 4.3 if t_1 had been 2 and t_2 and t_3 were both 1. The patterns of results would be the same, although written in a slightly different order, and the values of K would be identical.

To illustrate the use of Table F suppose in our example 4 women had undergone treatment I, 3 had undergone treatment II and 5 had undergone treatment III and we had obtained a K of 5.75. Then we set $t_1 = 5$ (the largest sample size), $t_2 = 4$ and $t_3 = 3$ (the smallest). With a significance level of 0.05, Table F gives the critical value of K as 5.63. Our value is larger than this, so we should reject the null hypothesis and conclude that the treatments differ.

Chi-square Approximation to K

When there are more than two samples, a distribution known as the chi-square (χ^2) distribution frequently plays a role similar to that of the normal distribution in the two-sample cases in providing an approximation to the null distribution of a test statistic. This is the case with K. Appendix Table G gives critical values of the χ^2 distribution that may be used with sample sizes beyond the scope of the exact Table F.

To obtain the relevant critical value we need to know the number of samples being compared; this determines what is known as the degrees of freedom (df for short) associated with χ^2. Degrees of freedom are given by the number of samples minus 1. In our simplified example, we were comparing 3 samples, so we have $3 - 1 = 2$ df. The degrees of freedom determine which row of the χ^2 table to use, since the shape of the χ^2 distribution depends on the number of df. The term degrees of freedom arises from the amount by which the computation of the test statistic is constrained by the data. In the present context, the calculation of K depends on the rank-sums of the samples being compared. For our simplified example with 3 samples, once we know the rank-sums of any two of the samples, we automatically know the rank-sum of the third, since the three rank-sums must add up to 10, the sum of all ranks in the experiment ($1 + 2 + 3 + 4$ in our case). Thus, any two of the rank-sums are free to vary, but once they have been decided on, the third one is completely constrained. Hence we have 2 df in our example.

Having calculated the df, the use of Table G is very simple. Looking along the row determined by the df, we find the critical value of χ^2 associated with the chosen significance level. This critical value is then compared with our obtained value of K in the same way as we did with the exact Table F. For example, with 3 samples and hence 2 df, the critical value of χ^2 associated with an α of 0.05 is 5.991. If our obtained value of K is as large as this or larger, then we reject the null hypothesis. Notice that we do not need to make any changes in K to be able to use the χ^2 distribution. This has already been done and is the reason K has a slightly more complicated form than it need have.

As with our previous approximations, this one gets better as sample sizes increase. As a general rule, with three samples the χ^2 approximation will be good if all samples contain more than 5 observations. With more than three samples, it will be good if all samples contain more than 4 observations.

The use of the χ^2 approximation is illustrated in Examples 4.2 and 4.3.

The Treatment of Ties

As with the Rank-Sum Test, our calculation of the null distribution of K has assumed that the response variable is continuous. When there are ties, this assumption is violated, but the test may still be used. The procedure for dealing with ties is identical to that recommended in the case of the Rank-Sum Test. When computing K with ties, the midrank technique is used, any scores tied at a particular value being given the average of the ranks they would have received had they been distinct. Rather than going through the tedious procedure of computing a null distribution anew for each different combination of ties, it is usual to resort to one of the following approximate procedures.

If fewer than a quarter of the scores are involved in ties, computing K using formula 4.2 and using the exact null distribution given in Table F or the χ^2 approximation for sample sizes outside the range of Table F will generally give a reasonably accurate result.

When there are extensive ties, Table F will not give an accurate result. With extensive ties, the calculation of K should be modified slightly and the χ^2 approximation should be used. The necessary modification involves taking account of the number and extent of the tied values. The procedure is best demonstrated by an example. Suppose the percentage weight-losses of the four women had been those shown in Table 4.5. The relevant midranks are shown alongside the data. K (without the correction for ties) is then given by formula 4.2 as

$$K = -3 \times 5 + \frac{12}{4 \times 5} \times 27 = 1.2$$

Now, there are two scores tied at a rank of 1.5 and two tied at 3.5. We record these as below

Midrank	1.5	3.5
No. of scores tied at that value, u_i	2	2

We then calculate $\Sigma u_i(u_i - 1)(u_i + 1)$ which is $2 \times 1 \times 3 + 2 \times 1 \times 3 = 12$, and divide the result by $n^3 - n$ which is $4^3 - 4 = 64 - 4 = 60$ to give $12/60 = 0.2$.

The revised value of K is then given by dividing our original value, 1.2, by $1 - 0.2$ to give $1.2/(1 - 0.2) = 1.2/0.8 = 1.5$.

The following formula summarizes what we have just done:

$$K = \frac{-3(n+1) + \dfrac{12}{n(n+1)} \Sigma \dfrac{R_i^2}{t_i}}{1 - \dfrac{\Sigma u_i(u_i - 1)(u_i + 1)}{n^3 - n}} \qquad (4.3)$$

It is worth noting that correcting for ties in this way always lead to a value of K larger than that calculated using the uncorrected formula 4.2. Thus, if the uncorrected value is significant, the corrected value will be too. Also, if there are no ties at all, formula 4.3 reduces to formula 4.2, since the correction $\Sigma u_i(u_i - 1)(u_i + 1)/(n^3 - n)$ will be zero.

The use of this formula will be illustrated again in Examples 4.2 and 4.3.

Having calculated K using formula 4.3, the obtained value is referred to Table G. The approximation will be reasonably accurate for most cases as long as each of the sample sizes t_i is 5 or larger. For the example in Table 4.5, Table G will not give accurate results, since the sample sizes are too small.

Table 4.5. Steps in the calculation of K when there are ties

	Treatment						
	I		II		III		
	Score	Midrank	Score	Midrank	Score	Midrank	
	14	1.5	14	1.5	18	3.5	
			18	3.5			
R_i		1.5		5.0		3.5	
R_i^2		2.25		25.00		12.25	
R_i^2/t_i		2.25		12.50		12.25	$\Sigma \frac{R_i^2}{t_i} = 27$

Further Comments

For a further discussion of the Kruskal–Wallis Test, see Bradley (1968, Section 5.13) or Lehmann (1975, Section 5.2). For a method of estimating the size of the treatment effects, see Lehmann (1975, Section 5.7B) or Hollander and Wolfe (1973, Section 6.4).

At the beginning of our discussion of the Kruskal–Wallis Test, I stated that the test is a direct generalization of the Rank-Sum Test. The formulae 4.2 and 4.3 look rather different from the exact test statistic S and the approximate statistic z used in the Rank-Sum Test. However, it can be shown quite straightforwardly that, when there are only two independent samples, the Kruskal–Wallis Test is identical to the Rank-Sum Test, and that the corrections for ties are identical. This won't be attempted here, but Exercise 4.4 should help convince you.

When there are extensive ties in the response variable, it is still possible to use the Kruskal–Wallis Test, as we shall see in Example 4.3. If the ties become so extensive that the response variable has only two categories, it is not necessary to go through the laborious procedure of ranking all the scores, since *in this case only*, the Kruskal–Wallis Test is almost equivalent to the Chi-Square Test for Independence presented in Section 8.1, which involves simpler calculations. You are asked to demonstrate this in Exercises 4.5 and 8.3.

Example 4.1 The Kruskal–Wallis Test

Three types of telephone are compared for their ease of use. Two of the types (PB1 and PB2) are push-button telephones distinguished by different keyboards, while the third (D) has a dial instead of push-buttons. Fifteen volunteers agree to use one of the telephones for a period of six months and to record, among other things, the number of times they use the telephone to make outgoing calls and the number of

Table 4.6. Hypothetical data and calculations for Example 4.1

	Type of telephone						
	PB1		PB2		D		
	Proportion of errors	Rank	Proportion of errors	Rank	Proportion of errors	Rank	
	0.081	7	0.030	4	0.301	14	
	0.010	1	0.102	9	0.214	13	
	0.098	8	0.043	5	0.163	12	
	0.123	11	0.072	6	0.103	10	
	0.028	3	0.021	2			
R_i		30		26		49	
R_i^2		900		676		2401	
R_i^2/t_i		180		135.2		600.25	$\Sigma \frac{R_i^2}{t_i} = 915.45$

errors they make when doing this. Each type of telephone is used by five people, the assignment of telephones to people being made randomly. One of the people given a dial telephone drops out after two months for reasons unrelated to the study. For the remaining 14 people, the proportion of errors made in the final three months is calculated and is shown in Table 4.6. We wish to know whether the telephones differ in this respect. Since we have three independent samples, we may use the Kruskal–Wallis Test. The necessary calculations are shown alongside the data. In this case, we have $n = 14$, $t_1 = 5, t_2 = 5$ and $t_3 = 4$. There are no ties, so K is given by

$$
\begin{aligned}
K &= -3(n+1) + \frac{12}{n(n+1)} \Sigma \frac{R_i^2}{t_i} \\
&= -3 \times 15 + \frac{12}{14 \times 15} \times 915.45 \\
&= -45 + 52.31 \\
&= 7.31
\end{aligned}
$$

Using a significance level of 0.05, Table F gives the critical value of K as 5.64. Our obtained value is larger than this, so we reject the null hypothesis and conclude that there are differences in the proportions of errors made with the three telephones. From the data, it looks as though there is not much to choose between the two push-button telephones, but that the dial telephone leads to more errors than the other two. However, before we can draw such detailed conclusions, we should need to do further tests on the data (see Section 4.2 and Example 4.4).

Example 4.2 Ties in the Kruskal–Wallis Test

In a comparison of four secretarial courses, the typing speeds (in words per minute) of five people from each course were obtained. These are shown in Table 4.7. The Kruskal–Wallis Test will allow us to test for any differences in typing speed among the four courses, since we have four independent samples. The relevant calculations are shown alongside the typing speeds. For this example, we have $n = 20$, $t_1 = 5$, $t_2 = 5$, $t_3 = 5$, and $t_4 = 5$. Since there is a large proportion of ties, we shall use the midrank technique. The number and extent of the ties are given below

Midrank	1.5	3	4	5	8.5	12.5	15	18	20
u_i	2	1	1	1	6	2	3	3	1

Table 4.7. Hypothetical data and calculations for Example 4.2

	Course							
	A		*B*		*C*		*D*	
	Speed	Midrank	Speed	Midrank	Speed	Midrank	Speed	Midrank
	40	1.5	60	8.5	55	5	60	8.5
	60	8.5	60	8.5	60	8.5	75	18
	60	8.5	40	1.5	70	15	75	18
	45	3	50	4	75	18	80	20
	65	12.5	65	12.5	70	15	70	15
R_i		34		35		61.5		79.5
R_i^2		1156		1225		3782.25		6320.25
R_i^2/t_i		231.2		245		756.45		1264.05
								$\Sigma \frac{R_i^2}{t_i} = 2496.7$

so we have

$$\Sigma u_i(u_i - 1)(u_i + 1) = 2 \times 1 \times 3 + 1 \times 0 \times 2 + 1 \times 0 \times 2 + 1 \times 0 \times 2$$
$$+ 6 \times 5 \times 7 + 2 \times 1 \times 3 + 3 \times 2 \times 4$$
$$+ 3 \times 2 \times 4 + 1 \times 0 \times 2$$
$$= 270$$

and $n^3 - n = 20^3 - 20 = 7980$
With the correction for ties, K is then given by

$$K = \frac{-3(n+1) + \dfrac{12}{n(n+1)} \Sigma \dfrac{R_i^2}{t_i}}{1 - \dfrac{\Sigma u_i(u_i - 1)(u_i + 1)}{n^3 - n}}$$

$$= \frac{-3 \times 21 + \dfrac{12}{20 \times 21} \times 2496.7}{1 - 270/7980}$$

$$= \frac{-63 + 71.334}{1 - 0.034}$$

$$= 8.63$$

We cannot use the exact Table F in this case for two reasons: we are comparing four samples, and there is a large proportion of ties in the data. We therefore use the χ^2 approximation with 3 df (since there are four samples). Using a significance level of 0.05, Table G gives 7.815 as the critical value. Since our obtained K of 8.63 is larger than this, we reject the null hypothesis and conclude that there are differences in the typing speeds of people from the four courses. From the data, it looks as though courses C and D lead to higher speeds than courses A and B, but we should need to carry out further tests to state this conclusively (see Section 4.2).

Example 4.3 The Kruskal–Wallis Test with Extensive Ties

At the end of the courses at a particular college, each student either fails, passes or passes with distinction. The results from three of the courses which have no students in common are compared. Since there are no students doing more than one course, it may be reasonable to treat the data as independent. In such a situation, there are bound to be extensive ties in the response variable, since there are only three levels (fail, pass and distinction), so it is usually more convenient to record the data in the form of a contingency table (c.f. Section 2.3). Suppose the results are those given in Table 4.8. Notice that the explanatory variable (course) is categorical while the response variable (result) is ordinal, so this contingency table is not the same as the ordered contingency tables in Chapter 2, for which *both* variable were considered to be ordinal. For this reason, the Kruskal–Wallis Test is applicable here.

To use the Kruskal–Wallis Test, we need to rank the data using the midrank method and find rank-sums associated with the three courses. To do this we note that the column marginal totals (the u_i's) record the extent of the ties in the response variable. Thus 12 people obtained the lowest score – they failed! The rank associated with each of them would therefore have to be $(1 + 2 + 3 + \ldots + 10 + 11 + 12)/12$. To save the bother of actually working this out, we already know that the mean of the first n ranks is $(n + 1)/2$ (see p. 150). This gives the midrank for these 12 students as $13/2 = 6.5$.

To obtain the midrank for the 30 students who passed, we should need to calculate $(13 + 14 + 15 + \ldots + 40 + 41 + 42)/30$. We can simplify the calculation by noticing that it is the same as $12 + (1 + 2 + 3 + \ldots + 28 + 29 + 30)/30$, the last part of which is just the mean of the first 30 ranks. So the midrank required is $12 + 31/2 = 27.5$.

Table 4.8. Hypothetical data for Example 4.3

		Fail	Pass	Distinction	t_i
Course	A	5	10	5	20
	B	4	5	1	10
	C	3	15	2	20
	u_i	12	30	8	50

The midrank for the 8 students who passed with distinction is obtained similarly, either directly by calculating $(43 + 44 + \ldots + 49 + 50)/8$, or more simply by calculating $42 + (1 + 2 + \ldots + 7 + 8)/8$ to give $42 + 9/2 = 46.5$.

With these midranks, the rank-sum for course A is easily computed. Since there are 5 students each with midrank 6.5, 10 with midrank 27.5 and 5 with midrank 46.5, the rank-sum will be $5 \times 6.5 + 10 \times 27.5 + 5 \times 46.5 = 540$. The rank-sums for all three courses calculated in this way are shown below together with the other calculations necessary to arrive at K.

	Course			
	A	B	C	
R_i	540	210	525	
R_i^2	291600	44100	275625	
R_i^2/t_i	14580	4410	13781.25	$\Sigma \frac{R_i^2}{t_i} = 32771.25$

We also need $\Sigma\, u_i(u_i - 1)(u_i + 1)$ which is given by

$$12 \times 11 \times 13 + 30 \times 29 \times 31 + 8 \times 7 \times 9 = 29190$$

and $n^3 - n$ which is $50^3 - 50 = 124950$
Then from formula 4.3, we obtain K as follows

$$K = \frac{-3 \times 51 + \dfrac{12}{50 \times 51} \times 32771.25}{1 - \dfrac{29190}{124950}}$$

$$= \frac{-153 + 154.218}{1 - 0.234}$$

$$= \frac{1.218}{0.766}$$

$$= 1.59$$

Since there are 3 courses being compared and the sample sizes are sufficiently large, we may use Table G with 2 df to obtain a critical value for K. When $\alpha = 0.05$, the critical value is 5.99. Our obtained K is smaller than this, so we cannot reject the null hypothesis. We conclude that there is no reliable evidence that the courses differ.

4.2 MULTIPLE COMPARISONS USING THE RANK-SUM TEST

When a significant result has been obtained with the Kruskal–Wallis Test, all we know is that there is some difference in location between the samples. We do not know the locus of the difference, however. Thus, in Example 4.1, we are not justified in concluding that the dial-'phone leads to reliably more errors than the push-button ones on the basis of the significant Kruskal–Wallis Test. We may only conclude that the three telephones lead to different proportions of errors. This was not a problem with two-sample tests such as the Rank-Sum Test, because a significant result means that one sample has higher scores than the other. With more than two samples, the possibilities increase. A significant result in Example 4.1 could have been obtained if D had more errors than PB1 or PB2, which did not differ; or if D had more errors than PB1 which had more errors than PB2; or for a variety of other reasons.

To help choose between the various possibilities, it is frequently useful to compare the samples in pairs. Since the Kruskal–Wallis Test is identical to the Rank-Sum Test when there are only two samples, it is natural to use the Rank-Sum Test for this purpose. Thus, for Example 4.1, we should carry out three Rank-Sum Tests, on PB1 versus PB2, PB1 versus D and PB2 versus D. However, this procedure introduces a complication. The way in which the null distribution of the Rank-Sum Test was constructed makes it accurate only if exactly one test is carried out. When more than one test is carried out, the significance levels become distorted. The significance level is the probability of falsely rejecting the null hypothesis (a Type I error). The more tests we carry out the more likely we are to make a Type I error.

Whether this problem bothers us will depend on our purposes. To put the problem in a slightly different context, suppose 100 investigators each independently carry out the same experiment for which we in our wisdom know the null hypothesis to be true. If they each use a significance level of 0.05, it is almost certain that at least one of them will commit a Type I error. While acknowledging such a danger, the usual procedure is to set the significance level separately for each experiment. This of course effectively ignores what the other investigators are doing. Thus, the single experiment is treated as a unit for these purposes. This seems quite a natural procedure, since it allows us not to be ultraconservative, thereby decreasing the probability of a Type II error (see section 1.7). Within a single experiment, however, the procedure implies that we should be relatively conservative.

This motivates the distinction frequently drawn between error rate *per comparison* and error rate *per experiment.* To return to our example, if we carry out the three separate Rank-Sum Tests each using a significance level of 0.05, the *per comparison* error rate is 0.05, since this is the probability of a Type I error for each test considered individually. The *per experiment* error rate is the probability of at least one Type I error for the three tests considered as a package. It can be shown that this never exceeds the sum of the per comparison error rates. Thus, in our example, the per experiment error rate will be no larger than 0.15. These arguments provide a rough-and-ready method of carrying out multiple comparisons. If we are concerned to keep the per experiment error rate at a particular value, say α, then if we are carrying out c comparisons, each comparison should be tested using a significance level of α/c. In our example, to keep the per experiment error rate as low as 0.05, each of the three comparisons should use a significance level of

$0.05/3 = 0.017$. This procedure is rough-and-ready because it errs on the conservative side; the resulting per experiment error rate will certainly be no larger than α, but it may be considerably smaller than α. Several alternative methods which are not so conservative have been suggested, but they are outside the scope of this book (see Lehmann, 1975, for references). However, our method will be satisfactory for most purposes. For standard significance levels, such as 0.05 or 0.01, it tends to be fairly accurate for a small number of comparisons, but gets increasingly less accurate as the number of comparisons increases.

Multiple comparison procedures provide a method of searching through the data in an attempt to locate differences that might be interesting. They are most appropriately carried out *only* if the overall Kruskal–Wallis Test is significant. Once we know there is some sort of difference between the samples, it is usually acceptable to be a little less conservative in carrying out multiple comparisons by making use of a larger per experiment error rate than was used for the overall test. Thus, if we reject the null hypothesis using the Kruskal–Wallis Test with $\alpha = 0.05$, it may be acceptable to set α as high as 0.20 when carrying out a large number of multiple comparisons. Values of α between 0.05 and 0.20 are frequently used for this purpose. If we choose a larger value of α than we used for the overall test we are in effect saying 'the evidence so far implies that at least one of the defendants is guilty; knowing this, I'm prepared to be a bit more reckless in attempting to convict the villain(s)'. Whether such recklessness is justified can only be determined on substantive grounds. If the villain you wish to convict is important enough, it might be worth risking the possibility of convicting some innocent people too.

How many comparisons should be performed? In most situations, we want to compare all pairs of samples. If there are k samples in the original Kruskal–Wallis Test, the number of pairs is given by $k(k - 1)/2$. In our example, there are 3 samples, so $k = 3$ and the number of pairs is $3 \times 2/2 = 3$, which we know to be correct in this case. When all $k(k - 1)/2$ comparisons are performed, each comparison should be tested using a two-tailed test with a significance level of $\alpha/[k(k - 1)/2]$, where α is the per experiment error rate.

However, there are situations in which we might not want to compare all the pairs. For example, suppose that, before carrying out the experiment in Example 4.1, we knew that the dial-'phone was about to be replaced by the telephone company because it was difficult to use and the experiment was an attempt to find which type of push-button 'phone lead to reliably fewer errors than the dial-'phone. In such a case, we might think of the D sample as providing baseline control data against which the other samples are to be compared. So we should want to perform only two comparisons: D versus PB1 and D versus PB2. In general, if one of the k samples is a control group while the remaining $k - 1$ samples represent treatment groups each of which is to be compared only with the control, there will be $k - 1$ comparisons. In such a case, each of the $k - 1$ comparisons should be performed using a significance level of $\alpha/(k - 1)$, where α is the required per experiment error rate.

Contrast with this the situation where we notice after the Kruskal–Wallis Test has been found to be significant that two of the samples look particularly different.

Thus we might notice that D and PB2 are very different, and we might be able to explain this *post hoc* in a convincing way. To support our *post hoc* explanation, we should only need to perform the one comparison, D versus PB2. You might think that this comparison should then be done using α as the significance level. However, it is important to notice here that our explanation for the difference was suggested by the data. Since the Kruskal–Wallis Test has produced a significant result, we know that the groups differ in some way. It might have turned out that there was a large difference between PB1 and PB2 and we might then have found some equally convincing *post hoc* explanation for this. To guard against this problem, we should treat this situation as though we were actually performing all pairs of comparisons, and carry out the comparison using a significance level of $\alpha/[k(k-1)/2]$. The important distinction here is between comparisons suggested independently of the data and those suggested by the data.

Our discussion of multiple comparisons has only skimmed the surface of the problems that arise. However, it should give some rough guidelines as to how to proceed in most situations.

Suggested Procedure for Performing Multiple Comparisons

In this Section I suggest a standard procedure to be used when doing multiple comparisons following a significant Kruskal–Wallis Test. Its use will be illustrated in Example 4.4. Suppose for the time being we are comparing four samples, A, B, C, and D.

We first need to choose α, the per experiment error rate. Suppose we set $\alpha = 0.10$. With four samples, we should need to do $4 \times 3/2 = 6$ comparisons of pairs. Therefore, the per comparison error rate should be $\alpha/6 = 0.017$. Now, since we are using the Rank-Sum Test for the comparisons, we need to consult Table A to find critical values of S. Unfortunately, Table A does not give critical values associated with a significance level of 0.017. The closest we can get would be to use 0.02 as the per comparison error rate. This in turn would change the per experiment error rate to $6 \times 0.02 = 0.12$, which is still acceptable and is close to our original required value of 0.10. So we set $\alpha = 0.12$ and perform each comparison using a significance level of 0.02.

We now list the samples in order of increasing average rank. This is easily calculated for each sample, since we have already computed rank-sums, R_i, in carrying out the Kruskal–Wallis Test; the average ranks are then simply R_i/t_i. Suppose sample B has the smallest average rank, A the next, C the next, and D the largest. We list them in order $BACD$.

The first Rank-Sum Test is done between the sample with the smallest average rank and the one with the largest, i.e. B and D. If this is significant we go on to compare B with C and then B with A. As soon as we get a non-significant result we stop and draw a line joining the samples in the ordered list that have been shown not to differ. Thus if the BD comparison is significant but the BC one is not, we draw a line stretching from B to C, which gives $\overline{BAC}D$. Having found a non-significant result, we do not need to compare any of the other pairs joined by the line, since if B does not differ from C, then it should not differ from A which lies between B and C in average rank; similarly, A should not differ from C.

Having compared B, the sample with smallest average rank, with all the others until a non-significant result is obtained, we then compare the next smallest, A, with the others in the same way. Thus A would be compared with D only in this case (since A and C are already joined by a line). If that comparison is significant, we then compare C with D, which completes the series. If AD is not significant, we draw a line from A to D to give $\overline{B\overline{AC}D}$, and no further comparisons are required (since C and D are joined by the line AD).

This procedure prevents any inconsistencies from occurring. When it is adopted, we should never be able to draw conclusions such as French is an easier language to learn than German, German is easier than Dutch, but French and Dutch are equally difficult.

The results may be summarized using the line convention. Thus, if the final analysis produces $B\overline{ACD}$, we know that B leads to reliably smaller ranks than the other 3 samples, which do not differ amongst themselves. $B\overline{AC}D$ means that B has smaller ranks than the rest, D has larger ranks, but A and C do not differ reliably. A more complicated outcome would be $\overline{B\overline{AC}D}$; this occurs if the only significant comparison is between B and D. It may be interpreted as a sort of partial ordering of the samples, since it implies that A and C are somewhere between B and D, even though they are not reliably different from either B or D. However, care should be taken in interpreting such an outcome. For a list of the other possible outcomes in this situation, see Exercise 4.9.

Example 4.4 Multiple Comparisons after a Significant Kruskal–Wallis Test

Let us continue the analysis of the telephones experiment. In Example 4.1, we were able to reject the null hypothesis that there was no difference between the three types of telephone using a significance level of 0.05. We must first decide on a significance level for the comparisons, which need not be the same as the one used with the Kruskal–Wallis Test. Suppose we set $\alpha = 0.10$. In so doing, we are taking a greater risk of making a Type I error, but believe this to be worthwhile in order to demonstrate an effect. Since there are three samples, we need to perform $3 \times 2/2 = 3$ comparisons of the pairs. Each comparison should be performed with a two-tailed significance level of $\alpha/3 = 0.033$. Table A does not give critical values associated with 0.033, however. The closest we can get is 0.02 which implies an α of 0.06. This is an acceptable per experiment error rate.

From Table 4.6, we know the rank-sums for PB1, PB2 and D to be 30, 26, and 49, so the average ranks will be $30/5 = 6$, $26/5 = 5.2$ and $49/4 = 12.25$, since there are 5 people in the first two samples and 4 in the last. We therefore write the samples in the order PB2 PB1 D.

Carrying out a Rank-Sum Test on PB2 and D first, we find $S = 20$.

From Table A, with $t_1 = 5$, $t_2 = 4$ and a two-tailed significance level of 0.02, the critical values of S are -20 and 20, so we reject the null hypothesis, and conclude that PB2 and D differ reliably. No lines are drawn yet.

We now compare PB2 and PB1. In this case $S = -3$. The critical values from Table A with $t_1 = 5$, $t_2 = 5$ and a significance level of 0.02 are -23 and 23. Thus PB2 and PB1 do not differ reliably, so we join them to give $\overline{\text{PB2 PB1}}$ D.

Finally we compare PB1 with D. In this case $S = 18$ and the critical values are -20 and 20, so PB1 and D do not differ reliably.

The final result is therefore $\overline{\text{PB2 }\overline{\text{PB1}}\text{ D}}$, which means that D leads to more errors than PB2 with PB1 somewhere in the middle. Notice that this is a slightly more complicated result than provided by our cursory glance at the data at the end of Example 4.1.

4.3 SUMMARY OF SUGGESTED PROCEDURE

General Points

1. Do you have more than two independent samples? If not, look elsewhere; see the table at the front of the book for suggestions.
2. Do you wish to test a predicted ordering of the samples? If so, try the tests in Chapter 5.
3. Are the scores on the response variable ordinal? If not, try the Chi-Square Test for Independence in Chapter 8.

The Kruskal–Wallis Test

1. Select significance level α.
2. Find n, the total number of scores, and t_i, the number of scores in the ith sample. Check that $\Sigma t_i = n$.
3. Rank order all n scores, using midranks if there are ties.
4. Find the sum of the ranks in each sample. Denote the rank-sum of the ith sample R_i. Check that $\Sigma R_i = n(n + 1)/2$.
5. Calculate

$$K = -3(n + 1) + \frac{12}{n(n + 1)} \Sigma \frac{R_i^2}{t_i} \tag{4.2}$$

6. If more than a quarter of the response scores are involved in ties, go to 9.
7. If more than three samples are being compared or if any of the sample sizes is larger than 5, use the chi-square approximation in 10.
8. Find the relevant critical value in Table F. Reject the null hypothesis if the obtained K is larger than or equal to the critical value. If the null hypothesis is rejected, use multiple comparisons to locate the effects. Otherwise, stop.

9. For extensive ties, find u_i, the number of scores at each particular value of the response variable and divide the value of K obtained in 5 by

$$1 - \frac{\Sigma u_i(u_i - 1)(u_i + 1)}{n^3 - n}$$

10. *Chi-square approximation*
Find df, the number of samples minus 1. Find the relevant critical value in Table G. Reject the null hypothesis if the obtained K (corrected for ties as in 9 if necessary) is larger than or equal to the critical value. If any of the sample sizes is smaller than 5, the approximation may not be accurate. If the null hypothesis is rejected, use multiple comparisons to locate the effects. Otherwise, stop.

Multiple Comparisons

1. Select the per experiment significance level α, which may be larger than the α used in the overall Kruskal–Wallis Test if you are prepared to take the risk.
2. Decide on c, the number of comparisons you wish to make. Normally you will wish to compare all possible pairs of samples. If there are k samples, the number of pairs will be $c = k(k - 1)/2$.
3. Find the closest significance level in Table A to α/c.
4. Order the k samples with respect to their average ranks (given by R_i/t_i) and write the sample names in order.
5. Using a two-tailed test with significance level as calculated in 3, carry out Rank-Sum Tests as follows. Using the ordering given in 4, compare the left-most sample first with the right-most, next with the second from the right, and so on until a non-significant result is obtained. When this happens, join the two sample names with a line. Then take the second sample from the left and compare it first with the right-most, next with second from the right, and so on until either a non-significant result is obtained or two samples are being compared that are already joined by a line. Continue in this way until all comparisons have been exhausted. (See Section 4.2 for more details.)

4.4 EXERCISES

Section 4.1

1. A class of 12 students is randomly divided into three groups of four. Each group receives statistics lectures from a different lecturer. The table below shows the results of an exam marked 'blind' by an independent person who does not know which students have been lectured by which lecturer. Do the results suggest any differences between the lecturers?

Lecturer		
A	*B*	*C*
72	55	64
65	59	74
67	68	61
75	70	58

2. In a weight-reduction study, four treatments are compared. 24 men are randomly assigned to one of the four treatments, with 6 men being assigned to each treatment. At a follow up session, percentage weight-losses are recorded for each man; these are shown below. Do the treatments differ in effectiveness?

Treatment			
1	2	3	4
20.2	18.7	21.7	19.4
18.5	17.3	19.6	18.0
17.7	16.1	19.4	17.8
17.2	14.6	18.8	16.5
17.0	13.9	18.3	15.0
15.7	12.2	17.5	12.5

3. In a study comparing the effects of different ways of presenting evidence, three films of a criminal trial are made. The films show the same evidence, but edited in different ways. Each film is shown to a separate group of 30 people. The people are then asked to judge the defendant's guilt or innocence by saying either 'guilty', 'not sure', or 'innocent'. Some hypothetical results are shown below. Do the films differ in the likelihood of a person being judged guilty?

	Guilty	Not sure	Innocent
Film *A*	10	10	10
Film *B*	12	8	10
Film *C*	2	6	22

4. (Optional) (a) Show that the critical values of χ^2 with 1 df in Table G are equal to the squares of the two-tailed critical values of z in Table B(ii). (b) Compute the Kruskal–Wallis statistic K for the data from Example 2.2 where there are only two samples. Show that $K = z^2$, where z is the z-score computed in Example 2.2. (You have now demonstrated that the Rank-Sum Test and the Kruskal–Wallis Test are equivalent in the limiting case.)
5. 100 people taste a new biscuit and state whether or not they like it. The results are shown below. Do the four samples differ in their preferences?

	Like	Dislike	t_i
Men	10	10	20
Women	14	16	30
Boys	20	5	25
Girls	16	9	25
u_i	60	40	100

6. Does it affect the obtained value of K if we rank the scores high to low rather than low to high?

Section 4.2

7. Complete the analysis of Exercise 2 by carrying out multiple comparisons. Use a per experiment error rate of 0.06.
8. Complete the analysis of Exercise 3 by carrying out multiple comparisons. Use a per experiment error rate of 0.15.
9. When there are four samples, the possible outcomes of multiple comparison tests are listed below. The samples are written in order of increasing average rank – B having the smallest and D the largest average rank. State briefly what each outcome means.

(a) $BACD$, (b) $\overline{BA}CD$, (c) $B\overline{AC}D$, (d) $BA\overline{CD}$, (e) $\overline{B\overline{A}C}D$, (f) $\overline{BA}\,\overline{CD}$,

(g) $B\overline{A\overline{C}D}$, (h) $\overline{BAC}D$, (i) $B\overline{ACD}$, (j) $\overline{BA\overline{C}D}$, (k) $\overline{B\overline{A}CD}$, (l) $\overline{BACD}$, (m) $\overline{B\overline{AC}D}$.

---

10. Which of the examples in this chapter are experimental studies and which are correlational studies?

CHAPTER 5

Life has a way of setting things in order and leaving them be.

Jean Anouilh, *The Rehearsal*

Tests for Several Independent Samples – Both Variables Ordinal

The tests in this chapter assume that both variables are ordinal. This means that when several samples are being compared (i.e. there are several levels of the explanatory variable) it must be possible to order these in some meaningful way independently of the data. In this way, specific ordered predictions may be tested for a number of independent samples. For example, if we wish to test whether reaction time increases with dosage level of a particular drug, we might obtain reactions times from four independent groups of subjects, the four groups being given, say, 5, 10, 15, and 20 mg of the drug respectively. Here, the explanatory variable, dosage level, is considered to be ordinal because our interest centres on whether increased dosage levels lead to increased reaction times (cf. Example 1.12). If we are not specifically interested in testing an ordered prediction for such data, the tests of Chapter 4 should be used.

For each of the tests, the data are assumed independent. Each person in the experiment must therefore contribute only one score on the explanatory variable and one score on the response variable, and should not be able to influence the scores of any other person.

This chapter includes two tests, due to Kendall and Spearman, that are generally thought of as being tests of correlation or association (see Section 1.4). That is, they are normally used in situations where it is not possible to label one of the variables explanatory and the other response (see Section 1.5). For example, we may wish to know whether there is a correlation between the two variables height and weight, i.e. whether tall people tend to weigh more than short people. The natural way to investigate this is to take, say, 100 people and measure their height and weight. This can be seen to be a special case of the situation illustrated by the drug example above. To see this, one of the variables, say height, is arbitrarily defined as the explanatory variable. This variable has 100 levels, being the different heights of the people. We can then think of this problem as being one of comparing 100 independent samples, each sample containing the response (weight) of a single person. The explanatory variable is ordinal, since we are testing the prediction that weight increases with height.

It is important to stress this similarity between the two situations, even though the conclusions that may be drawn from them are different (see Section 1.4). In Section 5.4, we shall see that the Kendall Test for Correlation can profitably be viewed as the mother and father of all the tests that use the test statistic S. The other tests may be considered to be special applications of the Kendall Test in which ties occur in either the explanatory variable or the response variable or both.

5.1 THE JONCKHEERE TEST

The Jonckheere Test provides an alternative way of generalizing the Rank-Sum Test to more than two samples. We have already seen in Chapter 4 that the Kruskal–Wallis Test is a general version of the Rank-Sum Test. The Kruskal–Wallis Test focuses on the notion of the rank-sum of each of the samples being compared to provide an omnibus test of the differences between the samples. The Jonckheere Test focuses on the more direct ways of arriving at S, the Rank-Sum test statistic (see Section 2.1), to provide a generalization that is sensitive to directional differences between the samples. It assumes that the data collected are independent and that the scores on the response variable are continuous ordinal data. Thus, it is similar in its requirements to the Kruskal–Wallis Test. The crucial difference between the two tests is that the Jonckheere Test assumes also that the explanatory variable is ordinal, so that it tests an ordered prediction about the samples being compared. For the test to be valid, the predicted ordering of the samples should be made independently of the data.

In this section, we discuss the Jonckheere Test as it may be applied to data without ties in the response variable. Section 5.2 shows how ties may be handled.

Simplified Example

As part of a study investigating whether increasing knowledge of results (KR) improves performance in an industrial sorting task, four people are randomly assigned to one of three groups, which differ in the degree to which they are given knowledge of results after each trial. The first group is given no knowledge of results, the second is given partial knowledge of results and the third is given complete knowledge of results. Suppose the first and third groups contain only one person each while the second group contains two people. Let n be the total number of people in the study, and t_i be the number in the ith group. Thus, $n = 4$, $t_1 = 1$, $t_2 = 2$ and $t_3 = 1$. The number of correct responses made in 20 trials for each of the people is shown below:

No KR	Partial KR	Complete KR
10	12	15
	16	

These data are independent and the response variable (number of correct responses) is ordinal, so we could quite happily carry out a Kruskal–Wallis Test to discover whether the three samples differ in any way. However, such an analysis ignores the predicted ordering of the groups implicit in the reason for carrying out the study. We are interested in whether the number of correct responses increases as knowledge of results increases, so we are predicting that the No KR group should have the smallest scores, while the Complete KR group should have the largest scores, with the Partial KR group somewhere in between. Thus, we have an ordinal explanatory variable, so the Jonckheere Test will give us a test that is more sensitive to our predicted ordering. Notice particularly that the predicted ordering arose from the question we wished to ask of the data and was not determined by the way the data turned out.

Looking at the data, it is clear that they are somewhat in line with our prediction, since the lowest score (10) is obtained in the No KR group, the other groups obtaining higher scores, but they are not clearcut, since the highest score (16) is in the Partial KR group and not the Complete KR group.

Test Statistic – S

An obvious extension of the direct method of computing S for the Rank-Sum Test (Section 2.1) provides the test statistic for the Jonckheere Test. We shall present two ways of arriving at S, the second of which is more useful when there are ties in the data and which is used in Section 5.2.

Computing S directly

To compute S, the three samples must be written in the order determined by the prediction made, i.e. in the order No KR, Partial KR, Complete KR. A different ordering will result in a different value of S. With the samples in the predicted order, if the prediction (i.e. the alternative hypothesis) is correct, as we go from the left-most to the right-most samples the scores on the response variable should increase. S is computed by taking each score in turn and counting how many scores in samples to the right are larger and also counting how many scores in samples to the right are smaller. These are the positive and negative contributions, respectively, of that score to S, which we label p and q as in the Rank-Sum Test. Notice that we do not have to find p and q for any of the scores in the right-most sample, since there are no other samples to the right of it. S is then given by summing all the p

Table 5.1. Direct calculation of S

No KR			Partial KR			Complete KR
Score	p	q	Score	p	q	Score
10	3	0	12	1	0	15
			16	0	1	

$S = P - Q = (3 + 1 + 0) - (0 + 0 + 1) = 3$

scores to give P, summing all the q scores to give Q and subtracting one from the other, so $S = P - Q$. The calculations for our data are shown in Table 5.1. The score of 10 in the No *KR* group contributes 3 to P and 0 to Q, since all three scores in the other two groups are larger than 10, while the score of 16 in the Partial KR group contributes 0 to P and 1 to Q, since the only score (15) in the group to the right of it is smaller than 16. The resulting value of S is 3. As with the Rank-Sum Test, small values of S favour the null hypothesis that there is no difference between the three samples in the direction predicted, while large values of S favour the alternative hypothesis.

Computing S *from an ordered contingency table*

S may also be computed from data represented in the form of an ordered contingency table in exactly the same way as described in Section 2.3. Remember that the rows of an ordered contingency table show all the levels of the explanatory variable, written in the predicted order, while the columns show all the levels of the response variable in order, and the numbers in the body of the table show the frequency of particular combinations of scores. The ordered contingency table for our example data is shown in Table 5.2. For each non-zero cell of the table p is given by multiplying the frequency in the cell by the sum of the frequencies to its south-east and q is given by multiplying the frequency in the cell by the sum of the frequencies to its south-west. Cells in the same row and column are always ignored. There is also no need to consider the last row of the table since there is nothing

Table 5.2. Ordered contingency table representation of data for the Jonckheere Test

	Number correct				
	10	12	15	16	t_i
No KR	1				1
Partial KR		1		1	2
Complete KR			1		1
u_i	1	1	1	1	$4 = n$

below. As before S is obtained by subtracting Q, the sum of the q's, from P, the sum of the p's. For our example we have

$$P = 1 \times 3 + 1 \times 1 + 1 \times 0 = 4$$

$$Q = 1 \times 0 + 1 \times 0 + 1 \times 1 = 1$$

$$S = P - Q = 3,$$

which is the same as the value obtained by the direct method. With the data in this form, S will be large and positive if all the frequencies fall on or around the NE–SE diagonal of the table; S will be large and negative if all the frequencies fall on or around the SW–NE diagonal.

Null Distribution of S

The possible patterns of results that could have occurred in this situation will be the same ones that were investigated in the Kruskal–Wallis Test (see Section 4.1). The only difference is that S is emphasizing different aspects of the data from K. The 12 possible patterns for our example with $t_1 = 1, t_2 = 2$ and $t_3 = 1$ are given in Table 5.3, together with S computed for each pattern. These patterns contain only the rank order of the scores on the response variable, since this is really all that we use in computing S by the methods given, even though we did not explicitly rank order the scores. Our obtained data are equivalent to those shown as pattern 9 in the table. We can immediately see that large values of S favour the alternative hypothesis, since pattern 7 has the scores in exactly the order predicted and has the largest value of S. Pattern 6 on the other hand has the scores rather jumbled and so favours the null hypothesis and has a correspondingly low value of S.

Table 5.3. The 12 possible patterns of results when $t_1 = 1$, $t_2 = 2$, $t_3 = 1$, together with associated values of S. Roman numerals show groups, arabic show ranked scores

Pattern	I	II	III	S
1.	3	1, 2	4	$S = 1$
2.	4	1, 2	3	$S = -1$
3.	2	1, 3	4	$S = 3$
4.	4	1, 3	2	$S = -3$
5.	2	1, 4	3	$S = 1$
6.	3	1, 4	2	$S = -1$
7.	1	2, 3	4	$S = 5$
8.	4	2, 3	1	$S = -5$
9.	1	2, 4	3	$S = 3$
10.	3	2, 4	1	$S = -3$
11.	1	3, 4	2	$S = 1$
12.	2	3, 4	1	$S = -1$

Table 5.4. Null distribution of S for the case $t_1 = 1$, $t_2 = 2$, $t_3 = 1$

S	−5	−3	−1	1	3	5
Probability	1/12	2/12	3/12	3/12	2/12	1/12

From Table 5.3 we can easily compute the null distribution of S in the standard way as shown in Table 5.4. Thus, the probability of getting an S of 3 or larger is $2/12 + 1/12 = 0.25$. So we should need to use a significance level of at least 0.25 before being able to reject the null hypothesis for our example data. As usual, our simplified example is too small for us to be able to use a sensible significance level such as 0.05.

One-tailed and Two-tailed Tests

The procedure given above is appropriate for a one-tailed test. However, S may also be used in a two-tailed form in the same way as discussed for the Rank-Sum Test. A two-tailed test for our example would be asking whether the data provide evidence of *either* increasingly better performance with increasing KR *or* increasingly worse performance. Thus, while pattern 7 in Table 5.3 shows data that indicate increasingly better performance, pattern 8 indicates increasingly worse performance. The two patterns have S's of the same magnitude but different signs. A two-tailed test may be carried out in the same way as described in Section 2.1. Thus, from the null distribution of S in Table 5.4, we know that if α is set at 0.17, we should need to obtain an S greater than or equal to 5 in magnitude, since $\text{prob}(S \geqslant 5) + \text{prob}(S \leqslant -5) = 1/12 + 1/12 = 0.17$.

Notice that, whether a one-tailed or a two-tailed test is used, it is always related to the predicted ordering of the samples. As usual, the choice of which to use should be made independently of the data.

Table of the Null Distribution of S (Appendix Table H)

Table H in the Appendix gives critical values of the null distribution of S for both one- and two-tailed tests. It is appropriate only when three samples are being compared and each sample size is less than or equal to 5. There is a separate entry for each combination of sample sizes, t_1, t_2 and t_3; t_1 is always the largest and t_3 is always the smallest, so that $t_1 \geqslant t_2 \geqslant t_3$. It can, however, be used to obtain critical values in other cases, since the null distribution of S turns out to be the same when the sample sizes occur in different orders.

Table H is used in the same way as Tables A and C. As an illustration, suppose that in our example 4 people had been assigned to the No KR group, 3 to the Partial KR group, and 5 to the Complete KR group and we had obtained an S of 27. Then we set $t_1 = 5$ (the largest sample size), $t_2 = 4$ and $t_3 = 3$ (the smallest). For a one-tailed test with significance level of 0.05, Table H gives the critical value of S as 25. Our value is larger than this, so we should reject the null hypothesis and conclude that the data indicate that performance improves with increasing KR. Had we wished to use a two-tailed test with $\alpha = 0.05$, the relevant critical values would be -29 and 29. In this case we should not reject the null hypothesis.

Normal Approximation to S

As with the Rank-Sum Test, the standard normal distribution may be used to approximate the null distribution of S for those cases not covered by Table H. The possible values that S may take for the Jonckheere Test will always have a mean of zero and a variance given by

$$\text{Variance} = \frac{2(n^3 - \Sigma t_i^3) + 3(n^2 - \Sigma t_i^2)}{18} \tag{5.1}$$

where n is the total number of observations and t_i is the number of observations in the ith sample. To show that this formula works, we can compute the variance for our simplified example with $t_1 = 1$, $t_2 = 2$ and $t_3 = 1$ directly from the values of S given in Table 5.3 using the method of Section 1.1. This gives a value of 7.667. To use formula 5.1, we first compute $\Sigma t_i^3 = 1^3 + 2^3 + 1^3 = 10$ and $\Sigma t_i^2 = 1^2 + 2^2 + 1^2 = 6$. We then obtain

$$\text{Variance} = \frac{2(4^3 - 10) + 3(4^2 - 6)}{18} = \frac{2 \times 54 + 3 \times 10}{18}$$

$$= 7.667,$$

as required.

When there are no ties in the response variable, the difference between consecutive possible values of S is always 2, so the normal approximation may be improved by making use of a continuity correction of 1. This should be subtracted from positive values of S and added to negative values of S.

The use of the normal approximation is illustrated in Example 5.2. It will usually be quite accurate if at least two of the samples contain 5 or more observations. If there are ties in the response variable, the approximation given in Section 5.2 should be used rather than the present one.

It may straightforwardly be demonstrated that, when there are only two samples, formula 5.1 reduces to the formula for the variance of S for the Rank-Sum Test given as formula 2.1 in Section 2.2. This is left as an exercise for the interested reader.

Further Comments

For more on the Jonckheere Test, see Jonckheere (1954a) or Lehmann (1975, Section 5.5B), who also discusses an alternative test due to Chacko and Shorack that may be preferable to the Jonckheere Test in some cases. For a method of estimating the size of the treatment effects, see Lehmann (1975, Section 5.7B) or Hollander and Wolfe (1973, Section 6.4). Alternatively, the methods of association described in Section 5.6 may convey useful information about the size of the effects.

Example 5.1 The Jonckheere Test

In a study investigating whether people learn better when training is distributed over a period of time than when the training is massed all at once, 19 people are assigned to one of three groups. Four of the people (Group I) learn a list of items for 10 trials with no interval between trials. Another five (Group II) learn the list for 10 trials with 20 seconds between each trial, while the remaining five (Group III) have 40 seconds between trials. Suppose we wish to know whether increasing the interval between trials improves learning. The total number of correct responses for each person is given in Table 5.5, together with the calculations necessary for computing S by the direct method, which is the quickest way when there are no ties in the response variable. The Jonckheere Test is applicable here, since the data are independent and we are testing the ordered prediction that Group I should do worst, Group III should do best, with Group II somewhere in between. To use Table H, we set $t_1 = 5$ (the largest sample size), $t_2 = 5$ and $t_3 = 4$ (the smallest). Our prediction implies that we require a one-tailed test – we are not interested in whether distributed training leads to fewer correct responses than massed training. With $\alpha = 0.05$, the one-tailed critical value of S is 31. Our obtained value of 53 is larger than the critical value, so we reject the null hypothesis and conclude that the data support our prediction.

We must be careful, however, not to go beyond our data in the conclusions we draw. While there may well be a straight increase in number of correct responses when the intertrial intervals are between 0 and 40 seconds, we may find that increasing the interval beyond 40 seconds leads to a decrease in performance. So extrapolating beyond

Table 5.5. Total number of correct responses and calculation of S for Example 5.1 (Hypothetical data)

Group						
I(0 sec)			II(20 sec)			III(40 sec)
Score	p	q	Score	p	q	Score
15	10	0	20	5	0	24
21	8	2	22	5	0	23
14	10	0	25	3	2	28
10	10	0	18	5	0	27
			26	3	2	30

$S = P - Q = 59 - 6 = 53$

the levels of the explanatory variable used in our study may be misleading. Similarly, interpolation between the levels used may be misleading. Thus, had we included intertrial intervals of 10 seconds and 30 seconds in our study, we may have found that the neat monotonic increasing relation breaks down. Therefore, we must be wary of drawing conclusions beyond the levels of the explanatory variable used in the study.

Example 5.2 Using the Normal Approximation to the Jonckheere Test

In a study of alcoholism and drug addiction carried out by Peter Grant (1975), it was predicted that alcoholics should have lower self-esteem than addicts, who should have lower self-esteem than a group of therapists from the clinic at which both the alcoholics and the addicts were being treated. Self-esteem was measured inversely by the discrepancy between actual self and ideal self in a repertory grid administered to each of 10 alcoholics, 5 drug addicts and 5 therapists. The data are shown in Table 5.6, together with the calculations necessary for computing S by the direct method, which give $S = 83$. We may use a one-tailed Jonckheere Test to test Grant's prediction, since the data may quite reasonably be assumed independent and the prediction implies an ordering of the levels of the explanatory variable.

Since one of the samples has 10 observations, we are not able to use Table H to find an exact critical value of S. However, the normal approximation should be accurate with the present data. There are 5 observations in each of the first two samples and 10 in the last, so we have $t_1 = 5$, $t_2 = 5$, $t_3 = 10$ and $n = 20$. Therefore, $\Sigma t_i^3 = 5^3 + 5^3 + 10^3 = 1250$ and $\Sigma t_i^2 = 5^2 + 5^2 + 10^2 = 150$. The variance of S is thus computed using formula 5.1 as

$$\text{Variance} = \frac{2(n^3 - \Sigma t_i^3) + 3(n^2 - \Sigma t_i^2)}{18}$$

$$= \frac{2(20^3 - 1250) + 3(20^2 - 150)}{18}$$

$$= \frac{13500 + 750}{18}$$

$$= 791.667$$

Subtracting a continuity correction of 1 from the obtained S of 83, we get $S_c = 82$ and

$$z = \frac{S_c}{\text{S.D.}} = \frac{82}{\sqrt{791.667}} = 2.91$$

Using a significance level of 0.05, we find from Table B(ii) that the one-tailed critical value of z is 1.645. Since the obtained z is larger than this, we reject the null hypothesis and conclude that the data conform to Grant's prediction.

Table 5.6. Self-esteem scores for 3 groups of people; low scores mean high self-esteem (From Grant, 1975)

Therapists			Addicts			Alcoholics	
Score	p	q	Score	p	q	Score	
3	15	0	9.5	10	0	20	
4	15	0	11.5	10	0	21.5	
17	13	2	25.5	6	4	23	
18.5	13	2	44	5	5	25	$n = 20$
21	12	3	47	5	5	34	$t_1 = 5$
						56.5	$t_2 = 5$
						66	$t_3 = 10$
						70.5	
						72	
						76	

$S = P - Q = 104 - 21 = 83$

5.2 THE JONCKHEERE TEST WITH TIES

The calculation of the null distribution of the Jonckheere Test assumes that the response variable is continuous, so ties should not occur. If they do, we use the midrank technique described in Section 2.3. This involves little or no modification to the suggested methods of computing S. For the direct method, any ties that occur when comparing a particular score with scores in samples to the right are ignored when calculating p and q (see Example 5.3). No modification is required to the ordered contingency table method, which automatically takes care of the ties (see Examples 5.4 and 5.5).

When there are ties in the response variable, the critical values in Table H will no longer be accurate. To obtain accurate critical values, we should need to calculate the null distribution anew for each different combination of ties. As long as there are not too many ties, however, Table H will give a reasonably good approximation. As a very rough general rule, Table H should not be used when more than a quarter of the scores are involved in ties.

When more than a quarter of the scores are involved in ties, the normal approximation, corrected for ties as shown below, will generally be adequate.

Normal Approximation to S in the Tied Case

Ordinal response variable

When there are ties in the response variable the spacing between consecutive possible values of S becomes uneven, so there is no generally applicable continuity correction.

The required formula for the variance of S when there are ties looks very complicated. In fact it's quite straightforward to use, as we shall see in Example 5.4. It is given by

$$\text{Variance} = \frac{2(n^3 - \Sigma t_i^3 - \Sigma u_i^3) + 3(n^2 - \Sigma t_i^2 - \Sigma u_i^2) + 5n}{18} + \frac{(\Sigma t_i^3 - 3\Sigma t_i^2 + 2n)(\Sigma u_i^3 - 3\Sigma u_i^2 + 2n)}{9n(n-1)(n-2)} + \frac{(\Sigma t_i^2 - n)(\Sigma u_i^2 - n)}{2n(n-1)} \quad (5.2)$$

Here, the t_i's refer to the row marginal totals in the contingency table and the u_i's refer to the column marginal totals.

Two category response variable

A special case of the above situation occurs when the response variable has only two categories, as illustrated in Example 5.5. In this case, it is possible to use a continuity correction. This is given by $(2n - t_1 - t_k)/[2(k-1)]$, where k refers to the number of samples, t_1 is the first row marginal total in the contingency table and t_k is the last one.

A major advantage of the two category case is that formula 5.2 can be written in a much simpler form. The variance of S in this case becomes

$$\text{Variance} = \frac{u_1 u_2 (n^3 - \Sigma t_i^3)}{3n(n-1)} \quad (5.3)$$

The necessary calculations are illustrated in Example 5.5.

It is worth noting that this use of the Jonckheere Test is identical to the Rank-Sum Test with extensive ties illustrated in Example 2.4. The only difference is that the roles of the explanatory and response variables have been reversed.

Example 5.3 The Jonckheere Test with Few Ties

In a study of the effects of dogmatism in teachers on the academic self-concept of their pupils, Wendy McKane (1977) selected three groups of four teachers with high (H), medium (M) and low (L) scores

Table 5.7. Mean academic self-concept scores for children taught by teachers of high, medium and low dogmatism (From McKane, 1977)

Dogmatism score							
L			M			H	
Score	p	q	Score	p	q	Score	
10.1	6	2	10.3	3	1	7.3	
11.1	3	5	7.8	3	1	12.3	$S = P - Q$
12.0	3	5	12.5	0	4	10.4	$= 21 - 27$
10.6	3	5	12.5	0	4	10.5	$= -6$

on a dogmatism test. All twelve teachers taught 9- to 11-year-olds in similar schools. A random sample of eight children in each teacher's class was selected, each child being given the Barker–Lunn test of academic self-concept, which assesses the children's beliefs about their own ability in the classroom. High scores on this test reflect high self-concept. The mean score on the Barker–Lunn test for each of the twelve classes is shown in Table 5.7. McKane wanted to test the prediction that there is a negative relation between teachers' dogmatism and children's academic self-concept: the more dogmatic the teacher, the lower the average score of the children in that class should be. We can test this using a one-tailed version of the Jonckheere Test. Since only two of the twelve scores on the response variable are tied, Table H should be reasonably accurate. With $\alpha = 0.05$, the relevant lower tail critical value of S with $t_1 = 4$, $t_2 = 4$, and $t_3 = 4$ is -24. The obtained S is -6, so the prediction is not supported. One possible reason for this is that McKane could find no teachers who scored very high on the dogmatism scale, so the H group, although being more dogmatic than the others, would not be classified as highly dogmatic by the test. So the conclusion strictly refers only within the limits of the rather undogmatic group of teachers sampled. It would be heartening if the difficulty of finding dogmatic teachers extended beyond the schools used in this study and if it could be convincingly demonstrated that the dogmatism test was not subject to any sort of response bias that typically affects such tests.

Example 5.4 The Jonckheere Test with Extensive Ties

Lynne Chambers and Enid Rowlands (1975) obtained recall data from samples of 4-, 5-, and 6-year-old children. They wished to test the predication that recall improves with age. Their data were the number of items correctly recalled out of 9 and the complete data for one of their conditions are shown below:

4-year-olds	6,	7,	7,	7,	8,	8,	8,	9,	9,	9
5-year-olds	6,	7,	7,	8,	8,	8,	8,	9,	9,	9
6-year-olds	8,	8,	8,	9,	9,	9,	9,	9,	9,	9

There are ten children in each of the three samples and we may reasonably assume the data to be independent. A Kruskal–Wallis Test carried out on these data would indicate any overall differences between the three age groups, but would not be sensitive to the predicted ordering, so the Jonckheere Test is preferable. The data are shown in the form of an ordered contingency table in Table 5.8 from which we can easily compute S, as follows:

$$P = 1 \times 19 + 3 \times 17 + 3 \times 10 + 3 \times 0 + 1 \times 10 + 2 \times 10 + 4 \times 7 + 3 \times 0$$
$$= 158$$

$$Q = 1 \times 0 + 3 \times 1 + 3 \times 3 + 3 \times 10 + 1 \times 0 + 2 \times 0 + 4 \times 0 + 3 \times 3$$
$$= 51$$

$$S = 107$$

To compute the variance of S using formula 5.2, we first need some preliminary calculations. Since $n = 30$, we have $n^2 = 900$ and $n^3 = 27000$; also

$$\Sigma t_i^2 = 10^2 + 10^2 + 10^2 = 300$$

$$\Sigma t_i^3 = 10^3 + 10^3 + 10^3 = 3000$$

$$\Sigma u_i^2 = 2^2 + 5^2 + 10^2 + 13^2 = 298$$

$$\Sigma u_i^3 = 2^3 + 5^3 + 10^3 + 13^3 = 3330$$

Table 5.8. Ordered contingency table for the data of Example 5.4 (From Chambers and Rowlands, 1975)

		Recall score				
		6	7	8	9	t_i
	4	1	3	3	3	10
Age	5	1	2	4	3	10
	6	0	0	3	7	10
	u_i	2	5	10	13	$30 = n$

Fitting these values into formula 5.2, we get

$$\text{Variance} = \frac{2(27000 - 3000 - 3330) + 3(900 - 300 - 298) + 150}{18}$$

$$+ \frac{(3000 - 900 + 60)(3330 - 894 + 60)}{9 \times 30 \times 29 \times 28}$$

$$+ \frac{(300 - 30)(298 - 30)}{2 \times 30 \times 29}$$

$$= 2421.511$$

In this case, there is no continuity correction, so the z-score is given by

$$z = \frac{S}{\text{S.D.}} = \frac{107}{\sqrt{2421.511}} = 2.17$$

With $\alpha = 0.05$, Table B(ii) gives 1.645 as the one-tailed critical value of z. The obtained value is larger than this, so we reject the null hypothesis in favour of Chambers and Rowlands' prediction that recall improves with age.

Example 5.5 The Jonckheere Test – Two Category Response Variable

In an experimental study of reading, Elspeth Stirling (1977) asked 112 people to read a story. Afterwards, they were asked to judge whether a particular sentence had been present in the story. The people were randomly divided into four groups of 28 each. Group ID (for identical) were presented with a sentence identical to the sentence in the passage. Group CC (for case congruent) were presented with a sentence that had a different surface form but the same meaning as the sentence in the story. Group NOC (for noun order congruent) were presented with a sentence with the same surface structure but a different meaning. Group SR (for simply related) were given a sentence that had both a different surface structure and a different meaning from the original

Table 5.9. Ordered contingency table for the data of Example 5.5 (From Stirling, 1977)

		Same	Different	t_i
Group	ID	16	12	28
	CC	9	19	28
	NOC	8	20	28
	SR	4	24	28
	u_i	37	75	112

sentence. Each subject said either 'Same' or 'Different' to the presented sentence. Using a model of reading based on Case Grammar, Stirling predicted that the proportion of Same judgements should decrease from group to group, with group ID having the most, group CC the next and group SR the least. Her data are presented in Table 5.9. These data are already in the form of an ordered contingency table, since the rows are written in the predicted ordering. S is easily computed as 1036.

Now, since the response variable has two categories, a continuity correction is appropriate. It is given by

$$\frac{2n - t_1 - t_k}{2(k-1)} = \frac{2 \times 112 - 28 - 28}{2 \times 3} = 28,$$

since $k = 4$ is the number of samples.

The variance of S may be computed from formula 5.3. We first require $\Sigma t_i^3 = 28^3 + 28^3 + 28^3 + 28^3 = 87808$. Then, from formula 5.3,

$$\text{Variance} = \frac{37 \times 75 \times (112^3 - 87808)}{3 \times 112 \times 111} = 98000$$

The z-score then becomes

$$z = \frac{S_c}{\text{S.D.}} = \frac{1036 - 28}{\sqrt{98000}} = 3.22$$

With $\alpha = 0.001$, Table B(ii) gives the one-tailed critical value of z as 3.090. Even with such a stringent significance level, the obtained value is larger than the critical value, so we reject the null hypothesis and conclude that Stirling's prediction is upheld with these data.

5.3 THE KENDALL TEST FOR CORRELATION

When there is only one observation in each of the samples, the Jonckheere Test reduces to a well-known test due to Kendall. As noted at the beginning of the chapter, the Kendall Test is most frequently used as a test of correlation between two variables. It assumes that both the explanatory and the response variable are continuous ordinal variables and that the data are independent. This implies that there should be no ties in either the explanatory variable or the response variable. The treatment of ties is discussed in Section 5.4.

Simplified Example

Suppose we are interested in whether there is any relation between ability in mathematics and ability in music or whether the two abilities are independent. We obtain the scores for a sample of 3 people on both a test of mathematical ability and a test of musical ability, the scores being the following:

	Person		
	1	2	3
Mathematics	28	25	36
Music	34	35	53

Our interest centres on whether people scoring low on the mathematics test also score low on the music test and people scoring high in mathematics also score high in music (indicating a positive correlation) or whether people scoring low on one of the tests score high on the other (indicating a negative correlation). In such a problem we are not interested in whether the scores on one test tend to be different from the scores on the other. The tests are different, so the chances are that they are not strictly comparable anyway, since they may well be measured on different scales. However, had we been interested in such differences, the Wilcoxon Signed-Rank Test would be appropriate. In a correlational problem we are looking at the data from a different angle.

Test Statistic – *S*

The rationale and test statistic for the Kendall Test are identical to those of the Jonckheere Test. To compute S, we first choose one of the variables to be the explanatory variable – it doesn't matter which we choose, since the result will be the same for either choice. Suppose we choose the Mathematics score to be the explanatory variable, with the Music score taking the role of the response variable. As with the Jonckheere Test, we rearrange the data so that the levels of the explanatory variable are written in increasing order, i.e. the data from the subject with the lowest Mathematics score are put on the left and those from the subject with the highest Mathematics score are put on the right. This is done in Table 5.10.

Table 5.10. Direct calculation of S for the Kendall Test

	Person			
	2	1	3	
Mathematics	25	28	36	
Music	35	34	53	
p	1	1		$P = 2$
q	1	0		$Q = 1$
				$S = P - Q = 1$

Now, if the two sets of scores are perfectly positively correlated, then, since the Mathematics scores are in increasing order, the Music scores should also be in increasing order. If the two variables are perfectly negatively correlated, then the Music scores should be in decreasing order. On the other hand, if the two variables are independent, the Music scores should be in no particular order. The test statistic S gives just what we require here. Large positive values of S reflect positive correlation between the two variables, large negative values reflect negative correlation and values close to zero reflect independence.

Computing S *directly*

The calculation of S is identical to that shown for the Jonckheere Test, although it is slightly simpler here because there is only one response under each level of the explanatory variable. Take each Music score (except the right-most) in turn and count how many scores to the right are larger (the p contribution) and how many scores to the right are smaller (the q contribution). S is then given by subtracting the sum of the q's from the sum of the p's. The calculations for our example are shown in Table 5.10 and the resulting value of S is 1, indicating a slight positive correlation, as would be expected from the data, since the subject scoring highest in Mathematics also scores highest in Music, although the other two subjects are out of order.

Computing S *from an ordered contingency table*

S may also be computed by first representing the data in the form of an ordered contingency table as shown in Table 5.11 and then calculating S in the usual way as shown in Section 5.1. For our example, this gives $P = 1 \times 1 + 1 \times 1 = 2$, $Q = 1 \times 1 + 1 \times 0 = 1$; and $S = P - Q = 2 - 1 = 1$, as before. This method will generally be best when there are extensive ties in one or both of the variables. When there are no ties it takes longer than the direct method.

Table 5.11. Ordered contingency table representation for the data of Table 5.10

		Music			
		34	35	53	t_i
	25		1		1
Mathematics	28	1			1
	36			1	1
	u_i	1	1	1	$3 = n$

Null distribution of S

When using the Kendall Test, we are testing the null hypothesis that the two variables are independent. This implies that, once we have written one set of scores,

Table 5.12. The 6 possible patterns of results when $n = 3$ together with associated values of S

Mathematics	1. Music	2. Music	3. Music	4. Music	5. Music	6. Music
1	1	1	2	2	3	3
2	2	3	1	3	1	2
3	3	2	3	1	2	1
	$S = 3$	1	1	−1	−1	−3

say the Mathematics scores, in increasing order, all possible orderings of the other set of scores are equally likely. As with the Jonckheere Test, we need only concentrate on the rank order of the scores to compute the null distribution of S. The 6 possible patterns of results for our example with $n = 3$ are given in Table 5.12, together with the value of S computed for each. Our example data are equivalent to pattern 3 here. The null distribution of S for our case can then be written down immediately as in Table 5.13. Thus, the two-tailed probability of getting an S of 1 or more is $2/6 + 1/6 + 1/6 + 2/6 = 1.0$, so with our data we should not be able to reject the null hypothesis of independence for any sensible significance level.

To test the prediction that there is a positive correlation between the two variables, we use an upper tail test. To test for a negative correlation, a lower tail test should be used, since negative values of S indicate negative correlation. To test for a departure from independence in either direction, a two-tailed test should be used. These are all carried out in the usual manner described in Section 2.1.

Table 5.13. Null distribution of S for the case $n = 3$

S	−3	−1	1	3
Probability	1/6	2/6	2/6	1/6

Table of the Null Distribution of S (Appendix Table I)

Table I in the Appendix gives critical values of the null distribution of S for both one- and two-tailed tests for all values of n up to 40. To illustrate its use, when n is 8 and $\alpha = 0.05$, the lower and upper tail critical values of S will be −18 and 18 for a two-tailed test; we therefore reject the null hypothesis if our obtained S is $\leqslant -18$ or $\geqslant 18$. For a one-tailed test, the upper tail critical value is 16, so we reject the null hypothesis if our obtained S is $\geqslant 16$. If a lower tail test is required, we reject the null hypothesis if our obtained S is $\leqslant -16$.

Normal Approximation to S

As with the other tests involving S, it is possible to use the standard normal distribution to approximate the null distribution for cases not covered by Table I.

The mean of the possible values that S may take is always 0 and the variance is given by

$$\text{Variance} = \frac{n(n-1)(2n+5)}{18} \tag{5.4}$$

This is easily seen to give the correct value for our simplified example with $n = 3$ where we know from Table 5.12 that the 6 possible values of S are 3, 1, 1, −1, −1, and −3, the variance of these values being 11/3. The formula gives this immediately.

The approximation may be improved by using a continuity correction of 1, since, when there are no ties in either variable, the spacing between consecutive possible values of S will always be 2. As usual, the continuity correction should be subtracted from positive values of S and added to negative values.

Further Comments

For a full discussion of the Kendall Test and its relation to other tests to be outlined in the next section, see Kendall (1970).

To estimate the size of the effect demonstrated by using the Kendall Test, one of the measures of association described in Section 5.6 may be used.

Example 5.6 The Kendal Test for Correlation

To discover whether the final year results for a particular course could be predicted by performance on a first year examination, the results for 15 students were compared. These are shown below. The

	Student														
	1	2	3	4	5	6	7	8	9	10	11	12	13	14	15
First year	63	59	23	83	38	42	51	49	22	73	69	62	45	50	55
Final year	60	68	42	62	38	48	63	55	17	74	58	64	47	50	57

Kendall Test is appropriate here, since we are interested in whether students who score low (or high) in the first year also score low (or high) in the final year. Suppose we decide to use a one-tailed test, which implies we should not be interested in discovering a negative correlation, with a significance level of 0.05. Then from Table I we find the upper tail critical value of S when $n = 15$ to be 35.

We compute S using the direct method by rearranging the first year scores in increasing order. The calculations are shown in Table 5.14. The obtained S of 73 is larger than the critical value, so we reject the

Table 5.14. Rearranged data and calculation of S for Example 5.6 (Hypothetical data)

	Student														
	9	3	5	6	13	8	14	7	15	2	12	1	11	10	4
First year	22	23	38	42	45	49	50	51	55	59	62	63	69	73	83
Final year	17	42	38	48	47	55	50	63	57	68	64	60	58	74	62
p	14	12	12	10	10	8	8	3	6	1	1	2	2	0	
q	0	1	0	1	0	1	0	4	0	4	3	1	0	1	

$S = P - Q = 89 - 16 = 73$

null hypothesis and conclude that there is a positive correlation between the two examinations. Thus, in this case, it should be possible to predict students' final year performance from their first year results.

Example 5.7. The Mann Test for Trend

The world will always welcome lovers,
As time goes by

Dooley Wilson in *'Casablanca'*

It is possible to use the Kendall Test as a test of trend. When this is done the test is generally referred to as the Mann Test, since H.B. Mann first suggested this use.

Suppose we test a single subject on a set of related problems on each of 6 days, measuring the time taken to solve the problems in minutes. We wish to know whether there is evidence of a monotonically increasing or decreasing trend in the data, which are given in Table 5.15. (Monotonically increasing means that time taken either increases or stays constant over the 6 days, but never decreases. Monotonically decreasing means that time taken either decreases or stays constant, but never increases.) We may test this using the Kendall Test, by treating day number as the explanatory variable and time as the response variable. Notice that, because the data come from the same subject, the assumption of independence may be questionable. However, this use of the test is testing for a particular type of dependence (positive or negative correlation) against the general null hypothesis of lack of dependence

Table 5.15. Hypothetical data and calculation of S for Example 5.7

	Day 1	Day 2	Day 3	Day 4	Day 5	Day 6	
Time	30	32	27	24	20	17	
p	1	0	0	0	0		$P = 1$
q	4	4	3	2	1		$Q = 14$

$S = P - Q = 1 - 14 = -13$

of this sort. This will generally be acceptable as long as the data come from only one individual (in this context, see Example 2.11).

Since we are interested in whether there is either an improvement or a decrement in performance over time, a two-tailed test is appropriate. With $\alpha = 0.05$, Table I gives the critical values of S when $n = 6$ as -13 and 13.

The calculation of S for the obtained data is shown in Table 5.15. Since our obtained value of -13 is equal to the lower tail critical value, we must reject the null hypothesis and conclude that these data provide reliable evidence of a negative correlation. Thus, there is a downward trend – performance time decreases as time goes by.

5.4 THE KENDALL TEST WITH TIES

All generalizations are dangerous, even this one.

Alexandre Dumas, *fils*

The calculation of the null distribution for the Kendall Test assumes that there are no ties in either of the two variables. Thus, in Example 5.6, no students should have the same mark in the first year examination and none should have the same mark in the final examination. When ties occur in either or both of the variables they may be treated in the standard way, using midranks.

When there are ties, the Kendall Test turns into one of the other tests using S as the test statistic, so exact tables of the null distribution may be available. Thus, if there are ties only in the explanatory variable, we obtain the Jonckheere Test and Table H may be used to find critical values; with data beyond the scope of Table H, the normal approximation to the Jonckheere Test may be used. If the ties in the explanatory variable become so extensive that there are only two levels, we obtain the Rank-Sum Test; and so on. The tests using S, all of which may be viewed as the Kendall Test with ties in one or both variables, are summarized in the table at the back of the book, which includes information about appropriate exact tables and the use of the normal approximation when the exact tables are not available.

The expressions for the variance of S all look very different. However, it is possible to show that they are all special cases of the most complicated formula given as the variance of S for the Jonckheere Test (with ties), which represents the most general situation in which both variables have ties. For example, the much simpler formula for the variance of S in the Kendall Test without ties may be obtained from the more general expression by setting all the t_i's and all the u_i's equal to unity, since these represent the extent of the ties in each variable.

To find the appropriate table or formula using the table at the back of the book, it may be necessary in some cases to interchange the roles of the explanatory and response variables, as we shall see in Example 5.8. This will not affect the validity of the test, but for experimental studies, any conclusions drawn should be based on the way in which the study was originally carried out and not on the relabelling.

Example 5.8 The Kendall Test with Ties

In Example 5.6, we used the Kendall Test to assess whether there

Table 5.16. Hypothetical data for Example 5.8

	Student												
	1	2	3	4	5	6	7	8	9	10	11	12	13
First year	23	63	38	50	55	22	42	24	45	53	53	48	35
Final year	42	55	42	55	55	17	42	17	42	55	42	55	17

was a positive correlation between first year results and final year results for a particular course. Suppose the results had been those given in Table 5.16. Here we have ties in both variables; two of the first year scores are tied, while all the final year scores are involved in ties. From the table at the back of the book, we can see that the Jonckheere Test with ties is appropriate. Since one of the variables has very few ties, we may be able to use the exact table for the Jonckeere Test (Table H). To see whether this is possible, we label the variable with few ties (first year scores) the response variable and the variable with extensive ties (final year scores) the explanatory variable and rearrange the data as in Table 5.17, the form most convenient for the Jonckheere Test. In this form, we see immediately that we can use Table H with $t_1 = 5$, $t_2 = 5$ and $t_3 = 3$ to find critical values. For an upper tail test with $\alpha = 0.05$, the critical value of S of 27. The obtained value of S for these data is 46, so we reject the null hypothesis and conclude again that there is a positive correlation between first year results and final year results.

Table 5.17. Calculation of S for the data in Table 5.16

Final year score							
17			42			55	
Score	p	q	Score	p	q	Score	
22	10	0	23	5	0	63	
24	9	1	38	5	0	50	$P = 50$
35	9	1	42	5	0	55	$Q = 4$
			45	5	0	53	$S = 46$
			53	2	2	48	

5.5 THE SPEARMAN TEST FOR CORRELATION

The Spearman Test is a frequently used alternative to the Kendall Test which emphasizes slightly different aspects of the data, but which makes the same assumptions and is applicable whenever the Kendall Test is applicable.

Test Statistic – ρ

Consider again the simplified example used in Section 5.3, which is reproduced in Table 5.18 along with most of the calculations necessary to compute ρ (the Greek letter rho), the Spearman test statistic. For the Spearman Test, the scores on each variable must first be rank ordered. Thus, the lowest score in Mathematics (subject 2's) gets a rank of 1, the next gets a rank of 2, and so on. The rankings of the Mathematics and Music scores are shown in rows X_i and Y_i. In row $X_i - Y_i$, the Music ranking for each subject is subtracted from the Mathematics ranking, the result being squared in row $(X_i - Y_i)^2$. The sum of this final row gives D, 2 in this case.

Now, if there is a perfect positive correlation, the two rankings, X_i and Y_i, will be identical, so the difference score for each subject will be zero. D will then also be zero. If there is a perfect negative correlation, the rankings X_i and Y_i will be in reverse order and the differences $X_i - Y_i$ will be large. D will then also be large. If the two rankings are unrelated, D will be somewhere between these two extreme values.

D is frequently used as the test statistic for the Spearman Test. However, we shall find it more convenient to use a test statistic that takes the value zero when the two rankings are unrelated, a positive value when there is a positive correlation and a negative value when there is a negative correlation.

Such a test statistic is given by transforming D using the following formula to produce ρ, our final version of the test statistic:

$$\rho = 1 - \frac{6D}{n(n^2 - 1)} \tag{5.5}$$

For our example data with $D = 2$, ρ will be

$$1 - \frac{6 \times 2}{3 \times 8} = 0.5.$$

Table 5.18. Calculation of D for the Spearman Test

	Person			
	1	2	3	
Mathematics	28	25	36	
Music	34	35	53	
Maths rank, X_i	2	1	3	
Music rank, Y_i	1	2	3	
$X_i - Y_i$	1	−1	0	
$(X_i - Y_i)^2$	1	1	0	$D = \Sigma(X_i - Y_i)^2 = 2$

For any data, ρ will always lie between -1 and $+1$, taking the value $+1$ when there is a perfect positive correlation and the value -1 when there is a perfect negative correlation.

The most important difference between the Spearman and Kendall Tests is that the Spearman Test puts more weight on large differences between the two sets of rankings than on small differences. Had the two rankings for our example been

X_i	1	2	3
Y_i	3	1	2

the first difference, $1 - 3$, would contribute proportionately more to D than the other two, since differences are squared, so that large differences become even larger. This is not true of the Kendall Test, which does not involve any squaring.

Null Distribution of ρ

The null hypothesis of the Spearman Test is that the two variables are independent, which is the same as the null hypothesis of the Kendall Test. Thus, the patterns of results that need to be investigated are the same in both tests and are those given in Table 5.12 for the case $n = 3$. The D values for the 6 possible patterns of results shown there are 0, 2, 2, 6, 6 and 8, respectively; the corresponding values of ρ will then be 1, 0.5, 0.5, -0.5, -0.5, and -1, respectively. Under the null hypothesis, each of the 6 patterns is equally likely to occur, so we can immediately write the null distribution of ρ as shown in Table 5.19. From this, we can see that the one-tailed probability of getting a ρ of 0.5 or larger is $2/6 + 1/6 = 0.5$, so we should not be able to reject the null hypothesis of independence for our example data using any sensible significance level. This agrees with the conclusion of the Kendall Test for the same data. In general, the two tests rarely differ in their conclusions.

As with the Kendall Test, to test the prediction that there is a positive correlation between the two variables, we use an upper tail test. To test for a negative correlation, we use a lower tail test. To test for a departure from independence in either direction, a two-tailed test should be used.

Table 5.19. Null distribution of ρ when $n = 3$

ρ	-1	-0.5	0.5	1
Probability	1/6	2/6	2/6	1/6

Table of the Null Distribution of ρ (Appendix Table J)

Table J in the Appendix gives critical values of the null distribution of ρ for both one- and two-tailed tests for all values of n up to 30. To illustrate its use, when

$n = 8$, the critical values of ρ for a two-tailed test with $\alpha = 0.05$ are -0.738 and 0.738; we therefore reject the null hypothesis if our obtained ρ is $\leqslant -0.738$ or $\geqslant 0.738$. For a one-tailed test, the upper tail critical value is 0.643, so we reject the null hypothesis if our obtained ρ is $\geqslant 0.643$. If a lower tail test is required, we reject the null hypothesis if our obtained ρ is $\leqslant -0.643$.

Normal Approximation to ρ

For data beyond the scope of Table J, the standard normal distribution again comes to our rescue to provide an approximate test. When there are no ties in either variable, the mean of the possible values that ρ can take will always be zero, while the variance is given by

$$\text{Variance} = \frac{1}{n-1} \tag{5.6}$$

This is easily seen to give the correct answer for our example with $n = 3$, where the 6 possible values of ρ, 1, 0.5, 0.5, -0.5, -0.5 and -1, have a mean of 0 and a variance of 0.5.

A continuity correction of $6/(n^3 - n)$ generally improves the approximation. As usual, this should be subtracted from positive values of ρ and added to negative values.

The Treatment of Ties

The critical values of ρ given in Table J will only be accurate when there are no ties in either variable. When ties occur in practice, the midrank technique should be used. As long as no more than a quarter of the values on either variable are involved in ties, Table J or the normal distribution given above will give a reasonably good approximation.

When more than a quarter of the scores are involved in ties, a correction for ties should be used with the normal approximation. The relevant correction is given in Lehmann (1975, Section 7.3).

Further Comments

For a fuller discussion of the Spearman Test and a detailed comparison with the Kendall Test, see Kendall (1970). Kendall points out that the normal approximation is not nearly as accurate for the Spearman Test as for the Kendall Test. This makes the Kendall Test more attractive when exact tables are not available, particularly in the case of extensive ties. This is the main reason Kendall's Test with ties is used to provide a wealth of other tests.

The Spearman Test should generally be preferred to the Kendall Test only if it is considered important to emphasize large differences between the two rankings.

ρ is frequently used as a measure of association when there are few ties in either variable. Like Goodman and Kruskal's gamma and Kendall's tau to be discussed in

Section 5.6, it varies between −1 and +1, with values close to zero indicating little or no association. We shall not, however, consider it further in this light, mainly because it does not have such a natural probabilistic interpretation as gamma.

A major advantage of the Spearman Test is that it is closely related to the Friedman Test discussed in Chapter 6.

Example 5.9 The Spearman Test for Correlation

For this example we reanalyse the data of Example 5.6. The necessary steps in calculating D are given in Table 5.20, from which we obtain $D = 80$. We therefore have

$$\rho = 1 - \frac{6D}{n(n^2 - 1)} = 1 - \frac{6 \times 80}{15 \times 224} = 1 - 0.143 = 0.857.$$

Using a one-tailed test with $\alpha = 0.05$, Table J gives the critical value of ρ when $n = 15$ as 0.446, so we reject the null hypothesis since our obtained value is larger than this. As with the analysis using the Kendall Test, we conclude that there is a positive correlation between the first year results and the final results for these students.

Table 5.20. Hypothetical data for Example 5.9, together with the calculation of D

	Student															
	1	2	3	4	5	6	7	8	9	10	11	12	13	14	15	
First year	63	59	23	83	38	42	51	49	22	73	69	62	45	50	55	
Final year	60	68	42	62	38	48	63	55	17	74	58	64	47	50	57	
First year rank, X_i	12	10	2	15	3	4	8	6	1	14	13	11	5	7	9	
Final year rank, Y_i	10	14	3	11	2	5	12	7	1	15	9	13	4	6	8	
$X_i - Y_i$	2	−4	−1	4	1	−1	−4	−1	0	−1	4	−2	1	1	1	
$(X_i - Y_i)^2$	4	16	1	16	1	1	16	1	0	1	16	4	1	1	1	$D = 80$

5.6 MEASURES OF ASSOCIATION FOR ORDERED CONTINGENCY TABLES

To each thing belongs its measure

Pindar, *Odes*

In Section 2.4, we discussed two ways of estimating the size of the effect demonstrated by a significant S. The Hodges–Lehmann estimator is useful in the Rank-Sum situation when the response variable is measured on an easily interpretable scale. When the scale of the response variable does not have a simple interpretation, the other estimator, Somers' delta, might be more useful. In Section 2.6, we saw that delta provided useful information in the Fisher Exact situation where the data are most commonly represented in a 2 x 2 contingency table. In this section we shall discuss delta further together with two other commonly used estimators that are generally known as measures of association. These three measures of association are all useful for data that may be represented as an ordered contingency table, for which S is the appropriate test statistic. For a discussion of some measures that do not focus on the ordinal properties of the data, see Chapter 8.

Why do we need to discuss three measures of association and not just one, the best? The reason, as usual, is that the best measure for one purpose may not be the best for another purpose. As with the measures of location discussed in Section 1.1, the aim of a measure of association is to summarize a batch of data using a single number. Different ways of arriving at such a number will emphasize different aspects of the data. Those aspects that are important are determined largely by the purpose of the investigation, so no one measure will be appropriate for all purposes.

The aim of this section is to show which aspects of the data are emphasized by three of the most useful measures of association.

The first question to ask in choosing a measure of association is whether there is a particular reason to distinguish the explanatory variable and the response variable: does it matter to the conclusions drawn if the labelling is reversed? In experimental studies, the distinction is important. The aim of an experimental study is to demonstrate that variation on the explanatory variable causes variation on the response variable (see Section 1.4). In some correlational studies also, the distinction is important. For example, in many studies of sex differences it is usual to want to know how much the score on the response variable may be predicted from a knowledge of the person's sex (the explanatory variable); it is less common to want to turn the question the other way round and ask how much a person's sex may be predicted from the score on the response variable. Similarly, in Example 5.6, we are more likely to want to predict students' final year scores from their first year scores than the other way round. In all these cases, we require an asymmetrical measure of association such as delta that focuses on the explanatory variable.

In other correlational studies, there may be no particular reason for focusing attention on one of the variables. In discovering whether there is a relation between mathematical and musical ability, we may simply want to know the extent to which the two are related and not be particularly interested in the extent to which musical ability may be predicted from mathematical ability. In such a case, one of the symmetrical measures, gamma, or tau, is required.

Somers' Delta

Two-sample data

In Chapter 2 we have already seen that, for two-sample data with an ordinal response variable, delta is given by formula 2.4; i.e.

$$\delta = \frac{S}{t_1 t_2} \tag{2.4}$$

where t_1 and t_2 are the sizes of the samples (the extent of the ties on the explanatory variable).

The interpretation of delta depends on the following considerations. If we select two subjects at random, one from the first sample and one from the second, two possibilities interest us: (*a*) the subject from the first sample has a higher score on the response variable than the other one; (*b*) the subject from the second sample has a higher score than the other one. Delta measures the extent to which *a* is more likely than *b*.

2 x 2 contingency tables

Since the 2 x 2 case occurs so frequently in practice, it is worth paying particular attention to it. As a further example of 2 x 2 data, suppose 8 students are cross-classified according to whether they passed (P) or failed (F) their first year examination and also according to whether they passed or failed their final examination. Some possible sets of data are shown in Table 5.21. For such data, we should normally wish to predict final performance from a knowledge of first year performance. For the data in (a), $\delta = 4/7$ or 0.57 (using formula 2.4). This means that if we select two students, one of whom has passed and one of whom has failed in the first year, it is 57% more likely that the student who has passed will be the better one in the final year than that the student who has failed will be the better one. If we were interested instead in asking how students' first year performance is related to their final year performance, we could do this by turning the data round as in (b), from which we obtain $\delta = 4/16$ or 0.25, which shows that δ is asymmetrical. This time, the obtained value means that if we select two students, one of whom has passed and one whom has failed in the *final* year, it is only 25% more likely that the student who has passed will be the better one in the first year than that the student who has failed will be the better one. The asymmetry results from the fact that in this case we are better able to predict final results given knowledge of first year results (a) than we are to predict first year results given knowledge of final year results (b). This is due to the difference in the marginal totals – only one of the eight passed in the first year while four passed in the final year.

The other outcomes in Table 5.21 show some of the possibilities for delta. (d) and (e) show that delta attains its maximum (minimum) value of 1 (–1) when each column of the table has at most one non-zero cell. In the 2 x 2 case, this can only occur when the marginal totals for the two variables are the same, so we should never be able to obtain a delta of 1 or –1 for data with marginal totals like those in (a), (b), or (c). (f) shows that $\delta = 0$ when there is no association between the two variables – here, knowing the first year results tells us nothing about the final year results.

r x c *ordered contingency tables*

When there are more than two levels on the explanatory variable, the data may be recorded in an $r \times c$ ordered contingency table, where r is the number of rows (levels of the explanatory variable) and c is the number of columns (levels of the response variable). In this case delta will still be useful but will no longer be given by

Table 5.21. Various outcomes when 8 students are cross-classified according to whether they pass (P) or fail (F) their first and final year exams. Also shown are the associated values of S, delta, gamma, and tau b

(a)

First \ Final	P	F	t_i
P	1		1
F	3	4	7
u_i	4	4	

$S = 4$

$\delta = 0.57, \gamma = 1, \tau_b = 0.38$

(b)

Final \ First	P	F	t_i
P	1	3	4
F		4	4
u_i	1	7	

$S = 4$

$\delta = 0.25, \gamma = 1, \tau_b = 0.38$

(c)

First \ Final	P	F	t_i
P	2	1	3
F	2	3	5
u_i	4	4	

$S = 4$

$\delta = 0.27, \gamma = 0.50, \tau_b = 0.26$

(d)

First \ Final	P	F	t_i
P	1		1
F		7	7
u_i	1	7	

$S = 7$

$\delta = 1, \gamma = 1, \tau_b = 1$

(e)

First \ Final	P	F	t_i
P		1	1
F	7		7
u_i	7	1	

$S = -7$

$\delta = -1, \gamma = -1, \tau_b = -1$

(f)

First \ Final	P	F	t_i
P	2	2	4
F	2	2	4
u_i	4	4	

$S = 0$

$\delta = 0, \gamma = 0, \tau_b = 0$

formula 2.4. The more general formula is

$$\delta = \frac{2S}{n^2 - \Sigma t_i^2}, \tag{5.7}$$

where, as usual, n is the total number of scores and t_i is the number tied at the ith level of the explanatory variable. When there are only 2 samples ($r = 2$), formulae 5.7 and 2.4 are exactly equivalent.

As an illustration, suppose the examination results for our 8 students are recorded as distinction (D), pass (P), or fail (F). Table 5.22 shows some possible

Table 5.22. Ordered contingency tables for various outcomes when 8 students are cross-classified according to whether they obtain a distinction (D), pass (P), or fail (F) in their first and final year exams. Also shown are the associated values of S, delta, gamma, and tau b

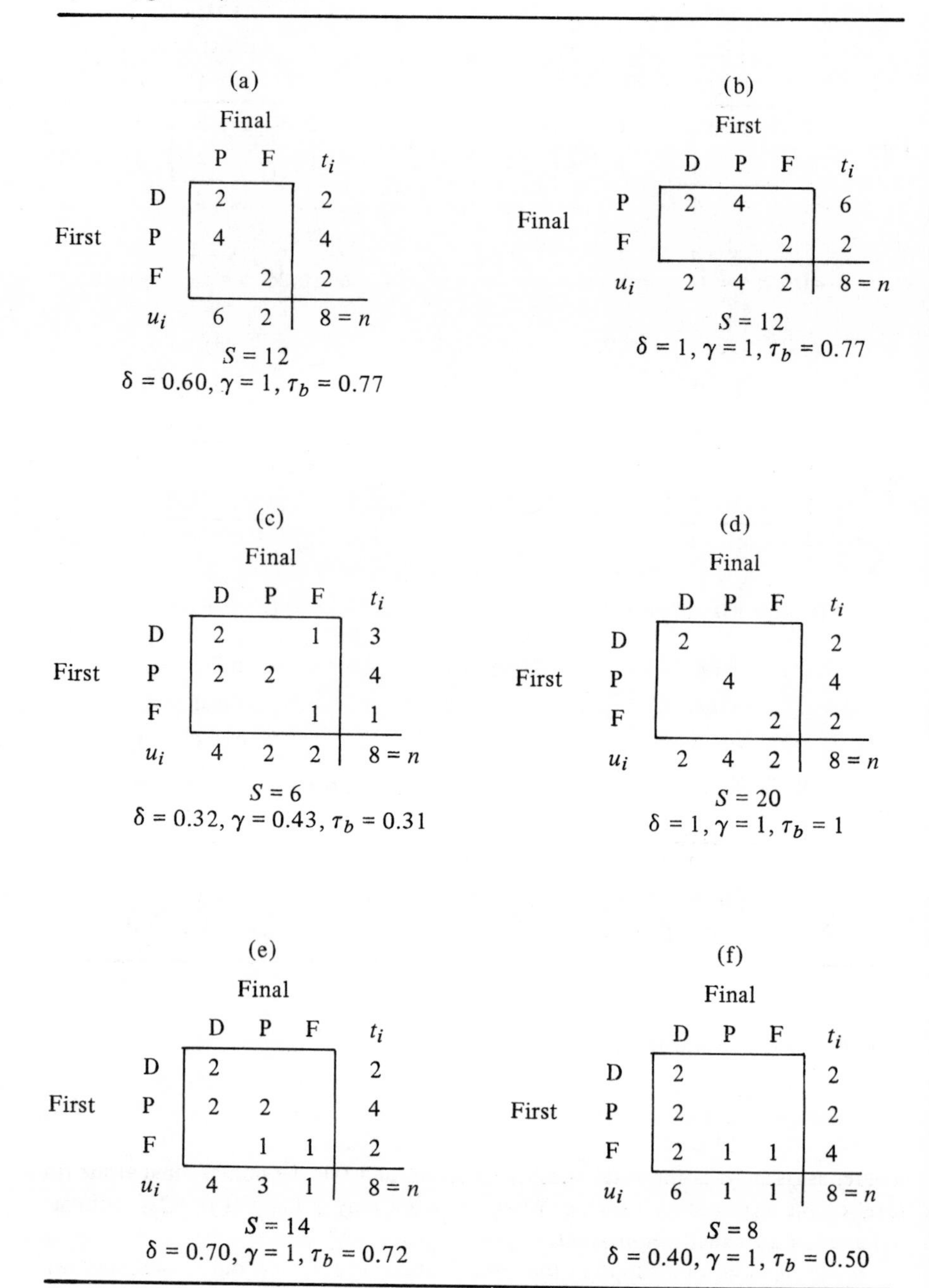

(a)

First \ Final	P	F	t_i
D	2		2
P	4		4
F		2	2
u_i	6	2	$8 = n$

$S = 12$
$\delta = 0.60, \gamma = 1, \tau_b = 0.77$

(b)

Final \ First	D	P	F	t_i
P	2	4		6
F			2	2
u_i	2	4	2	$8 = n$

$S = 12$
$\delta = 1, \gamma = 1, \tau_b = 0.77$

(c)

First \ Final	D	P	F	t_i
D	2		1	3
P	2	2		4
F			1	1
u_i	4	2	2	$8 = n$

$S = 6$
$\delta = 0.32, \gamma = 0.43, \tau_b = 0.31$

(d)

First \ Final	D	P	F	t_i
D	2			2
P		4		4
F			2	2
u_i	2	4	2	$8 = n$

$S = 20$
$\delta = 1, \gamma = 1, \tau_b = 1$

(e)

First \ Final	D	P	F	t_i
D	2			2
P	2	2		4
F		1	1	2
u_i	4	3	1	$8 = n$

$S = 14$
$\delta = 0.70, \gamma = 1, \tau_b = 0.72$

(f)

First \ Final	D	P	F	t_i
D	2			2
P	2			2
F	2	1	1	4
u_i	6	1	1	$8 = n$

$S = 8$
$\delta = 0.40, \gamma = 1, \tau_b = 0.50$

outcomes. In (a), we have a 3 x 2 ordered contingency table, since no one gained a distinction in the final examination. The table is ordered, since D represents a better performance than P and P represents a better performance than F. In this case, with $S = 12$, we have $\Sigma t_i^2 = 2^2 + 4^2 + 2^2 = 24$, so

$$\delta = \frac{2S}{n^2 - \Sigma t_i^2} = \frac{24}{64 - 24} = 0.6$$

This value may be interpreted as saying that if two students with different first year results are selected (i.e. either D and P, D and F, or P and F), then it is 60% more likely that the one who did better in the first year also did better in the final year than that the one who did better in the first year did worse in the final year.

This example again illustrates the asymmetry of delta, since $\delta = 1$ when the data are turned round as in (b). This shows that if two students are selected, one who passed the final examination and one who failed, it is certain that the one who passed also did better in the first year than the one who failed.

The data in (b) and (d) show that, as in the 2 x 2 case, delta takes its maximum value of 1 when each column has at most one non-zero value. Notice that this is true of the *rows* in (a), but it is not true of the columns, so δ is not equal to 1 in this case.

Formula 5.7 may be used to calculate δ in all cases, but in some situations it may be easier to use a different formula. We have already seen that this is possible in the 2 x 2 case, where formula 2.4 is easier to use than 5.7. The table at the back of the book gives the simplest method of calculating δ for the various situations encountered. Some of these will be illustrated in the examples below.

Goodman and Kruskal's Gamma

In many cases, we may want a symmetric measure of association rather than an asymmetric one; for example, we may want a measure of the extent to which good or bad performances in first and final years go together rather than focusing on one of the years as we did with delta. One of the most useful symmetric measures was introduced by Leo Goodman and William Kruskal (1954). Their measure γ (the Greek letter gamma) is easy to compute, being defined in all cases by

$$\gamma = \frac{S}{P + Q} \tag{5.8}$$

where P and Q are the positive and negative contributions to S, calculated as shown in Section 5.1.

Like delta, gamma always lies between −1 and +1. Gamma has a simple probabilistic interpretation similar to that of delta. If we select at random two students whose results are not tied on either variable (i.e. they have performed differently on both the first year and the final examination), then we can find the probability that the student who did better in the first year also did better than the other in the final year – this is just $P/(P+Q)$. We can also find the probability that the student who did better in the first year did worse than the other in the final year – this is $Q/(P+Q)$. Gamma is then the difference of these two probabilities (since $P-Q=S$).

2 x 2 contingency tables

For the data in Table 5.21(a), we have $P=1 \times 4=4$, $Q=0 \times 3=0$ and $S=4$, so $\gamma=1$. In this case, since the two students selected must not be tied on either variable, it is certain that the student who did better in the first year also did better in the final year, so gamma is 1. (Had one of the students been selected from the three in the FP cell, no other student would meet the conditions imposed, since there are no students in the PF cell in this example.)

If the data are turned round, as in (b), gamma is still 1, illustrating the symmetry of gamma. This also shows that gamma, unlike delta, is not affected by unequal marginal totals, being able to attain its maximum or minimum value no matter what values are in the margins.

Table 5.21(c) shows an example where gamma does not attain its maximum or mimimum value. For this case, $P=6$, $Q=2$ and $S=4$, so $\gamma=0.50$. The data in (f) show that gamma is zero when there is no association between the two variables. The data in (d) and (e) show that, when delta is 1 or -1, so is gamma. In general, gamma will always be equal to or larger in magnitude than delta. Gamma attains its maximum (minimum) value of 1 (-1) whenever any one cell of a 2 x 2 table has a zero entry.

When gamma is 1 or -1 it is always possible to draw a line through the non-zero entries in the table so that it descends from the north-west to the south-east cell (or from the north-east to the south-west) in a staircase (monotonic) fashion without turning back – try this in (a), (b), (d), and (e). When this happens, we can produce a new scale of results by following the treads of the staircase. Thus, we can represent the data in Table 5.12(a) in the following way.

First year result	P	F	F	F	F	F	F	F
Final year result	P	P	P	P	F	F	F	F
New scale	*A*		*B*				*C*	

In this representation of the 8 students' data, as we go from left to right on either the first year results or the final results performance changes monotonically; i.e. it either stays the same or gets worse. The same is true of the new scale, where we combine the two sets of results, with *A* representing the best combined performance (passing both examinations) and *C* representing the worst (failing both), *B* being somewhere in between (failing the first but passing the final).

Such a combination of results to produce a new variable or scale is always possible when gamma is 1 or -1, but it is never possible when gamma is between these two extremes. If we try representing the data in Table 5.21(c) in this way we shall always end up with something like this.

First year result	P	P	P	F	F	F	F	F
Final year result	P	P	F	P	P	F	F	F
			↑					

Here, the 1 in the PF cell is messing things up. Although the first year results decrease monotonically as we go from left to right, the final year results change from P to F and then back up to P, so we shan't be able to create a new combined scale that decreases monotonically from left to right. We can clean up the mess in the final year results by shifting the offending F two places to the right, but this will then mess up the first year results.

To illustrate how to produce and interpret a new scale when gamma is −1, the required representation for the data in Table 5.21(e) is shown below.

First year result	P	F	F	F	F	F	F	F
Final year result	F	P	P	P	P	P	P	P
New scale	*A*				*B*			

Here, the first year results decrease monotonically from left to right, while the final results *increase* monotonically from left to right. (Remember that monotonic increasing means either staying the same or getting better, and monotonic decreasing means either staying the same or getting worse.) The new scale labels *A* and *B* also change monotonically from left to right, reflecting at the same time deteriorating first year results and improving final results.

r x c *ordered contingency tables*

Gamma is also useful for larger ordered contingency tables. For the data shown in Table 5.22, $\gamma = 1$ in all cases except (c). In (c), we have $P = 10$, $Q = 4$ and $S = 6$, so $\gamma = 6/14$ or 0.43. The interpretation of gamma is the same as in the 2 x 2 case. If two students are selected at random subject to the condition that they have performed differently from each other on both exams, then for the data in (c), it is 43% more likely that the student who did better in the first exam will also have done better in the final exam than that the student who did better in the first exam will have done worse in the final exam. The value of 0.43 in this case indicates a reasonable but by no means perfect association.

As in the 2 x 2 case, when gamma is 1 (or −1), the non-zero cells look like a staircase going down from the north-west to the south-east cell (or from the north-east to the south-west cell). In some cases, such as (d), we need take only short steps to descend the staircase, while in others, such as (f), we need large steps. As before, we can use this staircase property to replace our two variables by a new one. This is illustrated below for the data in (f).

First year result	D	D	P	P	F	F	F	F
Final year result	D	D	D	D	D	D	P	F
New scale	*A*		*B*		*C*		*D*	*E*

Both sets of results decrease monotonically from left to right, and so does our new scale. Note that our new variable is an ordinal variable with as many levels as there are non-zero cells in the ordered contingency table that gave rise to it (5 in this case).

Kendall's Tau *b*

In some cases we may require a symmetrical measure of association that only attains its maximum (or minimum) value when the non-zero entries fall exactly along one of the diagonals of the ordered contingency table, as in Table 5.21(d) or (e) or Table 5.22(d). To illustrate, suppose I cross-classify my acquaintances according to whether they are blind or not and according to whether they are friendly or not, resulting in a 2 x 2 table. I know only 1 blind person, who happens to be friendly, so the results might look something like those in Table 5.23(a). Here we have $P = 15$, $Q = 0$, so $S = 15$ and $\gamma = 1$, indicating complete association. This is reflecting the fact that all the blind people I know are friendly. However, it is not true that all the friendly people are blind. Both statements will be true only when the non-zero entries fall along one of the diagonals, as in Table 5.23(b). Gamma

Table 5.23. Hypothetical data illustrating a cross-classification of 30 people on two variables

(a)

	Friendly	Not friendly	t_i
Blind	1		1
Not blind	14	15	29
u_i	15	15	

(b)

	Friendly	Not friendly	t_i
Blind	15		15
Not blind		15	15
u_i	15	15	

does not distinguish between (a) and (b), taking the value 1 for both. The reason for this is simple. Both (a) and (b) represent the most complete association possible given the marginal totals (e.g. given that in (a) there is only one blind person); gamma reflects such complete association.

A symmetrical measure of association that does distinguish between (a) and (b) was devised by Maurice Kendall (1970) and is generally referred to as τ_b (the Greek letter tau with subscript *b*). The reason for the subscript is to distinguish this version of tau from two others, τ_a and τ_c, discussed by Kendall, which we shall not consider here, partly because they are not so generally useful as τ_b and partly because of lack of space; the reader is referred to Kendall (1970, Chapter 3) and Everitt (1977, Section 3.7.3) for a discussion of these measures. One disadvantage of the tau measures is that they do not have a simple probabilistic interpretation like those we have found useful for gamma and delta.

2 x 2 contingency tables

Tau *b* distinguishes between (a) and (b) in Table 5.23 by making use of the information in the marginal totals. For the 2 x 2 case only, tau *b* is given by

$$\tau_b = \frac{S}{\sqrt{t_1 t_2 u_1 u_2}}, \tag{5.9}$$

where, as usual, the *t*'s represent the extent of the ties on the explanatory variable and the *u*'s represent the extent of the ties on the response variable. For (a), we have $t_1 = 1, t_2 = 29, u_1 = 15, u_2 = 15$ and $S = 15$, so

$$\tau_b = \frac{15}{\sqrt{1 \times 29 \times 15 \times 15}} = 0.19,$$

indicating a very low degree of association. For (b), we have $\tau_b = 1$, indicating perfect association. In the 2 x 2 case, τ_b achieves its maximum (minimum) value of 1 (–1) *only* when both entries on a diagonal are zero, as in (b). To distinguish this extreme situation from the *complete* association indexed by gamma (all blind people are friendly but not necessarily the other way round), this case is frequently referred to as *absolute* association (all blind people are friendly *and* all friendly people are blind). Thus, gamma achieves its maximum or minimum value when there is complete or absolute association, while tau *b* achieves its maximum or minimum value *only* when there is absolute association.

In Table 5.23(a), we have complete but not absolute association, so $\gamma = 1$ but τ_b is small. This large discrepancy shows the most important difference between gamma and tau *b*. In this case, gamma is saying that we have the most perfect association possible given the marginal totals. It is just an accident of sampling that I know only one blind person. In a different situation, I might well have known 15 blind people and if I had to classify half of my 30 acquaintances as friendly and half as unfriendly, the best indication we have from (a) is that all the blind people will be the friendly ones, as in (b). On the other hand, tau *b* is saying that the single

Table 5.24. Hypothetical cross-classification of 30 people on two variables

	Friendly	Not friendly	t_i
Blind	9	6	15
Not blind	6	9	15
u_i	15	15	

blind person I know is telling us something important about my acquaintances – there are fewer blind people and we shouldn't ignore this. The fact that there is only one blind person means that we have very little information about the friendliness of blind people in general. If I had known 15 blind people, the most likely outcome would not be as in (b) (as argued by gamma) but would be something like that in Table 5.24, for which $\tau_b = 0.20$ and $\gamma = 0.38$. The tau value here is almost identical to the one calculated for Table 5.23(a).

For this example, the cautious arguments offered by tau b are probably the strongest. For an example where the choice goes in favour of gamma, consider again the data of Table 5.21(a), another case of complete but not absolute association, for which $\gamma = 1$ and $\tau_b = 0.38$. Here, gamma is saying that, if the papers for the first year examination were marked again less severely, the 3 people who failed the first exam but passed the final one are more likely to pass than those who failed both times. This will change the table into one indicating absolute association. These arguments seem reasonable in this case, and the value of gamma of 1 reflects this. On the other hand, tau is still cautious, saying that we have no grounds for assuming that the people who passed the final exam are more likely to have passed the first exam than those who failed the final exam had the marking been less strict. The value of 0.38 for τ_b reflects this caution.

These two examples illustrate one of the most important facts about measures of association. In most cases, the choice of a measure should be decided by those aspects of the substantive situation that are considered important. For this reason, no one measure will serve all purposes, as suggested in the introduction to this section.

Of the two symmetrical measures, gamma will always be equal to or larger in magnitude than tau b. This is illustrated by the other sets of data in Table 5.21.

r × c *ordered contingency tables*

The properties of tau b can be generalized to cover larger ordered contingency tables such as those shown in Table 5.22. For these cases, however, tau b is no longer given by formula 5.9, since that is clearly only appropriate when there are 2 marginal totals on each variable. In the general case, tau b is given by

$$\tau_b = \frac{2S}{\sqrt{(n^2 - \Sigma t_i^2)(n^2 - \Sigma u_i^2)}} \tag{5.10}$$

where, as usual, the t's show the extent of the ties on the explanatory variable, the u's show the extent of the ties on the response variable and n is the total number of scores.

For the data in Table 5.22(a), we have $n = 8$, $\Sigma t_i^2 = 2^2 + 4^2 + 2^2 = 24$, $\Sigma u_i^2 = 6^2 + 2^2 = 40$ and $S = 12$, so

$$\tau_b = \frac{24}{\sqrt{(64 - 24)(64 - 40)}} = 0.77,$$

indicating fairly good, but not perfect, association.

In general, tau b will only take its maximum (minimum) value of 1 (−1) when the non-zero cells lie completely along one of the main diagonals, as in Table 5.22(d). When the number of rows and columns differ ($r \neq c$), as in Table 5.22(a), tau b will never be able to achieve a value of −1 or 1, since in such cases absolute association is not possible.

Formula 5.10 may be used to calculate τ_b in all cases, but in some situations some savings in calculations may be obtained by using different formulae. For example, we have already seen that in the 2 x 2 case it is easier to use formula 5.9 rather than 5.10. The table at the back of the book gives the simplest method of calculating τ_b for the various situations encountered. Some of these will be illustrated in the examples below.

Choosing a Measure of Association for Ordered Contingency Tables

In deciding which of the three measures to use, we may be guided by the two main differences between them. The first is whether an asymmetrical or a symmetrical measure is required. If an asymmetrical measure is needed, Somers' delta should be used. Otherwise, the choice is between gamma and tau. The difference between these two is in their treatment of complete association. Gamma should be used when a measure that takes its maximum or minimum value in cases of complete association (e.g. Table 5.22(a), (b), (e), or (f)) is required. Tau should be used when a measure that takes its maximum or minimum value *only* in cases of absolute association (e.g. Table 5.22(d)) is required. In cases of doubt, the simple probabilistic interpretation of gamma makes it more attractive than tau.

When there are no ties in the response variable, the choice is simplified since delta and gamma are exactly equivalent, as indicated by identical formulae in the table at the back of the book for the Kendall, Jonckheere, and Rank-Sum situations.

When there are no ties in either the response variable or the explanatory variable, delta, gamma, and tau are all exactly equivalent. In this case, Spearman's rho discussed in Section 5.5, provides yet another symmetric competitor. As noted earlier, rho puts more weight on large differences between the two sets of rankings than tau, so if it is considered important to emphasize such large differences, rho will do the trick. When there are ties in either variable, rho becomes less attractive

Table 5.25. Hypothetical data on predicting the duration of an illness (in years) by score on a questionnaire

		H	M	L
Duration of illness	>2		4	
	1–2			4
	<2	2		

than the other symmetrical measures. In such cases, the correct expression for rho is complicated (see Kendall, 1970, Section 3.8, for relevant formulae), and rho shares with tau the lack of a simple probabilistic interpretation, so the simpler tau or gamma are preferable.

A further consideration in choosing a measure of association has to do with whether we really want to pay particular attention to the ordinal nature of the two variables. Consider the data in Table 5.25, which might result from attempting to predict the duration of illness for 10 people on the basis of a high (H), medium (M) or low (L) score on a questionnaire. Both variables, questionnaire score and duration of illness, can be considered ordinal. We can calculate S for these data to be 0, so delta, gamma, and tau will all be zero, indicating no association between questionnaire score and duration of illness. However, we might want to argue that there is such an association, since a high score guarantees short duration (less than 2 years), a medium score guarantees long duration (more than 2 years) and a low score guarantees intermediate duration (1–2 years) – there are no exceptions to this rule for the 10 people concerned. The reason the three measures do not pick thus up is that they are sensitive only to monotonic association, where each variable is considered ordinal. In this case, although the association is good, it is not monotonic, since increasing questionnaire scores are not associated with increasing (or decreasing) durations. If we want a measure that is sensitive to such non-monotonic association, we might consider using one of the measures such as lambda described in Chapter 8 that ignore the ordinal properties of the two variables. (For this example, lambda is 1, indicating perfect association in the sense that once we know the score for a person on one of the variables, we can accurately predict the score on the other variable.)

Further Comments

For a further discussion of the three measures considered here, see Everitt (1977, Section 3.7.3). The papers by Goodman and Kruskal (1954, 1963, 1972) give a full discussion of gamma (and other measures), the 1972 paper providing information about the standard errors of gamma and delta. Kendall's (1970) book gives a full discussion of tau and rho.

For the 2×2 case, gamma is equivalent to a frequently used measure of association labelled Q that was introduced by Yule in 1900, while tau b is equivalent to the well-known product moment correlation coefficient (frequently referred to in this case as the phi coefficient). For a good discussion of these and other related measures, see Bishop, Fienberg and Holland (1975, Section 11.2).

Example 5.10 Measuring Association for Example 5.4 using Delta

The data for the Chambers and Rowlands study discussed in Example 5.4 are given in Table 5.8. For these data, S was found to be 107 and the Jonckheere Test suggested a reliable improvement in recall with age. We now wish to assess the degree of improvement. Although this is a correlational study, we may still wish to use an asymmetrical measure of association here, since we are more likely to be interested in how age affects recall rather than the other way round. So we shall use Somers' delta here, treating age as the explanatory variable and recall score as the response variable. From the table at the back of the book, in this situation we must use the most complicated expression to obtain delta (formula 5.7), so we first calculate $\Sigma t_i^2 = 10^2 + 10^2 + 10^2 = 300$, and delta is then given by

$$\delta = \frac{2S}{n^2 - \Sigma t_i^2} = \frac{2 \times 107}{30^2 - 300} = 0.36.$$

This may be interpreted as saying that, if we selected two children from different age groups (i.e. one 4-year-old and one 5-year-old; one 4-year-old and one 6-year-old; or one 5-year-old and one 6-year-old), then it is 36% more likely that the older one recalls more items than that the younger one recalls more items.

Example 5.11 Measuring Association for Example 5.6 using Gamma

In Example 5.6, we found a reliable correlation between first year marks and final year marks using the hypothetical data in Table 5.14, for which $S = 73$. In this case, there are no ties in either variable, so delta, gamma, and tau are all equivalent and are given by $S/(P + Q)$. All three therefore also share the simple probabilistic interpretation of gamma. Whether our aim is to predict final year scores from first year scores or to measure the association symmetrically, the value obtained for the measure will be the same.

Calculating gamma gives $\gamma = \dfrac{S}{P + Q} = \dfrac{73}{89 + 16} = 0.70,$

which indicates a reasonably large effect. This says here that if we select two students, we are 70% more likely to find that the student who does better in the first exam also does better in the final exam than to find that the student who does better in the first exam does worse in the final exam.

Since there are no ties in either variable, we could have used Spearman's rho as a measure of association here. In Example 5.9 we have already found rho to be 0.86 for these data, which again indicates a reasonably large association. In most cases, rho will tend to be larger in magnitude than gamma calculated for the same data, as here. But remember that rho does not have the simple probabilistic interpretation that gamma has.

Example 5.12 Measuring Association between Constructs in Repertory Grids using Tau *b*

Several of the examples we have considered use data obtained from repertory grids. In a repertory grid a person is asked to classify a group of acquaintances using a number of bipolar constructs. These constructs are normally chosen by the person completing the grid to represent important ways in which he or she sees others. For example, Table 5.26 shows an example of two constructs used by Brother M, a monk who had asked for psychiatric help for a number of sexual and drinking problems that he couldn't reconcile with his chosen monastic life. These were obtained during the course of a session with a clinical psychologist. Brother M was asked to select 10 people (usually called the *elements* of the repertory grid) who were important in his life. Among these he chose to include God as the most important person. He was also asked to make judgements about himself as he saw himself (S), himself as he would like to be (IS) and himself as he believed God saw him (SSG). He then classified each of these 13 elements using constructs elicited from him in one of the standard ways (see Fransella and Bannister, 1977). The two constructs shown here have been selected from 13 that he used in completing the repertory grid.

Part of the analysis of such a repertory grid involves assessing the

Table 5.26. Two constructs used to classify 13 elements (acquaintances), where S = Self, IS = Ideal self, SSG = Self as seen by God, G = God, MF = Male friend, FF = Female friend

	Elements												
	S	IS	SSG	FF	G	MF	MF	FF	MF	FF	MF	FF	MF
Honest–Dishonest	H	H	H	H	H	H	D	H	H	H	H	H	H
Imperfect–Perfect	I	P	I	I	I	I	I	I	I	I	I	I	I

degree to which different constructs are used in similar ways to classify the elements. One way of doing this that doesn't get very far is to obtain a matching score for a pair of constructs by counting the number of acquaintances falling on the same side of each construct. For the two constructs shown we obtain a matching score of 11, since 11 of the 13 people were seen as being both honest and imperfect. Such a high matching score seems to imply that the two constructs are being used in a very similar way, but this is misleading. Saying that the two constructs are similar implies that honest people tend to be imperfect (which is true) and that dishonest people tend to be perfect (for which we have no evidence at all here). So matching scores can be misleading. This has led some authors (e.g. Bannister and Mair, 1968, Fransella and Bannister, 1977) to argue that repertory grids like this cannot be analysed sensibly. But this is going a bit too far, since Kendall's tau *b* gives us a way of measuring the similarity between constructs that doesn't have any of the problems associated with matching scores. To see how tau may be used, we can represent the information in Table 5.26 in the form of a 2 x 2 contingency table as in Table 5.27. In this

Table 5.27. The data from Table 5.26 in the form of a 2 x 2 contingency table

	Honest	Dishonest
Imperfect	11	1
Perfect	1	

form, it is clear that the repertory grid data are very much like those shown in Table 5.23 – Brother M has cross-classified his 13 elements in terms of the two constructs imperfect–perfect and honest–dishonest in the same way as I cross-classified my acquaintances in terms of the two constructs blind–not blind and friendly–not friendly. All the arguments favouring tau *b* as a measure of association for the data in Table 5.23 carry over to this example.

Calculating tau for the data in Table 5.27, we obtain $S = -1$ and $\tau_b = -1/12$ or -0.08, indicating a very small negative association for these constructs, the negative sign suggesting that the left-hand side of the first construct goes with the right-hand side of the second construct, i.e. there is a very slight tendency for honest people to be perfect and dishonest people to be imperfect. This conclusion seems to capture quite well what is going on in these two constructs.

5.7 SUMMARY OF SUGGESTED PROCEDURE

General Points

1. Do you have two or more independent samples? If not, look elsewhere; see the table at the front of the book for suggestions.
2. Do you wish to test a predicted ordering of the samples? If not, try the tests in Chapter 4.
3. Are the scores on the response variable ordinal or two-category? If not, try the tests in Chapter 4, interchanging the roles of the explanatory and response variables.
4. If neither the explanatory nor the response variable contains ties, try the Kendall Test or the Spearman Test.
5. If either variable has ties, consult the table at the back of the book for the most appropriate test using S.

Jonckheere Test

1. Select significance level α and decide whether a one- or a two-tailed test is required.
2. Are more than a quarter of the scores on the response variable involved in ties? If so, go to 7.
3. Write down the groups (levels of the explanatory variable) in the predicted order and calculate S using the direct method as follows. For each response score in each group, calculate p, the number of scores in groups to the right that are strictly larger, and q, the number of scores in groups to the right that are strictly smaller. Find P, the sum of the p's, and Q, the sum of the q's. Find $S = P - Q$.
4. Do you have three groups each with sample size less than 6? If not, go to 6.
5. Find t_1, the number of scores in the largest group, t_3, the number of scores in the smallest group, and t_2, the number of scores in the remaining group. From Table H, find the relevant critical value(s) of S and make decision as specified at the top of Table H. Calculate a measure of association as shown below, if required.
6. *Normal approximation*

   Find t_i, the number of response scores in the ith group and $n = \Sigma t_i$.

$$\text{Compute Variance of } S = \frac{2(n^3 - \Sigma t_i^3) + 3(n^2 - \Sigma t_i^2)}{18} \tag{5.1}$$

$$\text{Compute } S_c = \begin{cases} S - 1, \text{if } S \text{ positive} \\ S + 1, \text{if } S \text{ negative} \end{cases}$$

$$\text{Compute } z = \frac{S}{\text{S.D.}}, \text{ where S.D.} = \sqrt{\text{Variance}}$$

From Table B(ii), find critical value(s) of z and make decision. If there are ties in the response variable and the obtained z is close to the critical value, use the more accurate approximation given in 7. Calculate a measure of association as shown below, if required.

7. *Extensive ties*

   Calculate S using the ordered contingency table method and use the normal approximation illustrated in Example 5.4 to complete the test. If the response variable has only two categories, the method illustrated in Example 5.5 will be quicker. Calculate a measure of association as shown below, if required.

Kendall Test for Correlation

1. Select significance level α and decide whether a one- or a two-tailed test is required.
2. Write down the scores on the explanatory variable in order and write underneath them the associated scores on the response variable. Find n, the number of scores on either variable. For each response score, calculate p, the number of response scores to the right that are strictly larger, and q, the number of scores to the right that are strictly smaller. Find P, the sum of the p's, and Q, the sum of the q's. Find $S = P - Q$.
3. If n is larger than 40, use the normal approximation given in 5.
4. From Table I, find the relevant critical value(s) of S and make decision as specified at the top of Table I. For a measure of association, calculate

$$\gamma = \frac{S}{P + Q}$$

5. *Normal approximation*

$$\text{Compute Variance of } S = \frac{n(n-1)(2n+5)}{18} \tag{5.4}$$

$$\text{Compute } S_c = \begin{cases} S - 1, \text{if } S \text{ positive} \\ S + 1, \text{if } S \text{ negative} \end{cases}$$

$$\text{Compute } z = \frac{S_c}{\text{S.D.}}, \text{ where S.D.} = \sqrt{\text{Variance}}$$

From Table B(ii), find critical value(s) of z and make decision. For a measure of association, calculate

$$\gamma = \frac{S}{P + Q}$$

Spearman Test for Correlation

1. Do you want to emphasize large differences in the rankings? If not, use the Kendall Test.
2. Select significance level α and decide whether a one- or two-tailed test is required.
3. Rank order the scores on each variable separately and subtract each ranking on the response variable from its associated ranking on the explanatory variable. Compute D, the sum of the squares of the resulting differences. Find n, the number of scores on either variable.

4. Compute $$\rho = 1 - \frac{6D}{n(n^2 - 1)} \qquad (5.5)$$

5. If n is larger than 30, use the normal approximation given in 7.
6. From Table J, find the relevant critical value(s) of ρ and make decision as specified at the top of Table J. Use ρ as a measure of association.
7. *Normal approximation*

$$\text{Compute Variance of } \rho = \frac{1}{n - 1} \qquad (5.6)$$

Continuity correction of $6/(n^3 - n)$ should be subtracted from positive values of ρ and added to negative values.

$$\text{Compute } z = \frac{\rho}{\text{S.D.}}, \text{ where S.D.} = \sqrt{\text{Variance}}$$

From Table B(ii), find critical value(s) of z and make decision. Use ρ (without continuity correction) as a measure of association.

Measures of Association for Ordered Contingency Tables

1. If the distinction between the explanatory and the response variable is important and you wish to estimate the degree to which variation on the response variable is accounted for by variation on the explanatory variable, use Somers' asymmetrical measure delta as shown in 3.
2. For a symmetrical measure that doesn't depend on the prior labelling of one variable as explanatory and one as response, use Goodman and Kruskal's gamma as shown in 4, if you want a measure that takes its maximum or minimum value both in cases of *complete* association (e.g. Table 5.22(a), (e), or (f)) and in cases of *absolute* association (e.g. Table 5.22(d)). Use Kendall's tau as shown in 5 if you want a measure that takes its maximum or minimum value *only* in cases of *absolute* association.
3. *Somers' delta*

$$\text{Calculate } \delta = \frac{2S}{n^2 - \Sigma t_i^2}, \qquad (5.7)$$

where the t's refer to the extent of the ties on the explanatory variable and $n = \Sigma t_i$ is the total number of scores. Alternatively, find a simpler formula, if appropriate, in the table at the back of the book.

4. *Goodman and Kruskal's gamma*

$$\text{Calculate } \gamma = \frac{S}{P + Q} \tag{5.8}$$

5. *Kendall's tau*

$$\text{Calculate } \tau_b = \frac{2S}{\sqrt{(n^2 - \Sigma t_i^2)(n^2 - \Sigma u_i^2)}}, \tag{5.10}$$

where the t's refer to the extent of the ties on the explanatory variable, the u's to the extent of the ties on the response variable, and $n = \Sigma t_i = \Sigma u_i$ is the total number of scores. Alternatively, find a simpler formula, if appropriate, in the table at the back of the book. Remember that tau b does not have a simple probabilisitic interpretation like gamma and delta.

5.8 EXERCISES

Section 5.1

1. Each of 12 students is given a test of verbal ability. It is predicted that performance on the test should be best for final year students, worst for first year students, and intermediate for second years. Do the results shown below support the prediction? High scores reflect better verbal ability.

Year		
1st	2nd	Final
40	61	59
48	42	54
59	39	51
	41	49
		63

2. The reaction time of each of 18 people is measured after being given different dosages of a drug. 5 of the people received 5 mg of the drug, a further 5 received 10 mg, a further 4 received 15 mg and the remainder received 20 mg. Do the data shown below support the prediction that reaction time increases with increasing dosage level of the drug? The RTs are given in msec.

Dosage			
5 mg	10 mg	15 mg	20 mg
310	283	456	305
315	314	492	321
281	423	531	390
276	402	628	400
391	389		

Section 5.2

3. In a study investigating some of the factors underlying anorexia nervosa, Celia Lowenstein (1978) asked 10 men and 10 women, each with no history of weight-related problems, to make judgements about various aspects of their bodies, both as they saw themselves (actual self body image) and as they would like to be (ideal self body image). She also asked 9 people (8 women and 1 man) clinically diagnosed as having anorexia nervosa to do the same. An analysis of the judgements made allowed her to decide for each person whether or not their actual self body image was widely separated from their ideal self body image. Are the data shown below consistent with her prediction that 'normal' women are more likely to have separated body images than 'normal' men and anorexics are more likely to have separated body images than 'normal' women?

	Men	Women	Anorexics
Separated	5	9	8
Not separated	5	1	1

Section 5.3

4. Seven subjects are given each of two types of tracking task to carry out. Accuracy scores are given below (large scores reflect large accuracy) (a) Are the two tasks correlated? (b) Verify that you obtain the same value of S no matter which variable (Task A score or Task B score) you treat as the explanatory variable. Will this always be true?

	Subject						
	1	2	3	4	5	6	7
Task A	20	19	31	6	9	18	27
Task B	31	12	32	10	11	13	30

5. Two judges taste 10 beers and rank order them in terms of sweetness. Do the judges agree?

	Beer									
	1	2	3	4	5	6	7	8	9	10
Judge *A*	1	2	3	4	5	7	8	6	9	10
Judge *B*	7	10	4	1	6	9	5	8	2	3

6. What if Judge *B* had instead ranked the beers as follows? 10, 1, 2, 3, 4, 6, 7, 5, 8, 9.

Section 5.4

7. The following data are the number of correct responses on each of 6 trials for a single subject. Does this subject show evidence of learning?

Trial	1	2	3	4	5	6
Score	1	2	2	4	2	4

8. Fifteen 5-, 6- and 7-year-olds were rated on a 3-point scale for their level of attainment in a liquid conservation task. Do the results shown below indicate a significant increasing trend with age?

		Level of attainment		
		Complete	Partial	Absent
Age	5	1	5	9
	6	3	10	2
	7	9	5	1

9. A number of subjects, grouped according to age, either passed (P) or failed (F) a test. Is there a change in performance with age?

	Baby	Child	Adolescent	Adult
P	1	2	4	6
F	4	4	1	0

10. From each of 5 age groups 20 children were randomly selected and given a simple cognitive test. The table below shows the percentage of children passing the test at each age. Is there evidence of a significant increase with age in the ability to pass the test?

Age (in years)	2	3	4	5	6
% passing test	5	25	20	45	40

Section 5.5

11. Analyse the data given in Exercises 4, 5, and 6 using the Spearman Test.

Section 5.6

12. Assess the degree of association for the data from Example 5.2 shown in Table 5.6.
13. Assess the degree of association for the data from Example 5.5 shown in Table 5.9.
14. Brother M (see Example 5.12) included in his repertory grid the following two constructs. Assess the degree of association between these two constructs.

	S	IS	SSG	FF	G	MF	MF	FF	MF	FF	MF	FF	MF
Weak–Strong	W	S	W	W	W	W	W	W	W	W	W	W	W
False–True	F	T	F	T	F	T	F	T	T	T	T	T	F

CHAPTER 6

Tests for Several Related Samples – Categorical Explanatory Variable

The tests in this chapter are applicable when more than two related samples of data have been collected and when the response variable may be thought of as either ordinal or categorical with two categories (cf. Examples 1.14 and 1.15). Such related data frequently arise when a response is obtained at each level of the explanatory variable from each subject. For example, in comparing a number of sleeping pills, we might ask each subject to try each pill and rate its effectiveness. The explanatory variable is the sleeping pill while the response variable is the effectiveness rating. As should be obvious with this example, such a design brings with it all the dangers outlined in Section 3.1 for the two-sample case. Thus, we must assume that there is no carryover effect that might bias the results. By randomising or counterbalancing the order of administration of the pills, it is possible to reduce any such bias somewhat. Unfortunately, it is rarely possible to avoid carryover effects entirely. We saw in Section 3.5 that it is possible to test whether a carryover effect is present in the two-sample situation. When there are more than two samples, such simple tests are not available. The problems introduced by carryover effects in interpreting results from a related samples design have led some workers, notably Poulton (1973), to recommend that such designs not be used at all. In view of these difficulties, great caution should be used in interpreting the results of the tests in this chapter when there is the possibility of a carryover effect.

One variation on the related samples design that is not open to such criticisms is to use matched groups of subjects, with one member of each homogeneous group being randomly assigned to each level of the explanatory variable. The main difficulty with using matched groups is deciding on the relevant factors along which the matching should be carried out.

6.1 THE FRIEDMAN TEST–ORDINAL RESPONSE VARIABLE

The Friedman Test is the counterpart of the Kruskal–Wallis Test (Section 4.1) when there are several related samples. Like the Kruskal–Wallis Test, it provides an omnibus test of whether the locations of the samples differ in any way. It is equivalent to the Sign Test (Section 3.2) when only two samples are being compared. It assumes that the results from different subjects (or different matched groups) are independent and that the scores on the response variable consist of continuous ordinal data. Because of the way the test statistic is calculated, this implies that there should be no ties within a particular subject's (or matched group's) data.

Simplified Example

Suppose we ask three subjects to visit each of three restaurants and to rate each on a 10-point scale of enjoyment after the visit. We wish to discover whether the three restaurants are equally liked (the null hypothesis) or whether there are differences between the restaurants in their enjoyment ratings (the alternative hypothesis). In an attempt to reduce the bias due to carryover effects, we decide randomly for each subject the order in which the visits are made. The results are given below.

		Restaurant		
		A	*B*	*C*
	1.	4	5	6
Subject	2.	3	7	9
	3.	3	2	5

We note that there are no ties within each subject's results. The two ties that occur between subjects do not matter for the present test, since the first stage in the analysis is to rank order the scores separately for each subject.

In what follows, to allow us to talk in general terms, the number of subjects (or matched groups) in the experiment will be labelled n and the number of samples will be labelled k. In our example $n = 3$, the number of subjects, and $k = 3$, the number of restaurants.

Test Statistic – Q

The first step in constructing a test statistic is to rank the data for each subject separately. (This is the only point at which the Friedman Test differs conceptually from the Kruskal–Wallis Test.) The rankings, together with the other calculations discussed below, are given in Table 6.1. If the null hypothesis is true, there should be no systematic tendency for any one of the restaurants to be given low (or high) scores by all subjects. Therefore, if we find the sum of all the ranks for each restaurant, the three totals should be very close together and all should be close to the average of the totals. On the other hand, if the null hypothesis is false, and there is, for example, a systematic tendency for one of the restaurants to be given

Table 6.1. The calculations involved in the Friedman Test

		Restaurant ($k = 3$)			
		A	B	C	
	1.	1	2	3	
Subject	2.	1	2	3	
($n = 3$)	3.	2	1	3	
Rank-sum, R_i		4	5	9	$\bar{R} = n(k+1)/2 = 6$
$R_i - \bar{R}$		−2	−1	3	
$(R_i - \bar{R})^2$		4	1	9	$\Sigma(R_i - \bar{R})^2 = 14$

low ranks across all subjects, then the three totals should differ. The Friedman Test investigates this in a manner identical to the Kruskal–Wallis Test. Notice that, with the Friedman Test, we can work with totals instead of averages, since the design forces us to have the same number of responses for each restaurant.

Each subject's ranked scores will be some ordering of the numbers from 1 to k. Therefore, the average rank score for each subject will be $(k + 1)/2$, in our case $(3 + 1)/2 = 2$. Since there are n subjects, the average total rank score summed across all subjects will be $n(k + 1)/2$, or $3(3 + 1)/2 = 6$ in our case. Under the null hypothesis, none of the three rank totals should be very different from this average value, which we shall call $\bar{R}$. We can get a measure of how different the three rank totals are by finding the sum of the squared deviations of each total from $\bar{R}$. The sequence of calculations is shown in Table 6.1, where the rank totals are labelled R_i.

Thus far we have obtained a value for $\Sigma(R_i - \bar{R})^2$, which is 14 in our case. Now, we could use this as the test statistic for the Friedman Test. However, as with the Kruskal–Wallis Test, we go one stage further and multiply it by a constant which simplifies the form of the approximate test to be described below. We therefore use as our test statistic the value Q given by

$$Q = \frac{12}{nk(k+1)} \times \Sigma(R_i - \bar{R})^2 \tag{6.1}$$

For example, we obtain

$$Q = \frac{12}{3 \times 3 \times 4} \times 14 = 4.67$$

It is easily seen that values of Q close to zero favour the null hypothesis while large values favour the alternative hypothesis. As with the Kruskal–Wallis test statistic, it is not possible to obtain negative values of Q.

Table 6.2. The 36 distinct patterns of results when $n = 3$, $k = 3$, and associated values of Q

1.	A	B	C	2.	A	B	C	3.	A	B	C	4.	A	B	C	5.	A	B	C	6.	A	B	C
	1	2	3		1	2	3		1	2	3		1	2	3		1	2	3		1	2	3
	1	2	3		1	2	3		1	2	3		1	2	3		1	2	3		1	2	3
	1	2	3		1	3	2		2	1	3		2	3	1		3	1	2		3	2	1
	$Q = 6.00$				$Q = 4.67$				$Q = 4.67$				$Q = 2.00$				$Q = 2.00$				$Q = 0.67$		
7.	A	B	C	8.	A	B	C	9.	A	B	C	10.	A	B	C	11.	A	B	C	12.	A	B	C
	1	2	3		1	2	3		1	2	3		1	2	3		1	2	3		1	2	3
	1	3	2		1	3	2		1	3	2		1	3	2		1	3	2		1	3	2
	1	2	3		1	3	2		2	1	3		2	3	1		3	1	2		3	2	1
	$Q = 4.67$				$Q = 4.67$				$Q = 2.67$				$Q = 2.67$				$Q = 0.67$				$Q = 0.67$		
13.	A	B	C	14.	A	B	C	15.	A	B	C	16.	A	B	C	17.	A	B	C	18.	A	B	C
	1	2	3		1	2	3		1	2	3		1	2	3		1	2	3		1	2	3
	2	1	3		2	1	3		2	1	3		2	1	3		2	1	3		2	1	3
	1	2	3		1	3	2		2	1	3		2	3	1		3	1	2		3	2	1
	$Q = 4.67$				$Q = 2.67$				$Q = 4.67$				$Q = 0.67$				$Q = 2.67$				$Q = 0.67$		

19.

A	B	C
1	2	3
2	3	1
1	2	3

$Q = 2.00$

20.

A	B	C
1	2	3
2	3	1
1	3	2

$Q = 2.67$

21.

A	B	C
1	2	3
2	3	1
2	1	3

$Q = 0.67$

22.

A	B	C
1	2	3
2	3	1
2	3	1

$Q = 2.00$

23.

A	B	C
1	2	3
2	3	1
3	1	2

$Q = 0.00$

24.

A	B	C
1	2	3
2	3	1
3	2	1

$Q = 0.67$

25.

A	B	C
1	2	3
3	1	2
1	2	3

$Q = 2.00$

26.

A	B	C
1	2	3
3	1	2
1	3	2

$Q = 0.67$

27.

A	B	C
1	2	3
3	1	2
2	1	3

$Q = 2.67$

28.

A	B	C
1	2	3
3	1	2
2	3	1

$Q = 0.00$

29.

A	B	C
1	2	3
3	1	2
3	1	2

$Q = 2.00$

30.

A	B	C
1	2	3
3	1	2
3	2	1

$Q = 0.67$

31.

A	B	C
1	2	3
3	2	1
1	2	3

$Q = 0.67$

32.

A	B	C
1	2	3
3	2	1
1	3	2

$Q = 0.67$

33.

A	B	C
1	2	3
3	2	1
2	1	3

$Q = 0.67$

34.

A	B	C
1	2	3
3	2	1
2	3	1

$Q = 0.67$

35.

A	B	C
1	2	3
3	2	1
3	1	2

$Q = 0.67$

36.

A	B	C
1	2	3
3	2	1
3	2	1

$Q = 0.67$

Simplifying the calculation of Q

It is possible to arrive at the same result as given by formula 6.1 using the simpler, but equivalent, formula given below.

$$Q = -3n(k+1) + \frac{12\Sigma R_i^2}{nk(k+1)} \tag{6.2}$$

For our example, we have

$$\Sigma R_i^2 = 4^2 + 5^2 + 9^2 = 122,$$

so formula 6.2 gives

$$Q = -3 \times 3 \times 4 + \frac{12 \times 122}{3 \times 3 \times 4} = -36 + 40.67 = 4.67,$$

as before.

Null Distribution of Q

To find out how large Q must be before we are prepared to reject the null hypothesis, we must compute its null distribution, which is done as usual by investigating all the possible patterns of results that could occur with our given sample size.

Each subject gives a ranking of the k restaurants. Under the null hypothesis, all possible rankings are equally likely. In our example, there are 6 possibilities for each subject. These are 123, 132, 213, 231, 312, and 321. Any one of these rankings could have been given by subject 1, who in fact gave the first of them. In general, there will be $k!$ possible rankings that are equally likely for each subject. For each of these possibilities for subject 1, there are another $k!$ possibilities for subject 2's rankings, and so on. Thus, we should need to investigate $(k!)^n$, or $6^3 = 216$ for our example, possible patterns of results. Fortunately, it turns out to be sufficient to investigate only the 36 patterns shown in Table 6.2, in which subject 1's data are kept constant, but the 36 possible orderings of the remaining two subject's data are listed. We don't need to include all the possibilities, because, for each pattern shown, there are exactly 5 more with the same value of Q. For example, the other five possibilities associated with pattern 1 are

(a)

A	B	C
1	3	2
1	3	2
1	3	2

(b)

A	B	C
2	1	3
2	1	3
2	1	3

(c)

A	B	C
2	3	1
2	3	1
2	3	1

(d)

A	B	C
3	1	2
3	1	2
3	1	2

(e)

A	B	C
3	2	1
3	2	1
3	2	1

For each of these $Q = 6.00$. These five have been obtained by rewriting the 3 columns of numbers shown in pattern 1 in different orders; since the ordering of the groups is not taken into account in this test, all six versions of pattern 1 will have the same value of Q. Similarly, there will be six versions of each of the other patterns in Table 6.2, all with the same value of Q. This means that the null distribution will be identical whether or not we include all the possible rankings for subject 1.

From the values of Q given in Table 6.2, the null distribution can thus be seen to be

Table 6.3. Null distribution of Q for the Friedman Test with $n = 3$ and $k = 3$

Q	0.00	0.67	2.00	2.67	4.67	6.00
probability	2/36	15/36	6/36	6/36	6/36	1/36

Under the alternative hypothesis, large values of Q are more likely to occur. Thus, the largest value of Q is associated with pattern 1 in Table 6.2, which is the only pattern having all three subjects totally in agreement, liking restaurant C the most and A the least. On the other hand, pattern 23 has the minimum amount of agreement between subjects, with each subject favouring a different restaurant; this therefore has the smallest value of Q, 0, which indicates no systematic difference between the restaurants.

As with the Kruskal–Wallis Test, it is convenient to think of the Friedman Test as inherently two-tailed, since large values of Q occur for many different types of pattern. Thus, for our example, the same value of 6 is obtained from pattern 1 or any of its five partners shown in (a)–(e) above.

The actual data we obtained were associated with a Q of 4.67, so from the null distribution just computed, we find that the probability of getting a Q as large as or larger than this is $6/36 + 1/36 = 0.194$. Thus, we should reject the null hypothesis in our case only if we are using a significance level of 0.194 or larger. As usual, such a choice of significance level would be too high for most purposes. We therefore conclude that our example data provide no reliable evidence of a consistent difference between the restaurants.

Table of the Null Distribution of Q (Appendix Table K)

Table K in the Appendix gives critical values of the null distribution of Q. It is appropriate when there are three samples ($k = 3$), with sample size, n, between 2 and 13, or when $k = 4$, with n between 2 and 8.

To illustrate its use, when $k = 3$ and $n = 3$, as in our example, the critical value of Q when $\alpha = 0.20$ is 4.67. So we should reject the null hypothesis if our obtained value is as large as this or larger, which agrees with our calculations above. Using a more sensible significance level such as 0.05, we find that we should need to obtain a value of Q at least as large as 6.00 before rejecting the null hypothesis.

Chi-square Approximation to Q

As with the Kruskal–Wallis Test, the chi-square distribution given in Table G provides an approximation to the exact null distribution of Q for cases not covered by Table K. Degrees of freedom are given by $k-1$, the number of samples minus one.

To illustrate its use, with 3 samples we have 2 df, so the critical value of χ^2 associated with a significance level of 0.05 is given by Table G as 5.991. If our obtained value of Q is as large or larger than this, we reject the null hypothesis.

The larger the sample size, the better the approximation will be. It will typically be reasonably accurate if $nk \geqslant 30$, and the proportion of ties is not too large.

The Treatment of Ties

Our calculation of the null distribution has assumed that, for each subject, the response variable is continuous, so there should be no ties within a subject's results. When ties occur in practice, the midrank technique may be used, any scores tied at a particular value being given the average of the ranks they would have received had they been distinct. Rather than going through the tedious procedure of computing a different null distribution of Q for each different combination of ties, it is usual to resort to one of the following approximate procedures.

When there are few ties, computing Q using formula 6.2 and using the exact null distribution given in Table K or the χ^2 approximation for sample sizes outside the range of Table K will generally give a reasonably accurate result.

When there are extensive ties, the calculation of Q should be modified slightly and the χ^2 approximation should be used. The necessary modification involves taking account of the number and extent of the tied values for each subject. The procedure is best illustrated by an example. Suppose the ratings of the restaurants by our three subjects had been

		Restaurant		
		A	*B*	*C*
	1.	4	5	6
Subject	2.	3	7	7
	3.	3	3	3

Here there are no ties in subject 1's results, but there are ties in the other two subjects' data. Each subject's data are ranked separately, using midranks in the case of ties, as shown in Table 6.4. Using formula 6.2, Q (without the correction for ties) is then given as

$$Q = -3 \times 3 \times 4 + \frac{12}{3 \times 3 \times 4} \times (16 + 42.25 + 56.25) = 2.17$$

Now, the number and extent of the ties for subject 2's data are tabulated in the usual way as

Midrank	1	2.5
No. of scores tied at that value, t_i	1	2

We then calculate $\Sigma(t_i^3 - t_i)$ for this subject which is $(1^3 - 1) + (2^3 - 2) = 6$. Similarly, for subject 3, we have

Midrank	2
No. of scores tied at that value, t_i	3

which gives $\Sigma(t_i^3 - t_i) = 3^3 - 3 = 24$, for this subject. We don't need to follow this procedure for subject 1, since we shall necessarily obtain a value of 0 when there are no ties. The obtained values are recorded in the final column of Table 6.4 and summed to give T which in our case is $6 + 24 = 30$. T is then divided by $n(k^3 - k)$ which is $3(27 - 3) = 72$ to give $30/72 = 0.417$.

The revised value of Q is then given by dividing our original value, 2.17, by $1 - 0.417$ to give 3.72. The following formula summarizes what we have just done:

$$Q = \frac{-3n(k+1) + \dfrac{12\Sigma R_i^2}{nk(k+1)}}{1 - \dfrac{T}{n(k^3 - k)}}, \tag{6.3}$$

where n is the number of subjects, k is the number of samples, R_i is the rank-sum for the ith sample and T is the correction for ties, calculated as shown above.

Table 6.4. Steps in the calculation of Q with ties

		Restaurant ($k = 3$)			
		A	B	C	$\Sigma(t_i^3 - t_i)$
Subject ($n = 3$)	1.	1	2	3	
	2.	1	2.5	2.5	6
	3.	2	2	2	24
Rank-sum, R_i		4	6.5	7.5	$T = 30$
R_i^2		16	42.25	56.25	

Correcting for ties in this way will always lead to a value of Q larger than that calculated using the uncorrected formula 6.2. Thus, if the uncorrected value is significant, the corrected one will be too. Also, if there are no ties at all, formula 6.3 reduces to formula 6.2, since the correction T will be zero.

The Kendall Coefficient of Concordance – W

Instead of viewing the Friedman Test as a test of location differences between the samples, in some cases it is useful to think of it as reflecting agreement or disagreement between the subjects. Now, if there were only two subjects we could assess their agreement using one of the tests of correlation discussed in Chapter 5. In the present case, we have more than two subjects and it is frequently useful to have an index of agreement between the subjects which is similar to a measure of association (see Section 5.6). Such an index is given by

$$W = \frac{Q}{n(k-1)}, \tag{6.4}$$

where n is the number of subjects and k is the number of samples. W so defined is known as the Coefficient of Concordance, which was devised by Maurice Kendall.

For our original example, in which Q is 4.67, we have $W = 0.78$. If all the subjects agree perfectly, as in pattern 1 of Table 6.2, W attains its maximum value of 1. If the subjects differ a lot, then Q will be 0 and W will attain its minimum value of zero. In this respect, W differs from the measures of association in Section 5.6, which have a minimum value of -1. The reason for this is that when more than two subjects are involved, although they may all agree completely, it is not possible for them to disagree completely. Thus, with three subjects, if subject 1 disagrees with subject 2 in some respect and also disagrees with subject 3, then 2 and 3 must agree.

Suppose that, instead of computing W, we had computed a value of Spearman's correlation coefficient ρ (section 5.5) for each pair of subjects and then computed the average of these three ρ's which we shall label ρ_{av}. Since subjects 1 and 2 in our example agree perfectly, $\rho = 1$. The ρ between subjects 1 and 3 is 0.5, as is the ρ between subjects 2 and 3. Thus, $\rho_{av} = (1 + 0.5 + 0.5)/3 = 0.67$. It turns out that, for any set of data,

$$\rho_{av} = \frac{nW - 1}{n - 1} \tag{6.5}$$

This is easily seen to be true of our data, for which $W = 0.78$ and $n = 3$. From formula 6.5, we can see that when $W = 1$, $\rho_{av} = 1$, indicating perfect agreement between all subjects, while when $W = 0$, $\rho_{av} = -1/(n-1)$, which is the smallest value the average ρ can take, further illustrating the point made in the last paragraph.

Such a simple relation as that defined by formula 6.5 does not hold if Kendall's correlation coefficient τ (Section 5.6) is considered instead of Spearman's. This is one of the main advantages of the Spearman coefficient over the other measures of association discussed in Section 5.6.

Further Comments

For more on the Friedman Test, see Bradley (1968, Section 5.12) or Lehmann (1975, Section 6.2). For a method of estimating the size of the treatment effects, see Lehmann (1975, Section 6.5C) or Hollander and Wolfe (1973, Sections 7.4 and 7.8).

For more on the Coefficient of Concordance, see Kendall (1970, Chapter 6).

Example 6.1. The Friedman Test

As part of its annual prize-giving ceremony, the Phoenix Cinema invites five film critics to rank order the four directors, Don Siegel, Arthur Penn, Martin Scorsese, and Sam Peckinpah, who have each been nominated for the Best Director award. The one with the lowest average rank (indicating the most preferred one) gets the prize. The obtained rankings are given in Table 6.5. So Arthur Penn wins. A Friedman Test carried out on these data will tell us whether there is any reliable overall agreement between the critics, or, equivalently, whether there are consistent differences in preferences for the four directors. We have four related samples (directors), so $k = 4$, and five putatively independent subjects (the critics), so $n = 5$. Therefore, Q will be given by formula 6.2 as

$$Q = -3n(k+1) + \frac{12\Sigma R_i^2}{nk(k+1)}$$

$$= -3 \times 5 \times 5 + \frac{12 \times 698}{5 \times 4 \times 5}$$

$$= 8.76$$

Table 6.5. Hypothetical data for Example 6.1

		Director ($k = 4$)				
		Siegel	Penn	Scorsese	Peckinpah	
Critic ($n = 5$)	1.	1	2	4	3	
	2.	2	1	3	4	
	3.	2	1	4	3	
	4.	2	1	3	4	
	5.	3	2	4	1	
Rank-sum, R_i		10	7	18	15	
	R_i^2	100	49	324	225	$\Sigma R_i^2 = 698$

Setting $\alpha = 0.05$, Table K gives 7.80 as the relevant critical value of Q. Since large values of Q favour the alternative hypothesis and our obtained value is larger than the critical value, we reject the null hypothesis and conclude that there is reliable agreement between the critics.

In this case, it might be useful to calculate the Coefficient of Concordance which will give a simple numerical index of this agreement. Formula 6.4 gives

$$W = \frac{Q}{n(k-1)} = \frac{8.76}{5 \times 3} = 0.58$$

which suggests reasonable, but by no means perfect, agreement between the critics and provides a convenient summary statement of the data.

Example 6.2. Ties in the Friedman Test

In a study of the factors affecting story recall, 12 people are asked to read a passage and then to recall it as accurately as possible. The passage is so constructed that 10 of the 'ideas units' involve nested relations between animate objects (e.g. 'all the men in the village were farmers'), 10 involve overlapping relations between animate objects (e.g. 'some but not all of the women are married'), 10 involve nested relations between inanimate objects (e.g. 'all the houses were made of stone') and a further 10 involve overlapping relations between inanimate objects (e.g. 'some but not all of the roads led to the village square'). The interest centres on whether the four types of relation (NA, OA, NI, and OI) are recalled equally well. A content analysis of the recall data for each subject is carried out to determine how many of the ideas units for each type of relation were correctly recalled and the results are given in Table 6.6. We have four related samples, so $k = 4$, and 12 subjects, so $n = 12$. There is a fair proportion of ties, so we shall use the midrank technique together with the chi-square approximation, which should be reasonably accurate, since $nk = 48$ is quite large. We first convert each subject's scores into midranks. The result is shown in

Table 6.6. Hypothetical data for Example 6.2

		Subject ($n = 12$)											
		1	2	3	4	5	6	7	8	9	10	11	12
Type of Relation ($k = 4$)	NA	6	5	7	6	7	6	3	8	6	7	5	6
	OA	5	5	8	3	5	6	2	7	1	4	3	2
	NI	4	5	9	6	5	6	1	5	2	8	4	6
	OI	3	2	9	4	4	6	2	1	1	2	3	2

Table 6.7. Midranks and calculations for Example 6.2

	1	2	3	4	5	6	7	8	9	10	11	12	R_i	R_i^2
NA	4	3	1	3.5	4	2.5	4	4	4	3	4	3.5	40.5	1640.25
OA	3	3	2	1	2.5	2.5	2.5	3	1.5	2	1.5	1.5	26	676
NI	2	3	3.5	3.5	2.5	2.5	1	2	3	4	3	3.5	33.5	1122.25
OI	1	1	3.5	2	1	2.5	2.5	1	1.5	1	1.5	1.5	20	400
$\Sigma(t_i^3 - t_i)$	0	24	6	6	6	60	6	0	6	0	6	12	$\Sigma R_i^2 = 3838.5$	

Table 6.7, together with the other calculations necessary to compute Q. Since there are ties, we use formula 6.3. We need to compute T, which is just the sum of the corrections for ties, if any, summed across all subjects. The relevant corrections are shown at the bottom of Table 6.7. Subject 3, for example, has one midrank of 1, one of 2 and two of 3.5, so the t's are 1, 1 and 2, and the correction will be $\Sigma(t_i^3 - t_i) = (1^3 - 1) + (1^3 - 1) + (2^3 - 2) = 6$. The corrections for the other subjects are obtained similarly. So from Table 6.7, we get $T = 24 + 6 + 6 + 6 + 60 + 6 + 6 + 6 + 12 = 132$. Then formula 6.3 gives

$$Q = \frac{-3n(k+1) + \dfrac{12\Sigma R_i^2}{nk(k+1)}}{1 - \dfrac{T}{n(k^3 - k)}} = \frac{-3 \times 12 \times 5 + \dfrac{12 \times 3838.5}{12 \times 4 \times 5}}{1 - \dfrac{132}{12 \times 60}}$$

$$= \frac{-180 + 191.925}{1 - 0.183} = \frac{11.925}{0.817} = 14.60$$

Using a significance level of 0.05, we find from Table G that the critical value of χ^2 with $k - 1 = 3$ df is 7.815. The obtained value of Q is larger than this, so we reject the null hypothesis and conclude that there are differences in the recall of the four types of relation. From the rank-sums given in Table 6.7, it looks as though nested relations are easier than overlapping ones, with the nested animate type being easiest to recall and the overlapping inanimate type the most difficult.

However, as with the Kruskal–Wallis Test, the Friedman Test as it stands does not really allow us to make such detailed statements. We should need to continue the analysis using multiple comparisons as shown below.

6.2 MULTIPLE COMPARISONS USING THE SIGN TEST

Since the Friedman Test is equivalent to the Sign Test (Section 3.2) when only two samples are being compared, as you can easily demonstrate for yourself (see Exercise 6.3), it is natural to use the Sign Test in carrying out multiple comparisons following a significant Friedman Test. This will allow us to assess which differences between the samples are responsible for the overall significant result. The problems involved in carrying out multiple comparisons on the same set of data in this case are identical to those discussed in Section 4.2, and the suggested procedure is the same.

Thus, once a significant result has been obtained using the Friedman Test, a Sign Test is carried out between all pairs of samples using a two-tailed significance level of $\alpha/[(k(k-1)/2)]$, where α is the required per experiment error rate and k is the number of samples. To prevent inconsistencies, a Sign Test is first carried out between the samples with the lowest and highest rank-sums and then between the samples with the lowest and second highest rank-sums, and so on until a non-significant result is obtained. The second lowest is then compared with the highest, then with the second highest, and so on. Whenever a non-significant result is obtained or a comparison is to be made that should be non-significant by implication, that stage of the procedure stops. For full details, see Section 4.2.

Example 6.3 Multiple Comparison after a Significant Friedman Test

Let us continue the analysis of the story recall data, which led to a significant result using the Friedman Test with a significance level of 0.05 in Example 6.2. Suppose we wish to use a per experiment error rate, α, of about 0.10. In so doing, we are taking a slightly greater risk of making a Type I error, but believe this to be worthwhile in order to demonstrate an effect. Since there are four samples, we need to perform $4 \times 3/2 = 6$ comparisons of the pairs using the Sign Test. Each comparison should thus be performed using a two-tailed significance level of $\alpha/6 = 0.017$. Table E does not give critical values associated with 0.017; the closest we can get is 0.02 which implies an α of 0.12. This is close enough to our desired per experiment error rate to be acceptable.

From Table 6.7, the rank-sums for the four samples, NA, OA, NI, and OI are 40.5, 26, 33.5, and 20, so we write the samples in the order OI OA NI NA.

We carry out our first Sign Test on OI and NA, for which we find $N+ = 1$. With n set at 11 (since there is one tie in this comparison, which we drop), Table E gives 1 as the critical value of $N+$ with a two-tailed significance level of 0.02. Our value is the same as this, so we reject the null hypothesis and conclude that OI and NA differ reliably. No lines are drawn at this stage.

We now compare OI and NI. In this case $N+ = 1$ with n set at 10 (since there are two ties). The critical value in this case is 0; since our value is larger than this (remember that small values of $N+$ favour the alternative hypothesis), we cannot reject the null hypothesis. Thus OI and NI do not differ reliably, so we join them to give $\overline{\text{OI OA NI}}$ NA (see Section 4.2). We have found a non-significant result, so we stop comparing OI with the others.

The next comparison is therefore between OA and NA, for which $N+ = 1$, with $n = 10$, the relevant critical value being O, so we cannot reject the null hypothesis. Since OA and NA do not differ reliably we join them, which gives OI OA NI NA.

There is no other comparison that isn't already accounted for, (e.g. NI and NA don't differ, since we have just shown that OA and NA don't differ), so we stop. The final result suggests a partial ordering of the samples, since, although OI and OA do not differ, OI differs from NA while OA does not, and so on. Thus, as we suspected in Example 6.2, OI is the most difficult type to recall while NA is the easiest, with the others in between. (See Exercise 4.9 for more on the interpretation of such results.)

6.3 THE COCHRAN TEST – TWO CATEGORY RESPONSE VARIABLE

When the ties in the Friedman Test become so extensive as to result in only two categories of response for each subject (or matched group of subjects), the Friedman Test turns into a test devised by Cochran. To carry out the Cochran Test, we may proceed to compute Q as defined in formula 6.3 or alternatively use the simpler, equivalent, formula 6.6 given below. Since the Friedman Test reduces to the Sign Test in the two-sample case, you will not be surprised to learn that the Cochran Test reduces to the McNemar Test (Example 3.11) in the two-sample case.

Simplified example

To illustrate the calculations involved in the Cochran Test, let us consider a slightly different version of Example 6.1. Suppose that, instead of ranking the directors, the critics are asked either to endorse or not to endorse each of the four directors. They may endorse as many as they wish. The results are given in Table 6.8, where E stands for endorse and N for not endorse. Since we have only

Table 6.8. Hypothetical data and calculations for the Cochran Test

		Director ($k = 4$)					
		Siegel	Penn	Scorsese	Peckinpah	L_i	L_i^2
Critic ($n = 5$)	1.	E	E	E	E	4	16
	2.	E	E	N	N	2	4
	3.	N	E	N	N	1	1
	4.	E	E	E	N	3	9
	5.	N	N	N	E	1	1
	B_i	3	4	2	2	$11 = G$	
	B_i^2	9	16	4	4		

two categories of response, we may think of them as representing an ordinal variable, with, say, E being a higher score than N. We may then compute Q using formula 6.3. To use this we need to rank order the directors separately for each subject, obtaining, for example, the midranks 3.5, 3.5, 1.5, and 1.5 for subject 2's data. Following this standard procedure, which is left as an exercise, we obtain a Q of 2.54.

In the two category case, however, we can bypass the ranking stage and also avoid the complexities of formula 6.3, by using the following simpler formula

$$Q = \frac{(k-1)[k\Sigma B_i^2 - G^2]}{kG - \Sigma L_i^2} \qquad (6.6)$$

Here, the B_i's stand for the total number of endorsements for each director while the L_i's stand for the total number of endorsements given by each subject and G is the total number of endorsements in the whole table. In Table 6.8, Siegel receives 3 E's, so $B_1 = 3$, while subject 1 endorses all four directors, so $L_1 = 4$. There are 11 E's throughout the table, so $G = 11$.

Some of the necessary calculations are shown in Table 6.8. We need to compute ΣB_i^2 which is $3^2 + 4^2 + 2^2 + 2^2 = 33$ and ΣL_i^2 which is $4^2 + 2^2 + 1^2 + 3^2 + 1^2 = 31$. Since $k = 4$ (the number of directors), formula 6.6 then gives

$$Q = \frac{3[4 \times 33 - 121]}{4 \times 11 - 31} = \frac{33}{13} = 2.54,$$

the same result as obtained using the longer method.

In formula 6.6, it doesn't matter whether we calculate the number of E's or the number of N's. The result will be the same, as long as we stick with the one we've chosen throughout the calculation (see Exercise 6.7).

Since there are ties in the response variable, to assess the significance of Q in this case, we need to use the chi-square approximation with $k - 1$ df. For our present example, this is likely not to be accurate, since $nk = 20$ is rather small and there are a lot of ties.

Further Comments

For more on the Cochran Test, see Lehmann (1975, Section 6.2).

In the same way as it is possible to use the Sign Test for multiple comparisons following a significant Friedman Test, so the McNemar Test (Example 3.11) may be used for multiple comparisons following a significant Cochran Test (see Exercise 6.6).

Example 6.4. The Cochran Test

Twenty students either pass (P) or fail (F) each of three examinations, A, B, and C. The data are given in Table 6.9. The Cochran Test applied to these data will indicate whether the examinations differ in difficulty. Counting the number of **P**'s in each row and each column gives the totals in Table 6.9, so we have $G = 33$,

$$\Sigma B_i^2 = 17^2 + 9^2 + 7^2 = 419$$

and

$$\Sigma L_i^2 = 3^2 + 2^2 + 1^2 + \ldots + 2^2 + 2^2 + 2^2 = 65.$$

In this case $k = 3$, the number of examinations, so substituting these values in formula 6.6, we have

$$Q = \frac{2[3 \times 419 - 1089]}{3 \times 33 - 65} = \frac{336}{34} = 9.88$$

With 20 subjects, $nk = 60$, so even with all the ties the chi-square approximation should be reasonably accurate. With $\alpha = 0.05$ and $k - 1 = 2$ df Table G gives 5.991 as the critical value of χ^2. Our value of Q is larger than this, so we reject the null hypothesis and conclude that there are differences between the pass-rates of the three examinations. From the data, it looks as though examination A is easier to pass than the other two, assuming no carryover effects such as fatigue are affecting the results.

able 6.9. Hypothetical data and calculations for Example 6.4

		Student ($n = 20$)																					
		1	2	3	4	5	6	7	8	9	10	11	12	13	14	15	16	17	18	19	20	B_i	B_i^2
xamination	A	P	P	P	F	P	P	P	P	F	F	P	P	P	P	P	P	P	P	P	P	17	289
:= 3)	B	P	F	F	F	P	P	F	F	F	P	P	F	P	F	P	F	F	F	P	P	9	81
	C	P	P	F	F	F	F	F	F	P	P	F	P	F	F	P	F	F	P	F	F	7	49
	L_i	3	2	1	0	2	2	1	1	1	2	2	2	2	1	3	1	1	2	2	2	33 = G	
	L_i^2	9	4	1	0	4	4	1	1	1	4	4	4	4	1	9	1	1	4	4	4		

6.4 SUMMARY OF SUGGESTED PROCEDURE

General Points

1. Do you have more than two related samples? If not, look elsewhere (see the table at the front of the book for suggestions).
2. Do you wish to test an ordered prediction about the samples? If so, try Chapter 7.
3. If the responses are ordinal, try the Friedman Test.
4. If the responses have just two categories, try the Cochran Test.

Friedman Test

1. This test may be used to test whether there is any difference (normally of location) between a number of samples. For the test to be valid there must be no carryover effects. In some cases, the difficulties created by carryover effects may be mitigated by randomizing or counterbalancing the order of presentation of the different treatments.
2. Find n, the number of subjects (or matched groups), and k, the number of samples. Select the significance level α.
3. Rank order each subject's data separately, using midranks if there are ties.
4. Find the sum of the ranks for each sample, R_i.
5. Find the sum of the squares of these rank-sums, ΣR_i^2.
6. Find $$Q = -3n(k + 1) + \frac{12\Sigma R_i^2}{nk(k + 1)} \qquad (6.2)$$
7. If there is a large proportion of ties within each subject's data, use the chi-square approximation given in 9.
8. If $k > 4$, *or* if $k = 3$ and $n > 13$, *or* if $k = 4$ and $n > 8$, use the chi-square approximation given in 9. Otherwise, compare the obtained value of Q with the relevant critical value in Table K. and complete the test as indicated at the top of Table K.

   Go to 10.
9. *Chi-square approximation*

   Compare the obtained Q with the relevant critical value given in Table G with $k - 1$ df, completing the test as indicated at the top of Table G. If there are ties and the obtained value is close to the critical value, carry out the test with Q corrected for ties. To correct for ties, find $\Sigma(t_i^3 - t_i)$ for each subject, where t_i is the number of scores at a particular value; find T, the sum of $\Sigma(t_i^3 - t_i)$ across all subjects; and divide the value of Q obtained using formula 6.2 by

   $$1 - \frac{T}{n(k^3 - k)}$$

   Compare this corrected value of Q with the critical value given in Table G. If $nk \geqslant 30$ and there are not too many ties, the approximation should be reasonably accurate.
10. If a significant result is obtained, use multiple comparisons as shown below.
11. If a measure of agreement between subjects is required, use Kendall's Coefficient of Concordance by calculating

    $$W = \frac{Q}{n(k - 1)} \qquad (6.4)$$

    Values close to 1 indicate good agreement; values close to 0 indicate poor agreement.

Multiple Comparisons

1. Write the names of the samples in order of increasing rank-sums, R_i. Select a per experiment significance level α and carry out each test below using a significance level given by α/c, where c is the number of comparisons required. c will generally be $k(k-1)/2$, the total number of comparisons of pairs of samples.
2. Compare the left-most sample with the right-most using the Sign Test. If a significant result is obtained, compare the left-most sample with the second sample from the right.
3. Continue this process until a non-significant result is obtained. When this happens compare the second sample from the left with the right-most, continuing such comparisons until a non-significant result is obtained or until a comparison is to be made that should be non-significant by implication.
4. Continue this procedure (illustrated in Example 6.3) until all necessary comparisons have been made using the Sign Test.

The Cochran Test

1. This test may be used to test whether there is a difference between a number of samples. For the test to be valid, there must be no carryover effects. In some cases, the difficulties created by carryover effects may be mitigated by randomizing or counterbalancing the order of presentation of the different treatments.
2. Find k, the number of samples. Select significance level α.
3. Focus on one of the two categories of response, and count B_i, the total number of times that category is assigned in the ith sample, L_i, the total number of times it is assigned by the ith subject, and G, the total number of times it is used in the whole study.

$$\text{Find } Q = \frac{(k-1)[k\Sigma B_i^2 - G^2]}{kG - \Sigma L_i^2} \tag{6.6}$$

and compare the obtained value with the relevant critical value given in Table G. This gives an approximate test; the approximation will be reasonably accurate if $nk \geqslant 30$, where n is the number of subjects who have used both categories of the response variable.

5. If a significant result is obtained, use the McNemar Test and the procedure outlined above to carry out multiple comparisons.

6.5 EXERCISES

Section 6.1

1. The number of problems solved by each of 4 people is shown below. Are there any differences between the three types of problems, A, B, and C?

		Type of problem		
		A	*B*	*C*
Subject	1.	20	30	40
	2.	24	26	25
	3.	29	31	53
	4.	42	48	49

2. Ten people each watch 4 films made by Howard Hawks (shown in different random orders to each person). After seeing each film, they rate it on a five point scale of enjoyment, with high ratings indicating much fun. The data are shown below. (a) Are there consistent differences in preferences for these films? (b) How much agreement is there between the 10 people?

	Person									
	1	2	3	4	5	6	7	8	9	10
The Big Sleep	5	5	5	4	5	5	3	5	5	5
Rio Bravo	5	5	3	4	5	5	5	2	4	5
Scarface	5	4	3	2	5	4	4	4	3	3
Land of the Pharaohs	5	2	2	2	4	3	3	1	2	2

3. (Optional) For the simplified example in Section 6.1, suppose only 2 restaurants were being compared and the ratings of 3 subjects were as shown below. Show that the Friedman Test and the Sign Test are exactly equivalent in this case by computing the relevant null distributions.

		Restaurant	
		A	*B*
Subject	1.	4	5
	2.	3	7
	3.	3	2

Section 6.2

4. Carry out multiple comparisons for the data of Exercise 1 using a per experiment error rate of about 0.05.
5. Carry out multiple comparisons for the data of Exercise 2 using a per experi-

ment error rate of 0.12. Under what circumstances might you want to use such a large error rate?

Section 6.3

6. Suppose the data for Exercise 2 had been those shown below. Are there consistent differences in preferences for the films now. If so, carry out multiple comparisons to locate the differences between the films.

	Person									
	1	2	3	4	5	6	7	8	9	10
The Big Sleep	5	5	5	5	5	5	5	5	5	5
Rio Bravo	5	5	5	5	4	5	4	5	4	5
Scarface	5	5	4	5	4	5	4	5	5	4
Land of the Pharaohs	5	4	4	5	4	4	4	4	4	4

7. (a) Compute Q using formula 6.3 for the simplified example of Section 6.3 and check that you get the same result as obtained using formula 6.6.
   (b) Check that you get the same result using formula 6.6 for this example if you count the N's rather than the E's.

CHAPTER 7

We must all hang together or assuredly
we shall all hang separately

Benjamin Franklin, *At Signing of The Declaration of Independence*

Tests for Several Related Samples – Both Variables Ordinal

The tests in this chapter assume that both variables are ordinal and that related data have been collected. The paradigm example is a learning experiment (Example 7.1) in which each participant gives a single ordinal (or two category) response on each of a number of trials. In such a situation, our interest frequently centres on whether learning (or forgetting) has taken place, so we consider the explanatory variable (trial number) to be ordinal. We have already seen that Kendall's S statistic provides one way of approaching such a problem when only *one* subject is involved (the Mann Test for Trend, Example 5.7). The tests in this chapter show how such S values obtained from a number of different subjects may be combined to provide an overall test of whether or not the *group* is learning.

These tests are much more general than this example would seem to imply (cf. Example 1.17). We have already seen in Chapter 5 that the Kendall Test turns into several other frequently-used tests when there are ties in one or both of the variables. This property will be exploited again in Sections 7.2 and 7.3 where we shall see how to combine data from a number of subjects (or matched groups of subjects) in any situation where each individual subject's data may be analysed using S (in any of its applications) as the test statistic.

We shall also discuss in Section 7.4 a simple way of testing whether there are differences between the S values obtained from different subjects (or matched groups).

7.1 THE COMBINED S TEST

In this section, we discuss the simplest case in which there are no ties in either variable and each subject provides the same amount of data. Such data could be analysed using the Friedman Test (Section 6.1). The crucial difference between the Friedman Test and the Combined S Test presented here is that the latter test assumes that the explanatory variable is ordinal, so that it tests an ordered prediction about the samples being compared. For the test to be valid, the predicted ordering of the samples should be made independently of the data.

The Combined S Test, another test suggested by A. R. Jonckheere (1954b), may be seen as an alternative way of generalizing the Sign Test (Section 3.2) to more than two samples. The test may easily be used when there are ties in either or both variables, as we shall see in Section 7.2 and 7.3. When different subjects provide different amounts of data, the method of Section 7.3 should be used.

Simplified Example

Suppose we ask two people to attempt 90 problems that fall into three distinct types, A, B, and C, 30 problems of each type being presented. We predict that type C should be the easiest to solve while type A should be the most difficult, with type B in between. To guard against possible biases due to carryover effects, the 90 problems are presented in a different random order to each person. The number of problems of each type correctly solved are as follows:

Type	A	B	C
Person 1	15	18	22
Person 2	13	18	17

For each person, the explanatory variable here is type of problem while the response variable is number of problems solved. Notice that in this example there are no ties within either person's data, and each person gives only one response at each level of the explanatory variable. As with the Friedman Test, the tie occurring between people does not matter, since each person's data are initially analysed separately. The data from one of the people are assumed to be independent of those from the other person.

Our predicted ordering of the three types of problem makes it more sensible to use a Combined S Test rather than the omnibus Friedman Test. Looking at the data, it is clear that they are somewhat in line with the prediction, although not perfectly.

To allow the following discussion to be easily generalized, we shall label the number of samples (or responses from each person) n and the number of people m. In our case, $n = 3$ and $m = 2$.

Test Statistic – J

We can assess the degree to which each person is in line with the predicted ordering of the three samples by computing Kendall's S in one of the usual ways

Table 7.1. The 36 patterns of results when $n = 3$, $m = 2$ and associated values of J computed by adding S for the two rows

1. *A B C*	2. *A B C*	3. *A B C*	4. *A B C*	5. *A B C*	6. *A B C*
1 2 3	1 2 3	1 2 3	1 2 3	1 2 3	1 2 3
1 2 3	1 3 2	2 1 3	2 3 1	3 1 2	3 2 1
$J = 6$	$J = 4$	$J = 4$	$J = 2$	$J = 2$	$J = 0$
7. *A B C*	8. *A B C*	9. *A B C*	10. *A B C*	11. *A B C*	12. *A B C*
1 3 2	1 3 2	1 3 2	1 3 2	1 3 2	1 3 2
1 2 3	1 3 2	2 1 3	2 3 1	3 1 2	3 2 1
$J = 4$	$J = 2$	$J = 2$	$J = 0$	$J = 0$	$J = -2$
13. *A B C*	14. *A B C*	15. *A B C*	16. *A B C*	17. *A B C*	18. *A B C*
2 1 3	2 1 3	2 1 3	2 1 3	2 1 3	2 1 3
1 2 3	1 3 2	2 1 3	2 3 1	3 1 2	3 2 1
$J = 4$	$J = 2$	$J = 2$	$J = 0$	$J = 0$	$J = -2$
19. *A B C*	20. *A B C*	21. *A B C*	22. *A B C*	23. *A B C*	24. *A B C*
2 3 1	2 3 1	2 3 1	2 3 1	2 3 1	2 3 1
1 2 3	1 3 2	2 1 3	2 3 1	3 1 2	3 2 1
$J = 2$	$J = 0$	$J = 0$	$J = -2$	$J = -2$	$J = -4$
25. *A B C*	26. *A B C*	27. *A B C*	28. *A B C*	29. *A B C*	30. *A B C*
3 1 2	3 1 2	3 1 2	3 1 2	3 1 2	3 1 2
1 2 3	1 3 2	2 1 3	2 3 1	3 1 2	3 2 1
$J = 2$	$J = 0$	$J = 0$	$J = -2$	$J = -2$	$J = -4$
31. *A B C*	32. *A B C*	33. *A B C*	34. *A B C*	35. *A B C*	36. *A B C*
3 2 1	3 2 1	3 2 1	3 2 1	3 2 1	3 2 1
1 2 3	1 3 2	2 1 3	2 3 1	3 1 2	3 2 1
$J = 0$	$J = -2$	$J = -2$	$J = -4$	$J = -4$	$J = -6$

(e.g. as in Example 5.7). The S for person 1 will then be 3 and the S for person 2 will be 1, indicating that person 1 is more in line with the prediction than person 2. We could then if we wished test the significance of each person's results separately using Table I. However, more often than not, we should be more interested in a single test combining the results from both people rather than separate tests.

The test statistic we shall use to provide this overall summary statement of the results is simply the sum of the individual S values, which we label J. Thus $J = \Sigma S_i$, where S_i is the S value computed from the ith person. In our case $J = 3 + 1 = 4$. If each person provides data in line with the prediction, then each will produce a large S value, resulting in a large value for J. Small values of J may arise either because none of the people are in line with the prediction, all having small S's, or because some people are in line with the prediction and some go against it, some having large positive S's and some having large negative S's. We shall see in Section 7.4 how to distinguish between these possibilities.

Null Distribution of J

For each person, the null hypothesis is that all possible orderings of the response variable are equally likely. Thus, for person 1 there are 6 possible patterns of results (see Table 5.12). For each of these possibilities for person 1, there are 6 possible patterns of person 2's results that are equally likely. The 36 resulting equally likely patterns of results are shown in Table 7.1, together with J calculated for each. In general, we should need to investigate $(n!)^m$ possible patterns. It can easily be seen from Table 7.1 that large values of J favour the alternative hypothesis that the data are in line with the predicted ordering, while small values favour the null hypothesis.

The null distribution of J for our case with $n = 3$ and $m = 2$ may then be written down immediately as in Table 7.2. The one-tailed probability of getting a J of 4 or more is thus $4/36 + 1/36 = 0.139$, so with our data we should only be able to reject the null hypothesis if we were using a significance level of 0.139 or larger.

To test that the data are in line with the predicted ordering, we should use an upper tail test. Had we predicted instead that Type A problems should be the easiest and Type C the hardest, negative values of S would favour this prediction, so a lower tail test should be used. To test for departures from the null hypothesis in either direction, a two-tailed test should be used. These are all carried out in the usual way.

Table 7.2. Null distribution of J for the case $n = 3$ and $m = 2$

J	−6	−4	−2	0	2	4	6
Probability	1/36	4/36	8/36	10/36	8/36	4/36	1/36

Table of the Null Distribution of J (Appendix Table L)

Table L in the Appendix gives critical values of the null distribution of J for both one- and two-tailed tests. It may be used when there are no more than 8 samples ($n \leqslant 8$) and no more than 10 subjects ($m \leqslant 10$). All other cases may be adequately handled using the normal approximation given below. To illustrate the use of Table L, for our example with $n = 3$ and $m = 2$, the upper tail critical value of J for a one-tailed significance level of 0.10 is 6. We obtained a J of 4, so we cannot reject the null hypothesis. This is the same as the conclusion above.

Normal Approximation to J

The standard normal distribution provides a very good approximation to the null distribution of J. As usual, to use it we need to know the mean and variance of the possible values that J can take.

When combining independent S values from different subjects, it turns out that the mean and variance of the possible values that J can take is the sum of the individual means and variances. S always has a mean of 0, so J will too. Since there are no ties in either variable, the variance of the possible values that each S can take will be $n(n-1)(2n+5)/18$ (see the table at the back of the book). With m subjects' results all having the same variance, the variance of J is thus given by multiplying this value by m, to give

$$\text{Variance} = \frac{mn(n-1)(2n+5)}{18} \tag{7.1}$$

In our case, with $n = 3$ and $m = 2$, this gives $2 \times 3 \times 2 \times 11/18 = 7.33$, which is easily seen to be the variance of the possible values for J given in Table 7.1.

When there are no ties in either variable, the difference between consecutive possible values of J is always 2, so the normal approximation may be improved by using a continuity correction of 1. This should be subtracted from positive values of J and added to negative values.

The use of the normal approximation is illustrated in Example 7.2. It rapidly improves as either m or n or both get larger, so the approximation will be very good for all values outside the scope of Table L.

If there are ties in either variable, then one of the approximations given in Section 7.2 should be used rather than the present one.

Further Comments

For more on the Combined S Test see Jonckheere (1954b) or Jonckheere and Bower (1967). Some other interesting uses of this test for assessing trends more complicated than the monotonic sort considered here are suggested by Ferguson (1965, Chapter 9).

When a significant result is obtained with the Combined S Test, we know only that the data are consistent with the predicted ordering. For our example, a significant result would imply that Type C problems are the easiest and Type A are the hardest. Despite this, we are not justified in concluding that type A problems are reliably harder than Type B problems, since we know only that the B problems are somewhere between the A and the C problems. In many cases, we shall be quite happy merely to state that the data are consistent with the predicted ordering. However, if we want to go beyond this and look for specific differences making up the ordering, the multiple comparison technique described in Section 6.2 may be used. Similarly, the estimators referred to in the Further Comments section of Section 6.1 may be used to estimate the size of particular differences.

Example 7.1 The Combined S Test – No Ties

Table 7.3 gives the number of correct responses on 5 trials of a learning experiment for each of 4 subjects. Does the group of subjects show evidence of learning? We are predicting that the scores on the response variable (number correct) should increase as trial number increases, so the explanatory variable (trial number) is ordinal. Since each person gives one response at each level of the explanatory variable, we have related samples, so the Combined S Test is applicable. In this case, we have $n = 5$ (the number of trials) and $m = 4$ (the number of subjects). If we are only interested in whether learning occurs and we are not interested in the possibility of forgetting, a one-tailed test is appropriate. Setting $\alpha = 0.05$, we find from Table L that, when $n = 5$ and $m = 4$, the upper tail critical value of J is 16. We should thus reject the null hypothesis that there is no learning if we obtain a J of 16 or larger.

The values of S computed for each subject are shown alongside the data. The sum of these is 22, which is thus our obtained value of J. Since this is larger than the critical value, we reject the null hypothesis and conclude that this group of subjects does indeed show evidence of learning.

Table 7.3. Hypothetical data and calculation of J for Example 7.1

		Trial number ($n = 5$)					
	Subject	1	2	3	4	5	S_i
	1.	0	4	10	8	9	6
($m = 4$)	2.	2	0	7	6	8	6
	3.	1	2	5	8	7	8
	4.	3	0	2	1	5	2
							$J = 22$

Example 7.2 The Normal Approximation to the Combined S Test – No Ties

One of the predictions from a version of Attribution Theory is that increasing the nicotine content of cigarettes should lead to a decrease in the number of cigarettes smoked and thus to a decrease in the amount of tar absorbed. Twelve smokers took part in an experiment to test this prediction. For each of three months, they smoked only cigarettes supplied by the experimenter. In one of the months they were given cigarettes with a low nicotine content, in another month they were given medium nicotine content cigarettes and in the remaining month

Table 7.4. Hypothetical data and calculation of J for Example 7.2

	Nicotine content	Subject (m = 12)												
		1	2	3	4	5	6	7	8	9	10	11	12	
	Low	100	250	200	150	146	73	191	190	142	130	122	280	
(n = 3)	Medium	95	200	150	196	83	78	202	152	148	95	119	253	
	High	70	196	190	203	92	82	203	163	145	76	120	260	
	S_i	–3	–3	–1	3	–1	3	3	–1	1	–3	–1	–1	$J = -4$

they were given high nicotine content cigarettes. The order of presentation of each type of cigarette was randomized separately for each subject, to guard against possible carryover effects. The number of cigarettes smoked in the final week of each month is shown in Table 7.4. A Combined S Test is appropriate here since we are predicting that as nicotine content increases smoking will decrease. If the prediction is correct, we should therefore obtain a large negative value for J, so we require a lower tail test. With $n = 3$ and $m = 12$, we cannot use Table L, so we must use the normal approximation. Since there are no ties in the response variable (number of cigarettes smoked) for any of the subjects, the variance of J is given by formula 7.1 as

$$\text{Variance} = \frac{mn(n-1)(2n+5)}{18} = \frac{12 \times 3 \times 2 \times 11}{18} = 44$$

Computing an S for each subject and summing the resulting values as shown in Table 7.4, we obtain a J of -4. Adding a continuity correction of 1 (since J is negative), to give $J_c = -3$, the required z-score is then

$$z = \frac{J_c}{\text{S.D.}} = \frac{-3}{\sqrt{44}} = -0.45$$

With $\alpha = 0.05$, Table B(ii) gives the lower tail critical value of z as -1.645. Our obtained value is larger than this, so we cannot reject the null hypothesis. We conclude that the data do not support the prediction. However, we note that some of the subjects have large negative S's in line with the prediction while others have large positive S's which go strictly against the prediction, so we might attempt to locate any possible differences between the subjects, in terms of, say, personality variables that might account for this lack of homogeneity in the subjects' results here.

7.2 TIES IN THE COMBINED S TEST – EQUAL VARIANCE CASE

Ties may occur either in the response variable or in the explanatory variable. In Example 7.2, the response variable was number of cigarettes smoked; if one of the subjects had smoked exactly the same number of cigarettes under two of the conditions, there would be a tie in the response variable. The explanatory variable was nicotine content. If there were more than one score for a subject under any of the levels of the explanatory variable, we should have ties in the explanatory variable. This would occur, for example, if we had carried out the study twice with each subject and obtained two scores each for low, medium, and high nicotine content cigarettes.

When there are ties in either variable for any of the subjects, the midrank technique may be used in combination with a relevant normal approximation. Now, from Section 5.4 we know the appropriate formulae for the variance of S for each subject's data when there are ties in one or both variables. These are given in the table at the back of the book. If each subject has exactly the same number and extent of ties, the variance of S for each subject will be the same, so the variance of J will be given by

$$\text{Variance} = m \times \text{Variance of } S, \tag{7.2}$$

where Variance of S is the common variance for all subjects, which may be found in the relevant part of the table at the back of the book. Thus, when the ties in the data are such that the results for each subject lead to the same variance of S, we use formula 7.2 to calculate the variance of J and use the normal approximation as before. This allows us to generalize the Combined S Test to cover a wide variety of experimental situations, as illustrated in the following examples. When the ties lead to different values of the variance of S for each subject the situation gets slightly more complicated and one of the methods of Section 7.3 should be used instead of the present one.

When there are ties in only one of the variables, a continuity correction of 1 may be used.

Combining Data from Several Matched Groups

The examples so far in this chapter have illustrated how to combine S values from a number of different subjects. In a learning experiment like the one in Example 7.1, it is natural to want to compute a value of S separately for each subject and then combine the S's rather than collapsing the data over subjects and then computing a single S score based on, say, the total number of correct responses at each trial. Collapsing the data over subjects may be misleading since any differences between subjects will be masked by this procedure in a way that doesn't happen with the Combined S procedure.

It is perhaps not so clear that such a procedure may be misleading when matched groups of subjects are used. The following example illustrates that the same argument applies to matched groups as applied to data from a single subject. Suppose we are interested in whether students with an Arts background are any better or worse at statistics than students from a Science background. To investi-

Table 7.5. Incorrect method of combining data from several 2 x 2 tables

	College A					College B							
	Pass	Fail	t_i			Pass	Fail	t_i			Pass	Fail	t_i
Science	21	21	42	+		1	21	22	=		22	42	64
Arts	1	1	2			1	21	22			2	22	24
u_i	22	22			u_i	2	42			u_i	24	64	
	(a) $S = 0$					(b) $S = 0$					(c) $S = 400$		

gate this we obtain the results from the same statistics examination of students at two colleges teaching the same course. Suppose the results are as shown in the 2 x 2 contingency tables in Table 7.5(a) and (b). Here we have recorded the results separately for each college and it is clear that the Arts and Science students do not differ in either college since $S = 0$ for each of the tables. If we want a single combined statement we might be tempted to collapse the data over the two colleges as in Table 7.5(c). For the collapsed data, $S = 400$; using the normal approximation together with a continuity correction, we obtain $z = 2.16$, a significant result for a two-tailed test with $\alpha = 0.05$. So the collapsed data suggest that Science students are better at statistics than Arts students, a conclusion that is completely at variance with the data in (a) and (b) for which there is no association at all. Why should this be so? If we compare the data in (a) and (b), we note that College A has a smaller proportion of Arts students than College B; in addition, A has a higher pass rate than B. These differences in the marginal proportions in the two tables result in the spurious association shown in (c).

In this case, we may think of the colleges as providing us with 2 matched groups of students. Using the Combined S Test here is much more sensible than collapsing the data since it does not produce a misleading conclusion. Since $S = 0$ for both colleges, J will also be 0, giving us the correct combined conclusion that Arts students are no different from Science students at statistics.

Although a 2 x 2 contingency table has been used to illustrate the dangers of collapsing data across a number of matched groups, the problem is more general, as shown in Exercise 7.4.

For a more complete discussion of collapsing data, see Bishop, Fienberg, and Holland (1975, Chapter 2).

Example 7.3 The Combined S Test with Ties in the Explanatory Variable

Fifteen children from four different schools go to a sixth-form college. The headmaster believes that the schools tend to produce children of different abilities, with school A producing the most able children, school B the next, C the next, and D the least able. Four teachers independently rank order the 15 children in terms of their

Table 7.6. Hypothetical data and calculation of J for Example 7.3. The entries are ranks assigned to the students from each school

		School				
	Teacher	A	B	C	D	S_i
	1.	7,13,14,15	5, 6, 8,11,12	4,9,10	1,2,3	61
($m = 4$)	2.	8, 9,14,15	4,10,11,12,13	3,5, 6	1,2,7	55
	3.	10,11,12,13	6, 7, 9,14,15	1,2, 8	3,4,5	51
	4.	11,13,14,15	1, 8, 9,10,12	5,6, 7	2,3,4	69
						$J = 236$

ability. Do the teachers' judgements bear out the headmaster's belief? The data are given in Table 7.6, with high scores indicating high ability. In this case, we have no ties in the response variable (ranking of ability) for any of the teachers, but there are ties in the explanatory variable, since 4 children come from school A, 5 from school B, and 3 each from schools C and D. Since each teacher judges the same 15 children, the ties in the explanatory variable will be the same for each teacher. For each teacher, we have a situation equivalent to that of a Jonckheere Test for four independent samples with $t_1 = 4$, $t_2 = 5$, $t_3 = 3$, $t_4 = 3$ and $n = 15$, so from the table at the back of the book, the variance of S will be given by

$$\text{Variance of } S = \frac{2(n^3 - \Sigma t_i^3) + 3(n^2 - \Sigma t_i^2)}{18}$$

$$= \frac{2(3375 - 243) + 3(225 - 59)}{18}$$

$$= 375.67$$

Since there are $m = 4$ teachers, the variance of J will be

$$\text{Variance of } J = m \times \text{Variance of } S = 4 \times 375.67 = 1502.67$$

The S values, computed (remembering the prediction that $A > B > C > D$) for each teacher using the direct method given in Section 5.1, are shown alongside the data. The sum of these gives J, which is 236. Since there are ties in only one variable, we subtract a continuity correction of 1 from J, to give $J_c = 235$. The z-score then becomes

$$z = \frac{J_c}{\text{S.D.}} = \frac{235}{\sqrt{1502.67}} = 6.06$$

Using a one-tailed test with $\alpha = 0.05$, Table B(ii) gives the upper tail critical value of z as 1.645. The obtained value is larger than this, so we reject the null hypothesis and conclude that the teachers' judgements are in line with the headmaster's predicted ordering of the schools.

Example 7.4 The Combined *S* Test with Ties in the Response Variable

In 20 trials of a learning experiment, the response on each trial was classified as either correct (C) or incorrect (I). The sequences of responses shown in Table 7.7 were recorded for four subjects. Does this group of subjects show evidence of learning? For each subject, the two variables are trial number (explanatory variable) and response. There are ties in only the response variable. Since one variable is ordinal and one has two categories this is formally equivalent to a Rank-Sum Test

Table 7.7. Hypothetical data for Example 7.4

(m = 4)	Subject 1	C I I C I C I I C C I I I C C C C C C C	S_1 = 46
	Subject 2	I I I I C C I I I C I C C C C C C C C C	S_2 = 78
	Subject 3	C I I I I I C C C I C C C C C I C I C C	S_3 = 40
	Subject 4	I C C I C I C I C I C C I C C C C I I C	S_4 = 10
			J = 174

(see the table at the back of the book). To see this equivalence, it is necessary to exchange the roles of the explanatory and the response variables, since the Rank-Sum Test has a two-category explanatory variable and an ordinal response variable.

If t_1 represents the number of C's and t_2 the number of I's, we note that t_1 = 12 and t_2 = 8 for all subjects (a fortunate coincidence), so the variance of S will be the same for each subject and will be given by the formula for the variance of S in the Rank-Sum case, which is

$$\text{Variance of } S = \frac{t_1 t_2 (n+1)}{3} = \frac{12 \times 8 \times 21}{3} = 672$$

Since there are m = 4 subjects, we have

$$\text{Variance of } J = m \times \text{Variance of } S = 4 \times 672 = 2688$$

This will only be correct if the number of C's and the number of I's is the same for each subject. If this is not so, one of the methods described in Section 7.3 should be used. The value of S for each subject is given alongside the data, from which we obtain J = 174. With a continuity correction of 1 (since there are ties in only one variable), we have J_c = 173 and

$$z = \frac{J_c}{\text{S.D.}} = \frac{173}{\sqrt{2688}} = 3.34$$

Using a one-tailed test with $\alpha = 0.05$, Table B(ii) gives the upper tail critical value of z as 1.645. The obtained value is larger than this, so we reject the null hypothesis and conclude that this group of subjects does show evidence of learning. It is worth noting that the overall result just obtained is more significant than any of the individual subject's results, for which z is given by

$$(S_i - 1)/\sqrt{672} \text{ or } 1.74, 2.97, 1.50, \text{ and } 0.35,$$

respectively. This is as it should be, indicating that the Combined S Test is very powerful.

Example 7.5 The Combined *S* Test with Ties in Both Variables

In a study of the care of terminal patients, the morbidity of widows during the year following their husband's death was investigated. A random sample of 20 women whose husbands had died in a general hospital and 20 whose husbands had died in a special hospice were interviewed in each of three areas and were asked to state whether or not they had suffered any illness in the year following their husband's death. The interest of the study centres on whether hospice or hospital bereavement result in different morbidity rates. In this situation, we may think of the areas as providing us with three matched groups of subjects. The results are given in Table 7.8. The data from each area could be analysed separately using a Fisher Exact Test (Section 2.5). The relevant S values are shown alongside the data. However, we can provide a simple overall statement of the results by using the Combined S Test, since the three areas are independent. We can do this using the normal approximation given in formula 7.2, since we note that the marginal totals for all three tables in Table 7.8 are identical, so the variance of S for the data from each area will be the same. Thus, we have

$$\text{Variance of } S = \frac{t_1 t_2 u_1 u_2}{n-1} = \frac{20 \times 20 \times 30 \times 10}{39} = 3076.92$$

Combining $m = 3$ tables, we obtain

$$\text{Variance of } J = m \times \text{Variance of } S = 3 \times 3076.92 = 9230.76$$

For these data, $J = -200 - 40 - 80 = -320$, so the z-score will be

$$z = \frac{J}{\text{S.D.}} = \frac{-320}{\sqrt{9230.76}} = -3.33$$

With $\alpha = 0.05$, this is outside the two-tailed critical values of -1.96 and 1.96 given in Table B(ii), so we reject the null hypothesis and conclude that there is a reliable difference in morbidity rates. Women whose husbands died in a general hospital are more likely to have an illness within the year following the death than those whose husbands died in

Table 7.8. Hypothetical data for Example 7.5

	Area A			Area B			Area C		
	Illness	None	t_i	Illness	None	t_i	Illness	None	t_i
Hospice	10	10	20	14	6	20	13	7	20
Hospital	20	0	20	16	4	20	17	3	20
u_i	30	10		30	10		30	10	
	$S = -200$			$S = -40$			$S = -80$		

a hospice. Before leaving this example, we note that there seem to be differences in this respect between the three areas. Even though the data in each area go in the same direction, Area A seems to have a larger difference between the two groups (with $S = -200$) than the other two areas (with $S = -40$ and -80). We shall take up this problem again in Section 7.4.

7.3 TIES IN THE COMBINED TEST – UNEQUAL VARIANCE CASE

When combining S values from data with unequal variances, a new problem is introduced that is not present in the equal variance case. This concerns whether each subject's (or matched group's) S score is given the same weighting when the S values are combined.

Suppose, for example, that in comparing the effects on reaction time of two drugs, X and Y, we obtain 10 reaction times under drug X and 10 under drug Y from each of three subjects. A fourth subject provides only 5 reaction times under each drug. Such a situation might occur if the equipment breaks down before all the data from this subject are collected. The data from each subject may be analysed using a Rank-Sum Test. However, if we wish to include subject 4's data in a combined test, because this subject provides less data than the others, we may wish to weight these data differentially so that they will not be swamped in the overall analysis by the more extensive data from the other three subjects. The situation discussed in Example 7.7 provides another example of the desirability of unequal weighting of S scores.

On the other hand, in some learning experiments, interest is centred on the trial up to and including the trial on which the last error is made (see Example 7.6). For example, incremental learning theory suggests that in these trials the subject is learning a little on each trial and so will show an increasing tendency to give a correct response as the trials increase; all-or-none learning theory argues against this, saying that the subject learns the correct response in one go, so there should not be a slowly increasing tendency to give a correct response. To choose between these theories, we might note the sequence of correct and incorrect responses up to the trial of last error for each of a number of subjects. Since people differ in the amount of time they take to learn, we should expect the number of trials taken before the final error occurs to differ. In such a situation, the data to be combined would be more extensive for one subject than for another, so that the variance of S would be different for different subjects. For this example, the number of observations obtained from each subject gives us useful information; subjects with shorter sequences of responses might be thought to favour the all-or-none theory while subjects with longer sequences and large values of S favour the incremental theory. Here, it is quite proper for the S values to be given equal weight (as shown in Example 7.6), since *both* the S value itself *and* the number of trials are important components of the test.

Such examples are rare, however. It is more often the case that discrepancies in the numbers of observations obtained from each subject (or matched group) give little or no information that bears on the test; if this is so, then such discrepancies may be removed by weighting the S scores unequally as shown in Example 7.7.

Equal Weighting of S Scores

When equal weighting is desired, the modification required to the approach discussed in Section 7.2 is simple: all we have to do is to compute the variance separately for each S_i and add them up. To use the normal approximation, J is computed by finding the sum of the S values in the usual way and the variance of J is given by summing the variances of the S values, so the overall z-score is computed as follows:

$$z = \frac{J}{\sqrt{\Sigma(\text{Variance of } S_i)}} \tag{7.3}$$

This procedure is illustrated in Example 7.6.

Unequal Weighting of S Scores

When unequal weighting is required, one way of effecting it is to divide each subject's S by the number of observations, n, provided by that subject before combining the data. This has the effect of making each subject's contribution to the combined test independent of the number of observations obtained. We then obtain a modified test statistic defined by

$$J^* = \sum \frac{S_i}{n_i}, \tag{7.4}$$

where S_i and n_i are the S value and the number of observations for the ith subject (or matched group).

Since this procedure divides the S score for each subject by n, it also divides the variance of S by n^2 (see Exercise 1.3h). This means that in the combined test the variance of J^* is given by

$$\text{Variance of } J^* = \sum \frac{(\text{Variance of } S_i)}{n_i^2} \tag{7.5}$$

This procedure is illustrated in Example 7.7.

Example 7.6 The Combined S Test with Equal Weighting of S Scores

In a test of an all-or-none theory of learning, 6 pigeons were taught a simple pattern discrimination. The crucial data for the theory are the trials up to and including the last error for each pigeon. The data shown in Table 7.9 record whether each pigeon was correct or incorrect on

Table 7.9. Hypothetical data and calculations for Example 7.6

	Trial										
Pigeon	1	2	3	4	5	6	7	8	9	S_i	Var S_i
1.	I	I	I	C	I	C	C	C	I	10	$66\frac{2}{3}$
2.	I	I	C	I	C	C	I			4	32
3.	I	I	I	C	I					2	8
4.	I	I	I	C	C	C	I			6	32
5.	I	I	I	I	C	C	I			6	$66\frac{2}{3}$
6.	I	I	I	C	I	C	C	C	I	10	$66\frac{2}{3}$
										$J = 38$	$232 = \text{Var } J$

each trial. The theory predicts that these trials should show no evidence of trend. Is the theory supported?

For each pigeon, the explanatory variable (trial number) is ordinal with no ties while the response variable has two categories, so we can test whether there is evidence of trend using a Rank-Sum Test (see the table at the back of the book, interchanging the roles of the explanatory and response variables). However, since the number of responses and the pattern of ties is different for each pigeon, we must decide whether to give the S scores equal weighting. In this case, each pigeon's S score is equally important in testing the prediction, since a pigeon taking only three trials to learn supports the theory as much as a pigeon learning incrementally over fifteen trials goes against it. Thus, we should give each pigeon's S score equal weighting. We therefore need to compute J, the sum of the individual S's, as well as the sum of the individual variances, using formula 7.3 to carry out the combined test. The necessary calculations are shown alongside the data. To illustrate the calculation of the variances, since for each pigeon we have a Rank-Sum Test situation, the table at the back of the book shows that the variance of S for each pigeon will be given by

$$\text{Variance of } S = \frac{t_1 t_2 (n+1)}{3},$$

where n is the number of trials up to and including the last error for that pigeon, t_1 is the number of correct responses and t_2 is the number incorrect. Thus, for pigeon 1, we have

$$\text{Variance of } S = 4 \times 5 \times 10/3 = 66\tfrac{2}{3}$$

The other variances are worked out in a similar manner. From this we obtain $J = \Sigma S_i = 38$ and

$$\text{Variance of } J = \Sigma\ (\text{Variance of } S_i) = 232,$$

so formula 7.3 gives

$$z = \frac{J}{\sqrt{\Sigma(\text{Variance of } S_i)}} = \frac{38}{\sqrt{232}} = 2.49$$

Using a one-tailed test with $\alpha = 0.05$, Table B(ii) gives 1.645 as the critical value of z. The obtained value is larger than this, so we should probably conclude that the all-or-none theory is not supported by these data; since the individual S's are all positive, there is an increasing tendency to obtain a correct response as the trials increase.

Example 7.7 The Combined *S* Test with Unequal Weighting of *S* Scores

Suppose that the data obtained in the study illustrated in Example 7.5 had been those given in Table 7.10. In this case, the sample sizes in the three areas differ considerably, with $n = 100$ for area A, 40 for area B and 20 for area C. This may be because the three areas differ considerably in size of population and the sample sizes were chosen to reflect these differences. However, in combining the results, we should not want the overall test to reflect such differences, so we use the modified test statistic J^* defined in formula 7.4. Since the data for each area separately are amenable to a Fisher Exact Test, the relevant formula for the variance of S for each area will be

$$\text{Variance of } S = \frac{t_1 t_2 u_1 u_2}{n - 1}$$

The calculations necessary for computing J^* and its variance are given in Table 7.11. The relevant z-score will then be

$$z = \frac{J^*}{\sqrt{\text{Var } J^*}} = \frac{-11}{\sqrt{8.48}} = -3.78$$

With $\alpha = 0.05$, this is outside the range given by the two-tailed critical values of -1.96 and 1.96 in Table B(ii), so we again reject the null

Table 7.10. Hypothetical data for Example 7.7

	Area A			Area B			Area C		
	Illness	None	t_i	Illness	None	t_i	Illness	None	t_i
Hospice	25	25	50	11	9	20	9	1	10
Hospital	45	5	50	19	1	20	3	7	10
u_i	70	30		30	10		12	8	
	$S = -1000$			$S = -160$			$S = 60$		

Table 7.11. Calculation of J^* and Var J^* for Example 7.7

Area	S_i	n_i	S_i/n_i	Var S_i	(Var S_i)/n_i^2
A	−1000	100	−10	53030.30	5.30
B	−160	40	−4	3076.92	1.92
C	60	20	3	505.26	1.26
			J^* = −11		Var J^* = 8.48

hypothesis and conclude that there is a difference in morbidity rates. As with the data given in Table 7.8, women whose husbands died in a general hospital are more likely to have an illness in the year following bereavement than are those whose husbands died in a special hospice. However, even though the overall test is significant, the present data seem to suggest differences between the areas, with area C even going against the overall finding, so we again need to test for any differences between the areas before being satisfied with the overall conclusion. The necessary test of homogeneity for the present data is carried out in Example 7.9 below.

7.4 THE HOMOGENEITY TEST

Before being satisfied with a conclusion based on the Combined S Test, it is necessary to discover whether there are differences among the subjects (or matched groups) contributing to the overall test. For example, in a learning experiment such as that in Example 7.1, we may have data for which the null hypothesis of no trend using the Combined S Test cannot be rejected. In this case, we might have a situation where none of the subjects shows any substantial trend; alternatively, we might have a situation where the different subjects show strong trends, but in opposite directions. In this second situation, the different trends will cancel each other out in the overall test. We need a test to distinguish the two situations, since in the second situation it will be misleading to say that no learning has occurred in the group – some subjects have learned while others have actually got worse.

Similarly, even when the null hypothesis is rejected for the Combined S Test, as for the data in Examples 7.5 and 7.7, it would be useful to be able to say whether all subjects (or matched groups) are showing the trend to the same extent.

Test Statistic, H, and its Use

Such a test for homogeneity of individual trends is easily constructed. It will be illustrated initially using the data of Table 7.8. At the end of Example 7.5 we suspected that there might be differences in the three areas despite the overall test being significant. We first compute a z-score for each of the three areas (without using a continuity correction). Since the variance of S is identically equal to

3076.92 for each area, and the S's are -200, -40 and -80 for areas A, B, and C, respectively, the z-scores will be -3.61, -0.72, and -1.44. Now, if the three areas differ, their z-scores will also differ. We could get an indication of the degree to which this is so by calculating the time-honoured sum of the squared deviations of these z-scores from their mean. The test statistic that we shall use is closely related to this and is given by

$$H = \Sigma z_i^2 - z^2 \qquad (7.7)$$

where z_i is the z-score of the ith area and z is the overall z-score computed in the normal approximation to the Combined S Test (without using a continuity correction). To see that this is similar to a sum of squared deviations from the mean, compare Formulae 1.1 and 1.3.

In Example 7.5, z was found to be -3.33, so H will be

$$\begin{aligned} H &= (-3.61)^2 + (-0.72)^2 + (-1.44)^2 - (-3.33)^2 \\ &= 4.54 \end{aligned}$$

If there are reliable differences between the three areas, H will be large, while if the three areas are relatively homogeneous, H will be close to zero.

Chi-square Approximation to H

The null distribution of H may be approximated by the chi-square distribution with $m - 1$ df, where m is the number of subjects (or matched groups). In our example, $m = 3$ (the number of areas), so we find from Table G that the critical value of χ^2 with $\alpha = 0.05$ and 2 df is 5.991. The obtained value of H is smaller than this, so we cannot reject the null hypothesis of homogeneity. Thus we have no reliable grounds for our suspicion that the three areas differ with these data.

There is a difficulty with the use of this chi-square approximation. For the test to be at all accurate, the normal approximation based on the z-score for each subject (or matched group) must be good. This will be true for our example, since the sample sizes are sufficiently large in each of the three areas for the normal approximation to S in each case to be good. Had the sample sizes for one (or more) of the areas been so small that the normal approximation for that area was poor, the chi-square approximation to H should not be used. Unlike the Combined S Test, the approximation of H to the chi-square distribution is *not* improved by increasing the number of subjects or matched groups being compared. This means that we should not be able to use the chi-square approximation to test the homogeneity of the trends shown in Table 7.9, since the normal approximation to some of the S's would be expected to be poor; for example, the data for pigeon 3 have $t_1 = 1$ and $t_2 = 4$ and we know that the normal approximation to the Rank-Sum Test will not be good with such small values of t_1 and t_2. The same would be true of the data for Example 7.2 shown in Table 7.4, since the normal approximation to the Kendall Test is not very good when $n = 3$.

In cases where the chi-square approximation is not accurate, a more complicated approximation suggested by Jonckheere may help (see Jonckheere, 1970, or Jonckheere and Bower, 1967).

Further Comments

The two statistics J and H that we have been using in this chapter are independent. This means that any pattern of significance is possible between the two tests. Thus, a non-significant Combined S Test might be obtained in conjunction with a significant Homogeneity Test or with a non-significant Homogeneity Test. The first pattern would indicate differences between the subjects (or matched groups) while the second would suggest a conclusion of no overall trend because the subjects are all tending this way. Alternatively, a significant Combined S Test might arise together with a non-significant Homogeneity Test (as in Example 7.5), suggesting that all subjects are showing equally strong trends in the same direction, or with a significant Homogeneity Test, indicating differences in the strengths of the trends of the subjects, even though these tend to be in the same direction.

For a fuller discussion of the Homogeneity Test, see the papers by Jonckheere referred to above. Fleiss (1973, Chapter 10) gives a good discussion of the test and methods of providing a combined measure of association for 2 x 2 tables only.

Example 7.8 The Homogeneity Test with an Equally Weighted Combined S

Suppose that in the learning experiment discussed in Example 7.1, the data in Table 7.12 were obtained. The z-score for the Combined S Test (computed without using a continuity correction) will be 0.30, indicating no overall trend.

We first note that the Homogeneity Test is likely to give a reasonably accurate result here, since with 7 trials and no ties, the normal approximation to each subject's S score is likely to be quite good.

The sum of the squares of the individual z's (each computed without using a continuity correction) is given in Table 7.12. H is therefore given by

$$H = \Sigma z_i^2 - z^2$$
$$= 21.93 - (0.30)^2$$
$$= 21.84$$

Table 7.12. Hypothetical data and calculations for Example 7.8

Subject	1	2	3	4	5	6	7	S_i	z_i	z_i^2
1.	0	4	7	5	8	10	12	19	2.854	8.15
2.	0	7	5	10	6	11	9	11	1.652	2.73
3.	10	3	5	8	9	4	2	−7	−1.051	1.10
4.	8	7	5	4	3	1	0	−21	−3.154	9.95
								$J = 2$		$\Sigma z_i^2 = 21.93$

Since we are comparing the z-scores of 4 subjects, we have 3 df, so, with $\alpha = 0.05$, Table G gives 7.815 as the critical value of χ^2. The obtained value of H is larger than this, so we reject the null hypothesis of homogeneity and conclude that there are differences between the subjects, as we should expect from these data.

Example 7.9 The Homogeneity Test with an Unequally Weighted Combined *S*

In this example, we continue the analysis of the data from Example 7.7, where we obtained a significant overall result based on an unequally weighted Combined S Test. The z-score obtained was -3.78. The remaining calculations necessary to compute H are the same whether the Combined S Test was equally weighted or not. These are given in Table 7.13. H is then given by

$$\begin{aligned} H &= \Sigma z_i^2 - z^2 \\ &= 34.31 - (-3.78)^2 \\ &= 20.02 \end{aligned}$$

Since we are comparing 3 matched groups, we have 2 df. From Table G, with $\alpha = 0.05$, the critical value of χ^2 is 5.991. Our obtained H is much larger than this, so we conclude that there are reliable differences between the areas. Thus, we must modify our original conclusion with these data. Although there is a tendency for women whose husbands died in a general hospital to be more likely to have an illness in the year following bereavement than those whose husbands died in a special hospice, this is true only in two of the three areas.

Table 7.13. Calculations for Example 7.9

Area	S_i	Var S_i	z_i	z_i^2
A	−1000	53030.30	−4.342	18.86
B	−160	3076.92	−2.884	8.32
C	60	505.26	2.669	7.13
				$\Sigma z_i^2 = 34.31$

7.5 SUMMARY OF SUGGESTED PROCEDURE

General Points

1. Do you have two or more related samples? If not, look elsewhere (see the table at the front of the book for suggestions).
2. Do you wish to test an ordered prediction about the samples? If not, try Chapter 6.

3. If the responses are not ordinal or two category, try computing a Kruskal–Wallis Test separately for each subject or matched group and obtain a combined test using the approach suggested by Lehmann (1975, Section 6.5D).

Combined *S* Test

1. This test provides a combined test for a set of subjects or matched groups whose data may be analysed separately using the S statistic (see Chapter 5). It assumes that there are no carryover effects that might affect the outcome.
2. Find m, the number of subjects (or matched groups). Select the significance level α and decide whether a one- or a two-tailed test is required.
3. Compute S separately for each subject or matched group using one of the methods in Chapter 5.
4. Compute J, the sum of the S scores for each subject.
5. If there are ties in either variable or if the subjects provide different amounts of data, go to 8.
6. Find n, the number of scores for each subject (as in Chapter 5). If $n > 8$ or if $m > 10$, use the normal approximation given in 7. Otherwise, find the relevant critical value(s) in Table L and complete the test as indicated at the top of Table L. Go to 11.
7. *Normal approximation*

$$\text{Compute Variance of } J = \frac{mn(n-1)(2n+5)}{18} \tag{7.1}$$

$$\text{Compute } J_c = \begin{cases} J - 1, \text{ if } J \text{ positive} \\ J + 1, \text{ if } J \text{ negative} \end{cases}$$

$$\text{Compute } z = \frac{J_c}{\text{S.D.}}, \text{ where S.D.} = \sqrt{\text{Variance}}$$

and compare the obtained value with the relevant critical value(s) in Table B(ii) to complete the test. Go to 11.

8. If the ties are such that the variance of S is different for each subject (or matched group), go to 9. When the variances are the same, find the common variance using the table at the back of the book and use the following normal approximation.

$$\text{Compute Variance of } J = m \times \text{Variance of } S \tag{7.2}$$

$$\text{Compute } z = \frac{J}{\text{S.D.}}, \text{ where S.D.} = \sqrt{\text{Variance of } J}$$

and compare the obtained value with the relevant critical value(s) in Table B(ii) to complete the test. Go to 11.

9. If the variance of S is different for each subject, decide whether to use equal weighting or unequal weighting when combining the S's (see Section 7.3). If there is the same number of observations for each subject, use equal weighting.

If in doubt use unequal weighting. For unequal weighting go to 10. *For equal weighting*, Compute Variance of J as the sum of the individual variances of S, computed separately for each subject using the table at the back of the book.

$$\text{Compute } z = \frac{J}{\text{S.D.}}, \text{ where S.D.} = \sqrt{\text{Variance of } J}$$

and compare the obtained value with the relevant critical value(s) in Table B(ii) to complete the test. Go to 11.

10. *For unequal weighting*

$$\text{Compute } J^* = \sum \frac{S_i}{n_i}, \tag{7.4}$$

where S_i and n_i are the S value and the number of observations for the ith subject (or matched group). Find the variance of S for each subject using the table at the back of the book and compute

$$\text{Variance of } J^* = \sum \frac{\text{Variance of } S_i}{n_i^2} \tag{7.5}$$

$$\text{Compute } z = \frac{J^*}{\text{S.D.}}, \text{ where S.D.} = \sqrt{\text{Variance of } J^*}$$

and compare the obtained value with the relevant critical value(s) in Table B(ii) to complete the test.

11. Check that there are no differences between subjects or matched groups using the Homogeneity Test.

Homogeneity Test

1. Check that there are sufficient observations for each subject (or matched group) for the normal approximation to S to be good. If the normal approximation is likely to be poor for any subject, the Homogeneity Test given here may not be accurate.
2. Compute a separate z-score for each subject (or matched group) in the usual way (without continuity correction) as described in Chapter 5. Label the z-score for the ith subject z_i.
3. Compute Σz_i^2, the sum of the squares of the individual z-scores.
4. Compute z^2, the square of the overall z-score computed as shown in the Combined S Test (without continuity correction).
5. Find $H = \Sigma z_i^2 - z^2$ and compare the obtained value with the relevant critical value from Table G with $m - 1$ df, where m is the number of subjects (or matched groups). If a significant value is obtained, there are reliable differences between the subjects.

7.6 EXERCISES

Section 7.1

1. In a learning experiment, the number of correct responses on each of 6 trials is recorded for each of three subjects. Do the data below provide evidence that the group of subjects has shown learning?

		Trial number					
		1	2	3	4	5	6
Subject	1.	3	6	8	2	7	9
	2.	1	3	4	5	10	9
	3.	2	8	7	9	11	10

2. The number of problems of three distinct types solved by each of four subjects is shown below. It is predicted that Type *A* problems should be the hardest, while Type *C* problems should be the easiest, with Type *B* of intermediate difficulty. Is the prediction confirmed?

		Type of problem		
		A	*B*	*C*
Subject	1.	20	30	40
	2.	25	26	24
	3.	29	31	53
	4.	42	48	49

Section 7.2

3. Three schools take part in an experiment comparing two methods of teaching elementary arithmetical concepts. 10 children from each school are randomly selected to be taught by Method I for a term and a further 10 children are taught by Method II. At the end of the term each child is given a test of arithmetic achievement. Do the results given below suggest that either method is superior?

		School *A*		School *B*		School *C*	
		Pass	Fail	Pass	Fail	Pass	Fail
Method	I	7	3	6	4	8	2
	II	4	6	5	5	3	7

4. Suppose the results from the two colleges comparing Arts and Science students' performance in a statistics examination are as shown below. Show that collapsing the data over colleges is misleading but that the Combined S Test gives a sensible conclusion.

	College *A*			College *B*		
	Distinction	Pass	Fail	Distinction	Pass	Fail
Science	20	20	20	1	20	29
Arts	1	1	1	1	20	29

5. In another learning experiment, the following data are obtained. Does this group show evidence of learning?

		Trial number					
		1	2	3	4	5	6
Subject	1.	3	3	2	3	5	6
	2.	7	8	9	8	10	8
	3.	1	2	2	4	2	7

Section 7.3

6. In yet another learning experiment, the following data are obtained. Does this group show evidence of learning?

		Trial number				
		1	2	3	4	5
Subject	1.	3	3	3	6	10
	2.	1	2	3	8	9
	3.	4	2	5	5	6

Why does it not matter in this case whether we choose equal or unequal weightings of the S values? Which is easier to compute?

7. In a test of all-or-none theory along the lines of Example 7.6, four people produced the data shown below up to and including the trial of last error. Do these data show evidence of a trend in learning or do they support the all-or-none theory?

		Trial number							
		1	2	3	4	5	6	7	8
Person	1.	I	I	I	I	I	C	C	I
	2.	I	C	I	C	C	I	I	I
	3.	I	C	C	C	I			
	4.	I	I	I	I	C	I	I	

8. A further three schools take part in the study outlined in Exercise 7.4. This time, however, all the children available in each school take part in the experiment, half of those available being taught by Method I and half by Method II. Do the results given below suggest that either method of teaching arithmetical concepts is superior?

		School *A*		School *B*		School *C*	
		Pass	Fail	Pass	Fail	Pass	Fail
Method	I	10	2	11	12	13	3
	II	3	9	11	11	7	9

Section 7.4

9. Carry out the Homogeneity Test for the data in Exercises 1, 3, and 8.
10. Why would you expect the Homogeneity Test not to be accurate for the data in Exercise 2 and 7? What about Exercises 5 and 6?

CHAPTER 8

Tests for One Sample or Several Independent Samples – Both Variables Categorical

The tests described in this chapter are approximate tests based on the chi-square distribution which we used in Chapter 4 to provide an approximation to the Kruskal–Wallis Test. They are applicable to data involving several independent samples, when both the explanatory variable and the response variable are categorical (see Examples 1.6 and 1.11), or to one-sample data with a categorical response variable (see Example 1.3).

The most important assumption is the familiar one of independence. In the one-sample case, this means that each person in the experiment must contribute only one score on the response variable. In the other cases, each person must contribute only one score on the explanatory variable and one score on the response variable. In addition, in all cases, each person should not be able to influence the scores of any other person.

Since these tests are based on an approximation, they may not be accurate when sample sizes are small.

8.1 THE CHI-SQUARE TEST FOR INDEPENDENCE

The Chi-Square Test was suggested by Karl Pearson at the turn of the century and has proved a popular test ever since. It may be used to test whether two variables are independent or whether they are associated; in doing so, it treats both variables as categorical.

Simplified Example

120 people each see one film by Vincente Minnelli, 50 of them seeing *Some Came Running*, 30 seeing *Meet Me in St. Louis*, 20 seeing *On a Clear Day You Can See Forever* and the remaining 20 seeing *The Courtship of Eddie's Father*. Afterwards they are asked to state which one of the three main characters they found most

Table 8.1. Hypothetical data for the simplified example

	Leading Male	Leading Female	Supporting Female	t_i
Some Came Running	12	38	0	50
Meet Me in St. Louis	10	11	9	30
On a Clear Day You Can See Forever	10	10	0	20
The Courtship of Eddie's Father	4	1	15	20
u_i	36	60	24	$120 = n$

sympathetic. Suppose the data are those given in the contingency table in Table 8.1, and we wish to know whether there are reliable differences between the four movies in terms of the character found most sympathetic. Here the explanatory variable is the film seen and the response variable is the character chosen. We first note that the data are independent, each person providing us with a single score on both the explanatory and the response variable, since they see only one movie and name only one character. The requirement of independence also means we must assume that no person has influenced the choice of any other person in a way that might bias the results.

The Chi-Square Test is appropriate when both variables are categorical. This is so for our example. The explanatory variable is categorical, since we are making no ordered predictions about differences between the films. Similarly, the response variable is categorical, since there is no underlying ordering of the responses that we wish to take into account in our test.

This situation is to be contrasted with one in which we are predicting a specific ordering for one or both of the variables. For example, we may be interested in seeing whether Minnelli's films have changed as he has grown older. We might then consider ordering the films from the earliest, *Meet Me in St. Louis*, to the most recent, *On a Clear Day You Can See Forever*. To test such a prediction, we therefore treat the explanatory variable as ordinal, although the response variable is still categorical. The appropriate statistical test that focuses on this more specific question will then be the Kruskal–Wallis Test (interchanging the roles of the explanatory and the response variables to conform to the description given in Chapter 4). We can carry out the Kruskal-Wallis Test using the method of Example 4.3 after reordering the rows of the contingency table to conform with our predicted (chronological) ordering of the films.

As an example of the situation in which both variables are considered ordinal, suppose we wish to test the prediction that the most sympathetic character in the earlier films is the leading female while in the intermediate films the supporting female is the most sympathetic and the leading male is the most sympathetic in the later films. To test such a prediction, we should treat both variables as ordinal and use the Jonckheere Test (as in Example 5.4), after reordering the rows and columns of the contingency table to conform to the predicted ordering of both variables. This would involve rearranging the columns by writing the choices for the leading female on the left, the choices for the supporting female in the middle and the choices for the leading male on the right, and rearranging the rows by writing the films in chronological order.

The Jonckheere Test and the Kruskal–Wallis Test both home in on specific predictions about the data and ignore other possible differences. The Chi-Square Test, on the other hand, provides an omnibus test, asking whether there are any differences at all between the four films. For this reason, it is less sensitive to any specific ordered predictions than the other tests, but it will thereby also be able to identify other types of difference between the films. For example, the supporting female character played by Stella Stevens in *The Courtship of Eddie's Father* is particularly sympathetic, which makes this film unusual amongst the other Minnelli films here. The Chi-Square Test will pick out such unusual events.

The null hypothesis tested by the Chi-Square Test for Independence is that the proportion of people choosing each of the three characters is the same for each film. The alternative hypothesis is that these proportions differ in any way. The Chi-Square Test is a test for independence between the two variables because the null hypothesis will be true when there is no association (i.e. independence) between the films and the most sympathetic character.

Test Statistic – χ^2

Under the null hypothesis, we expect the proportion of people choosing, say, the leading man as the most sympathetic character to be the same for all four films. Any differences that are actually observed are then thought to be merely accidents of sampling. If this is so, our best bet for the proportion of people choosing the leading man will be given by the total proportion of people making this choice, which is 36/120 or 0.3, since 36 of the 120 people chose the leading man. Similarly, our best bet for the proportion of people choosing the leading woman will be 60/120 or 0.5 and our best bet for the proportion of people choosing the supporting woman will be 24/120 or 0.2. We know that 50 people saw *Some Came Running*, so if there is no difference between the films, we expect 0.3 x 50 or 15 of these to choose the leading male character, 0.5 x 50 or 25 to choose the leading

Table 8.2. Expected frequencies for the data in Table 8.1

				t_i
	15	25	10	50
	9	15	6	30
	6	10	4	20
	6	10	4	20
u_i	36	60	24	$120 = n$

Table 8.3. Contribution of each cell to χ^2, calculated as $(O - E)^2/E$

0.60	6.76	10.00	17.36
0.11	1.07	1.50	2.68
2.67	0.00	4.00	6.67
0.67	8.10	30.25	39.02
4.05	15.93	45.75	65.73 = χ^2

female and 0.2 x 50 or 10 to choose the supporting female. In a similar way we can work out expected frequencies for each of the other films under the null hypothesis. The resulting expected frequencies are shown in Table 8.2. A simple way of remembering how to compute the expected frequency for any particular cell in such a contingency table is to multiply the marginal total of the row in which the cell occurs (t_i) by the marginal total of the column in which it occurs (u_i) and divide the result by n, the total number of observations. This gives 50 x 36/120 = 25 as the expected frequency of people choosing the leading male as the most sympathetic character in *Some Came Running*, as we found above.

If the null hypothesis is false, then the observed frequencies given in Table 8.1 should differ from these expected frequencies. We can see immediately from the 15 in the lower right-hand cell of Table 8.1 that the supporting female in *The Courtship of Eddie's Father* is more sympathetic than she should be if there were no differences between the films. Similarly, more people (38) chose Shirley Maclaine, who played the leading female character in *Some Came Running*, as the most sympathetic than would be expected under the null hypothesis. We can get an idea of how much the observed frequencies (O) differ from the expected frequencies (E) by calculating $(O - E)^2/E$ for each cell. This is done in Table 8.3, where, for example, the 6.76 in the second cell is obtained by calculating

$$\frac{(O-E)^2}{E} = \frac{(38-25)^2}{25} = \frac{169}{25} = 6.76.$$

From this table we can see that the two cells mentioned above have large discrepancies between observed and expected frequencies. On the other hand, the zero in the cell representing the leading female character (played by Barbra Streisand) in *On a Clear Day You Can See Forever* reflects the fact that she is getting precisely the amount of support that would be expected if there were no differences between the films.

To convert the information given in Table 8.3 into a single test statistic, which we label χ^2 (the Greek letter chi, pronounced kye), we simply find the sum of all the entries. This gives $\chi^2 = 65.73$ in this case. For those who prefer to capture what we have done by a simple formula, χ^2 is given by

$$\chi^2 = \sum \frac{(O-E)^2}{E} \tag{8.1}$$

Small values of χ^2 favour the null hypothesis that there are no differences between the films, while large values favour the alternative hypothesis.

It is worth noting that the same value of χ^2 will be obtained no matter what order the rows and columns of the contingency table are written in.

Table of the Approximate Null Distribution of χ^2 (Appendix Table G)

Since the number of possible patterns of results rapidly gets unmanageably large, it is usually not practicable to calculate the exact null distribution as we did with our previous tests. Instead, we resort to an approximation given by the chi-square distribution (Table G). This will be reasonably accurate if the sample sizes are large. As a rule-of-thumb, Table G will generally be satisfactory if none of the expected frequencies (E) is less than unity and if relatively few (say, one in five) of the cells have expected frequencies less than five. In our case, two of the twelve cells have E's less than five and none have E's less than unity (see Table 8.2), so we expect the approximation to be satisfactory. The approximation improves as the expected values get larger – when all the E's are 10 or more, the approximation is generally very good.

Degrees of freedom (df)

To use Table G, we need first to know the degrees of freedom (df) associated with our value of χ^2. In general, degrees of freedom reflect the constraints imposed on the calculation of the test statistic. In the present context, this is equivalent to the number of observed frequencies that can change without necessitating a change in the expected frequencies. The expected frequencies were calculated by using each of the marginal totals in the observed data. In our example, each row of the observed data has 2 df, since we can change any two of the values in each row without necessitating a change in the row total. So once we know any two values in each row, we automatically know the third. There are four rows in the table. Once we know the values of any three of them, the final row is automatically determined, since the columns must all add up to their respective totals of 36, 60, and 24. Thus, since three of the rows are free to vary, each of which has 2 df, the whole table has 6 df.

A simpler way of arriving at the same result is to follow the general rule that df for a contingency table are given by

$$\text{df} = (r - 1) \times (c - 1), \tag{8.2}$$

where r is the number of rows and c is the number of columns. In our example, $r = 4$ and $c = 3$, so we have $\text{df} = (4 - 1) \times (3 - 1) = 6$, as before.

From Table G, using a significance level of 0.01, we find that the approximate critical value for χ^2 with 6 df is 16.812. Since large values of χ^2 favour the alternative hypothesis and the χ^2 obtained from our example data is 65.73, which is larger than 16.812, we reject the null hypothesis. We conclude that there are differences between the films in terms of the character chosen as most sympathetic. We have already suggested two of the particular differences that might be responsible for this.

χ^2 With 1 df

When χ^2 is calculated for a contingency table with 2 rows and 2 columns, it will have 1 df. However, such a 2 x 2 contingency table could be analysed using the Fisher Exact Test of Section 2.5. Since the normal distribution provides an approximation to the Fisher Exact Test, we should expect there to be an intimate relation between the normal distribution and the chi-square distribution with 1 df. In fact, the values of the chi-square distribution with 1 df are simply the squares of the values of the normal distribution. This is easily checked by seeing, for example, that 1.96 is the critical value for a two-tailed 0.05 test using the normal distribution (Table B(ii)), while the critical value using the chi-square distribution with 1 df is 3.841 which is simply $(1.96)^2$. The only difference is that the chi-square distribution is inherently two-tailed. This relation between the chi-square and the normal distribution only holds when χ^2 has 1 df.

This means that the Chi-Square Test with 2 x 2 tables is equivalent to the normal approximation to the Fisher Exact Test. (There is a trivial difference as may be seen in Exercise 8.4, but this is generally ignored as it rarely affects any conclusions drawn.) Thus, in the case of 2 x 2 tables that fall within the scope of Table C, the Fisher Exact Test should be used in preference to the Chi-Square Test, since Table C provides an exact null distribution. (See Example 2.10 for the use of the Fisher Exact Test.)

The equivalence of these tests shows that we could have introduced the Fisher Exact Test as a special case of the tests in this section rather than as a special case of the Rank-Sum Test. This demonstrates again the way in which a two-category variable may be viewed either as categorical (hence the equivalence of the Fisher Exact and Chi-Square Tests) or as ordinal with extensive ties (hence the equivalence of the Fisher Exact and Rank-Sum Tests).

Further Comments

The chi-square distribution has many interesting uses in statistics. In the next section we shall see how it may be used to test predictions for one-sample data. For a discussion of some of the other uses of chi-square including techniques for isolating the reason for a significant Chi-Square Test see Everitt (1977), who gives an interesting introduction to many of the ways in which chi-square may be used. For the whole story, see Fienberg (1977) and Bishop, Fienberg and Holland (1975). See also Mosteller and Rourke (1973, Chapters 8–11).

Example 8.1 The Chi-square Test for Independence with Two Samples

In a comparison of two British Pariamentary constituencies, *A* and *B*, prior to a General Election, a sample of 500 potential voters from

Table 8.4. Hypothetical data for Example 8.1 (Expected frequencies in brackets)

		Labour	Liberal	Conservative	Not Voting	Don't know	t_i
Constituency	A	130 (150)	100 (100)	20 (75)	150 (100)	100 (75)	500
	B	170 (150)	100 (100)	130 (75)	50 (100)	50 (75)	500
	u_i	300	200	150	200	150	1000

each constituency are asked about their voting intentions. Both constituencies have three candidates, one from each of the major parties. The results are recorded in the contingency table in Table 8.4. Are the constituencies similar? The Chi-Square Test is applicable here if we are prepared to assume that the data are independent. Each person contributes to only one cell in the table and we should not have more than one response from anybody. Also, we must assume that each person has not been able to influence the response of any other person in a way that might bias the results.

The expected frequencies are shown in brackets alongside the observed frequencies. We note that all the E's are large, so the Chi-Square Test is likely to be quite accurate.

The calculation of χ^2 is as follows:

$$\chi^2 = \sum \frac{(O-E)^2}{E} = \frac{(130-150)^2}{150} + \frac{(100-100)^2}{100} + \frac{(20-75)^2}{75}$$

$$+ \frac{(150-100)^2}{100} + \frac{(100-75)^2}{75} + \frac{(170-150)^2}{150}$$

$$+ \frac{(100-100)^2}{100} + \frac{(130-75)^2}{75} + \frac{(50-100)^2}{100} + \frac{(50-75)^2}{75}$$

$$= 152.67$$

There are 2 rows and 5 columns in the contingency table, so we have $(2-1) \times (5-1) = 4$ df. Using a significance level of 0.05, we find from Table G that the critical value of χ^2 with 4 df is 9.488. Our obtained value is larger than this, so we reject the null hupothesis and conclude that there are reliable differences in voting intentions between the two constituencies. The most noticeable differences seem to be in the proportion of people intending to vote Conservative and in the proportion intending not to vote at all.

Table 8.5. Pearson's data used in Example 8.2 (Expected frequencies in brackets)

Coat colour of mother	Coat colour of daughter					
	Black	Brown	Bay	Chestnut	Grey	t_i
Black	7(1.596)	7(5.738)	13(18.278)	6(9.158)	5(3.230)	38
Brown	8(7.266)	40(26.123)	95(83.213)	23(41.693)	7(14.705)	173
Bay	11(18.774)	75(67.497)	230(215.007)	113(107.727)	18(37.995)	447
Chestnut	11(9.660)	20(34.730)	101(110.630)	82(55.430)	16(19.550)	230
Grey	5(4.704)	9(16.912)	42(53.872)	17(26.992)	39(9.520)	112
u_i	42	151	481	241	85	1000

Example 8.2 The Chi-Square Test for Independence with more than Two Samples

Since the Chi-Square Test was suggested by Karl Pearson, it seems appropriate to use some of his data to illustrate one of its uses. While studying inheritance. Pearson tabulated from stud-books the coat colour of 1000 mother-daughter racehorse pairs. Suppose we want to test whether there is any association between the coat colour of mother and that of daughter. The Chi-Square Test allows us to do this. Pearson's data are shown in the contingency table in Table 8.5 together with expected frequencies (in brackets). These are calculated in the usual way by multiplying the relevant marginal totals together and dividing by n. Thus, the 1.596 in the first cell is given by 38 x 42/1000. For the Chi-Square Test to be appropriate here, we must have independent data. This means that each mother–daughter combination contributes once only to one cell. Also, we should be careful to check whether data from a mother with several daughters has been included. If this is the case, the Chi-Square Test may be biased.

Before carrying our the Chi-Square Test, we note that all the expected frequencies are larger than unity, but 3 of the 25 E's are less than 5. However, our rule-of-thumb that no more than one-fifth of the cells have E's less than 5 is satisfied, so we expect the Chi-Square Test to be reasonably accurate.
χ^2 is given by

$$\chi^2 = \sum \frac{(O-E)^2}{E} = \frac{(7-1.596)^2}{1.596} + \frac{(7-5.738)^2}{5.738} + \cdots$$

$$+ \frac{(17-26.992)^2}{26.992} + \frac{(39-9.520)^2}{9.520}$$

$$= 181.55$$

Since there are 5 rows and 5 columns, we have $(5-1) \times (5-1) =$ 16 df. Using a significance level of 0.001, Table G gives the critical value of χ^2 with 16 df as 39.252. The obtained value is larger than this, so we reject the null hypothesis and conclude that there is a reliable association between coat colour of mother and that of daughter.

8.2 THE ONE-SAMPLE CHI-SQUARE TEST

The chi-square distribution can be used for one-sample data to provide an approximate test of whether the data obtained are consistent with a specific prediction. The test outlined below is very similar to the Chi-Square Test for Independence described in Section 8.1. The test statistic is again given by χ^2, which reflects the departure of the observed frequencies from those expected if the prediction is correct. The only difference is in methods of computing the expected frequencies and the df, which will be illustrated in the simplified example below.

Simplified Example

35 children were independently asked to name their favourite day of the week. The choices were:

Sun. 0; Mon. 1; Tues. 3; Wed. 7; Thurs. 8; Fri. 5; Sat. 11.

We wish to know whether these data are consistent with having sampled children whose preferences were evenlyy distributed over all the days of the week (the null hypothesis). This implies that we should expect 5 of the 35 children to choose each day. 5 is therefore the expected frequency of choice for each day.

The response variable has seven categorical values (the names of the days). Degrees of freedom in the one-sample case are given by the number of categories minus one, 6 in our example. This is because any 6 of the 7 observed frequencies are free to vary without necessitating a change in the total number of children, which we used to calculate the expected frequencies. In general, if the response variable has k categories, there will be $k - 1$ df.

χ^2 is calculated in the standard way using formula 8.1 as

$$\chi^2 = \sum \frac{(O-E)^2}{E} = \frac{(0-5)^2}{5} + \frac{(1-5)^2}{5} + \frac{(3-5)^2}{5} + \frac{(7-5)^2}{5} + \frac{(8-5)^2}{5} + \frac{(5-5)^2}{5} + \frac{(11-5)^2}{5}$$

$$= 18.8$$

Since none of the E's is less than 5, we expect the Chi-Square Test to be reasonably accurate. Using a significance level of 0.05, Table G gives the critical value of χ^2 with 6 df as 12.592. Our obtained value is larger than this, so we reject the null hypothesis and conclude that the children did not prefer all days of the week equally. This conclusion will, as usual, only be valid if the choices of the children were independent.

χ^2 with 1 df

In the one-sample case, χ^2 has 1 df when there are only two categories of response, so we should expect the Chi-Square Test to be equivalent to using the normal approximation to the Binomial Test (Section 3.4), which it is. The one-sample Chi-Square Test thus provides an alternative perspective on the Binomial Test. Consider again the data from Example 3.10 in which 29 out of 100 students give the correct answer to a 5-alternative multiple-choice question. Since the question has 5 alternatives, only one of which is correct, we should expect one-fifth of the students to get it correct by chance and four-fifths to get it wrong. There are two categories of response, correct and incorrect, with expected frequencies of

$100/5 = 20$ and $4 \times 100/5 = 80$. We therefore have

$$\chi^2 = \frac{(29 - 20)^2}{20} + \frac{(71 - 80)^2}{80} = 5.06,$$

which has 1 df. With $\alpha = 0.05$, this value is larger than the critical value of 3.841 given in Table G, so we reject the null hypothesis and conclude as before that more students got the question correct than would be expected by chance. This test is equivalent to the test carried out on the same data in Example 3.10 except in two minor ways. The first is that the Chi-Square Test is inherently two-tailed, whereas we originally carried out a one-tailed test which seems more appropriate for these data. The second is that we haven't included a correction for continuity here, which is why the χ^2 value of 5.06 is not quite the square of the z-score of 2.125 obtained in Example 3.10. Again, the analysis including a continuity correction is likely to be more accurate. It is possible to include a continuity correction in the formula for χ^2 with 1 df (see, for example, Mosteller and Rourke, 1973, Section 9.5), which does make $\chi^2 = z^2$.

Example 8.3 The One-Sample Chi-Square Test

In one of his many famous experiments with peas, the geneticist Mendel obtained 556 peas from a number of plants and classified them as in Table 8.6. According to Mendelian theory, the proportions of the four types should be 9/16, 3/16, 3/16 and 1/16, respectively. We can use the Chi-Square Test to test whether the data are consistent with this theory, which implies, for example, that 9/16 of the 556 peas classified (i.e. 312.75) should be round and yellow. This and the other expected frequencies, calculated in a similar way, are shown in brackets alongside the observed frequencies. Since there are four categories, we have 3 df and

$$\chi^2 = \frac{(315 - 312.75)^2}{312.75} + \frac{(108 - 104.25)^2}{104.25} + \frac{(101 - 104.25)^2}{104.25} + \frac{(32 - 34.75)^2}{34.75} = 0.47$$

In this case, we should be wise to use a relatively large significance level, such as 0.20, to give us a powerful test (cf. Example 3.3). We note that all the E's are large, so Table G should be accurate. With $\alpha = 0.20$ and 3 df, the critical value of χ^2 is 4.642. Our obtained value is much smaller than this, so we cannot reject the null hypothesis and we conclude that the data are consistent with Mendel's theory. (For an interesting discussion of some of Mendel's other data on garden peas, see Bishop, Fienberg, and Holland, 1975, Example 9.5.3.)

Table 8.6. Mendel's data used in Example 8.3

Type of pea	Frequency
Round and yellow	315 (312.75)
Round and green	108 (104.25)
Angular and yellow	101 (104.25)
Angular and green	32 (34.75)
Total, n	556

8.3 MEASURES OF ASSOCIATION FOR (UNORDERED) CONTINGENCY TABLES

In this section, we discuss a number of measures of association that are appropriate for data that may be represented in the form of a contingency table in which both the explanatory and the response variable are categorical. These measure are more general than those considered in Section 5.6, which are applicable only to *ordered* contingency tables, i.e. those in which both variables are ordinal. As with those measures, in some cases we may require an asymmetrical measure of association that differentiates between the explanatory and response variable and gives an indication of how much we can predict about the response variable given knowledge of the explanatory variable. In other cases, we may require a symmetrical measure that gives an indication of the degree to which the two variables are related without focusing attention on any one of them. We shall discuss in detail a measure introduced by Goodman and Kruskal that has both an asymmetrical and a symmetrical version, but first we shall discuss briefly some symmetrical measures based on the χ^2 test statistic.

Measures Based on χ^2

Several popular measures of association are based on the test statistic for the Chi-Square Test for Independence. Since this test assesses departure from independence, with values of χ^2 close to zero reflecting independence and large values reflecting lack of independence of the two variables, it seems natural to base a measure of association on χ^2. χ^2 itself will not do, since its value is influenced by the number of observations obtained; most people want a measure of association that does not depend on the number of observations. We shall consider two measures here, both of which involve a simple transformation of χ^2 to make it independent of the number of observations.

Pearson's Mean Square Contingency Coefficient, ϕ^2

Karl Pearson suggested the simplest of the measures of association based on χ^2, which is labelled ϕ^2 (the Greek letter phi). This is given simply by dividing the obtained value of χ^2 by n, the total number of observations. So

$$\phi^2 = \chi^2/n. \tag{8.3}$$

Phi square is frequently called the *mean square contingency coefficient*.

To illustrate its use, suppose we ask a sample of 100 people to indicate which of three political parties, Labour, Liberal, or Conservative, they prefer and we also ask them to state whether or not they belong to a trade union. Some possible outcomes are shown in Table 8.7. In all cases we have $n = 100$. For the data in (a), the value of χ^2, computed as in Example 8.1, is 16.67, which is significant even when using an α as low as 0.001. The Chi-Square Test thus indicates a reliable departure from independence. Phi square allows us to assess the size of this association. In this case, $\phi^2 = 0.17$, suggesting a slight association between trade union membership and party preference.

For the data in (b), trade union membership and party preference are clearly independent and the χ^2 value of 0 reflects this. When the two variables are independent, ϕ^2 will also be 0. In fact, this is the smallest value ϕ^2 can take, since χ^2 can never be negative, so neither can ϕ^2.

The data in (c) indicate a very strong association between the two variables, which is reflected by the large χ^2 of 100. In this case, $\phi^2 = 1$. The same data are shown transposed in (d); obviously the same values of χ^2 and ϕ^2 will be obtained no matter which way round the data are recorded, so ϕ^2 provides a symmetrical measure of association.

Phi square has two major disadvantages as a measure of association. The first is that it has no simple interpretation, which makes it difficult to compare values of ϕ^2 obtained from different sets of data. Thus, it is not at all clear what meaning to attach to the ϕ^2 of 0.17 in Table 8.7 (a). This disadvantage is shared by all the measures of association based on χ^2.

The second drawback is that ϕ^2 is not guaranteed to lie between 0 and 1; in some cases it may be larger than 1, as illustrated by the data in Table 8.8, for which $\phi^2 = 2$. Many people prefer to use a measure of association that always lies between 0 and 1. Several ways of modifying ϕ^2 to achieve this have been suggested, the most useful of which was suggested by Harald Cramér.

Cramér's C

Suppose we have a contingency table with r rows and c columns. Let q be the smaller or r and c (or their common value if $r = c$). Cramér's measure of association is then given by

$$C = \frac{\chi^2}{n(q-1)} \tag{8.4}$$

For the data in Table 8.8, $r = 3$ and $c = 3$, so q will be 3 also and C will be

$$C = \frac{\chi^2}{n \times 2} = \frac{100}{50 \times 2} = 1.$$

Table 8.7. Some possible outcomes when cross-classifying 100 people according to preferred political party and membership of a trade union

(a)

	Lab.	Lib.	Cons.	t_i
Member	35	4	15	60
Non-member	15	16	15	40
u_i	50	20	30	$100 = n$

$\chi^2 = 16.67$; $\phi^2 = 0.17$; $C = 0.17$;
$\lambda_a = 0.02$; $\lambda = 0.08$

(b)

	Lab.	Lib.	Cons.	t_i
Member	30	12	18	60
Non-member	20	8	12	40
u_i	50	20	30	100

$\chi^2 = 0$; $\phi^2 = 0$; $C = 0$;
$\lambda_a = 0$; $\lambda = 0$

(c)

	Lab.	Lib.	Cons.	t_i
Member	50		30	80
Non-member		20		20
u_i	50	20	30	100

$\chi^2 = 100$; $\phi^2 = 1$; $C = 1$;
$\lambda_a = 0.40$; $\lambda = 0.57$

(d)

	Member	Non-member	t_i
Lab.	50		50
Lib.		20	20
Cons.	30		30
u_i	80	20	100

$\chi^2 = 100$; $\phi^2 = 1$; $C = 1$;
$\lambda_a = 1$; $\lambda = 0.57$

Table 8.8. Cross-classification of 50 dogs according to breed and size

		Size			
		Large	Medium	Small	t_i
Breed	Bulldog		10		10
	Alsatian	20			20
	Terrier			20	20
	u_i	20	10	20	$50 = n$

$\chi^2 = 100; \phi^2 = 2; C = 1;$
$\lambda_a = 1; \lambda = 1$

For the data in Table 8.7(a), $r = 2$ and $c = 3$, so q will be 2 and C will be

$$C = \frac{\chi^2}{n} = 0.17$$

which in this case is exactly the same as ϕ^2. This will always be true when there are 2 rows or 2 columns in the contingency table. In other cases, C will be smaller than ϕ^2. C always lies between 0 and 1, taking the value 0 in cases of complete independence (e.g. Table 8.7(b)) and the value 1 in cases of perfect association (e.g. Table 8.7(c) or Table 8.8). Like ϕ^2, it does not have a simple interpretation (although a rather complicated interpretation of C is possible, as shown by Kendall and Stuart, 1973, Section 33.51).

Goodman and Kruskal's Lambda Measures

In Section 5.6 we discussed Goodman and Kruskal's gamma which was applicable to ordered contingency tables. In the same 1954 paper they also presented a measure of association that is applicable to unordered contingency tables. They called this measure λ (the Greek letter lambda). Like gamma, lambda has a simple probabilistic interpretation, which makes it more generally attractive than the measures based on χ^2.

Asymmetrical version, λ_a

We first consider the asymmetrical version of lambda, labelled λ_a (a for asymmetrical). To introduce it, consider again the data in Table 8.7(c) for which $\chi^2 = 100$, indicating a reliable association between trade union membership and party preference. Now suppose that we want to be able to predict the preferred political party of one of the 100 people drawn at random. If we don't know whether or not the person belongs to a trade union, our best bet is to guess Labour, since 50 of the 100 people preferred Labour. If we guess Labour, we shall be wrong 50 times out of 100, since 50 (20 + 30) people indicated Liberal or Conservative preferences.

If we are also told that the person is a trade union member, our best bet will still be Labour, since 50 of the 80 trade union members preferred Labour. In this case, we shall be wrong 30 times out of 80, since 30 of the trade union members preferred Conservative rather than Labour. On the other hand, if we know that the person does not belong to a trade union, our best bet will be Liberal, since all 20 non-trade unionists preferred Liberal. This time we shall never be wrong.

Without considering trade union membership, our error rate in guessing party preference was 50 in 100. However, taking trade union membership into account, we made only 30 errors if the person concerned was a member and none if the person concerned was not a member – a total of 30 errors. Predicting party preference on the basis of trade union membership has allowed us to reduce our error from 50 to 30. We can summarize this reduction of error by expressing it as a proportion of the original error to give λ_a, the required measure of association.

$$\lambda_a = \frac{\text{Amount of reduction in error}}{\text{Amount of original error}} \tag{8.5}$$

In our case,

$$\lambda_a = \frac{50 - 30}{50} = 0.40$$

This says that 40% of our errors in guessing the preferred party for these 100 people can be eliminated if we take trade union membership into account. This indicates a fairly good degree of association.

In this case, we have treated trade union membership as the explanatory variable, with preferred party as the response variable. Lambda is indicating how much our prediction of the response category can be improved by knowledge of the explanatory category.

We can, of course, turn the problem round the other way and ask how much knowledge of the preferred party helps us to predict whether or not a person belongs to a trade union, thus treating preferred party as the explanatory variable and union membership as the response variable. Following our usual convention of recording the levels of the explanatory variable as the rows of a contingency table and the response variable as the columns, our data would now be recorded as in Table 8.7(d). If we try predicting trade union membership without knowledge of the person's preferred party, our best bet is to say that the person is a member, since 80 of the 100 people belong to a trade union. Our error will then be 20 out of 100. Knowing that a person prefers Labour makes membership of a union certain, so there will be no error. The same will be true if we know that the person prefers Conservative. If the person shows Liberal leanings, our best bet is non-member, again with no error. This time, knowing the party preference reduces our error from

20 to 0, so λ_a is given by

$$\lambda_a = \frac{\text{Amount of reduction in error}}{\text{Amount of original error}} = \frac{20 - 0}{20} = 1$$

This says that all of our errors in guessing trade union membership for these 100 people can be eliminated if we take preferred party into account.

Since λ_a takes different values for the data in Tables 8.7(c) and (d), it is asymmetrical. It summarizes the degree to which knowledge of the explanatory variable helps in guessing the values on the response variable.

The calculation of λ_a may be speeded up considerably by making use of the following simple procedure, which will always give the same value as the method outlined above. First, make sure that the rows of the contingency table represent the levels of the explanatory variable and the columns represent the levels of the response variable. Then find the largest frequency in each row – it doesn't matter which you choose if several entries are tied at the largest frequency. Label the largest frequency in the *i*th row rm_i (for row maximum). Find the largest column marginal total, i.e. the largest of the u's, calling it max(u). Then find λ_a by calculating

$$\lambda_a = \frac{\Sigma rm_i - \max(u)}{n - \max(u)} \tag{8.6}$$

where, as usual, n is the total number of observations. For the data in Table 8.7(c), the largest frequencies in each row are 50 and 20 and the largest column marginal total is 50, so $\Sigma rm_i = 50 + 20 = 70$, $\max(u) = 50$ and $n = 100$, giving

$$\lambda_a = \frac{70 - 50}{100 - 50} = 0.40,$$

as obtained before using the method of formula 8.5.

Similarly, for the data in Table 8.7(d), we have $\Sigma rm_i = 50 + 20 + 30 = 100$, $\max(u) = 80$ and $n = 100$, giving

$$\lambda_a = \frac{100 - 80}{100 - 80} = 1,$$

as before.

λ_a always lies between 0 and 1, taking the value of zero when the two variables are independent, as in Table 8.7(b). It takes its maximum value of 1 only when each row of the contingency table contains at most one non-zero entry, since only in that case is perfect predictability possible.

In some cases, λ_a may be zero even when the Chi-Square Test indicates an association between the two variables. For example, the data in Table 8.9 have $\chi^2 = 25$ but $\lambda_a = 0$. This shows that it is possible to have a reliable association between two variables even when knowledge of one variable does not help in predicting the other. Thus, the predictive association measured by λ_a is only one of

Table 8.9. Data showing that λ_a and λ may be zero even when the Chi-Square Test indicates a reliable association

	Lab.	Lib.	Cons.	t_i
Member	30	20	30	80
Non-member	20			20
u_i	50	20	30	100

$\chi^2 = 25; \lambda_a = \lambda = 0$

a number of types of association that may occur. In this instance, it is clear that more of the non-members prefer Labour and fewer prefer Liberal or Conservative than would be expected if there were no association between union membership and party preference.

Symmetrical version, λ

Goodman and Kruskal also suggested a symmetrical version of λ that allows us to assess the mutual predictability between two variables. It can be illustrated again with the data in Table 8.7(c). Suppose we are given information about a person's score on one variable and we want to predict the score on the other variable. Some of the time we are asked to predict party preference given knowledge of union membership. Some of the time we are told what party the person prefers and are asked to predict union membership. We already know from our calculations of λ_a that in the first case we reduce our error from 50 to 30, while in the second case we reduce our error from 20 to 0. The symmetrical version of λ puts these two pieces of information together to give

$$\lambda = \frac{\text{Amount of reduction in error in both variables}}{\text{Amount of original error in both variables}} \tag{8.7}$$

In our case,

$$\lambda = \frac{(50 - 30) + (20 - 0)}{50 + 20} = 0.57$$

This says that we should eliminate 57% of our errors in guessing each of our variables if we make use of our knowledge of the other variable.

The interpretation of λ is not quite so straightforward as that of λ_a where we are only concerned with prediction in one direction. However, the interpretation still provides useful information in many situations.

The calculation of λ may be speeded up in a similar way to that of λ_a. In this case, however, since λ is symmetrical, it doesn't matter which way round the contingency table is recorded. First, find rm_i, the largest frequency in the ith row, and cm_i, the largest frequency in the ith column. Then find max(u), the largest column marginal total, and max(t), the largest row marginal total. Then find λ by calculating

$$\lambda = \frac{\Sigma rm_i + \Sigma cm_i - \max(u) - \max(t)}{2n - \max(u) - \max(t)} \tag{8.8}$$

where n is the total number of observations. For the data in Table 8.7(c), the largest frequencies in each row are 50 and 20, so $\Sigma rm_i = 50 + 20 = 70$, the largest frequencies in each column are 50, 20, and 30, so $\Sigma cm_i = 50 + 20 + 30 = 100$, $\max(u) = 50$, $\max(t) = 80$ and $n = 100$, giving

$$\lambda = \frac{70 + 100 - 50 - 80}{200 - 50 - 80} = 0.57$$

as obtained before using the method of formula 8.7.

λ shares with λ_a the property of always lying between 0 and 1, taking the value 0 when there is no predictive association between the two variables (e.g. Tables 8.7(b) and 8.9) and taking the value 1 when perfect mutual predictability is possible (e.g. Table 8.8). λ will therefore only attain its maximum value of 1 when each row and each column of the contingency table contains at most one non-zero entry.

2 x 2 Contingency Tables

What happens to the measures discussed above for data in the form of a 2 x 2 contingency table? When a variable has only two categories, we know that it is possible to view it as either categorical or ordinal, so 2 x 2 tables may be treated either as ordered contingency tables or as unordered contingency tables. We have already seen in Section 5.6 that it is profitable to use the ordinal measures of association in the 2 x 2 case. Let us now see whether the measures of association just introduced are useful.

In the 2 x 2 case, Pearson's mean square contingency coefficient, ϕ^2, and Cramér's C will be identically equal to χ^2/n. The value obtained will always be the same as the square of the value of τ_b discussed in Section 5.6. (This is true only for 2 x 2 tables.) Thus, apart from the squaring, which does not change any of the crucial information, ϕ^2 provides identical information to τ_b.

The lambda measures do not reduce to any of the previously introduced ordinal measures in the 2 x 2 case and so provide yet another alternative measure of association for 2 x 2 tables. Like τ_b, however, they are particularly sensitive to changes in marginals totals. Unless a proportional reduction in error measure is particularly required, I would suggest restricting the choice of measures for 2 x 2 tables to the ones discussed in Section 5.6.

Choosing a Measure of Association for Unordered Contingency Tables

The measures of association based on χ^2 have the advantages of being easy to calculate once the Chi-Square Test for Independence has been completed. Cramér's

C is generally preferable to Pearson's ϕ^2, since it is guaranteed to lie between 0 and 1 for any contingency table. However, neither of these measures has a simple interpretation. All that can be said is that the larger the value obtained, the more the two variables depart from independence.

The lambda measures are useful if a measure of predictability is required. In such cases, they are clearly superior to the measures based on χ^2, since they have a very simple interpretation. The choice between λ_a and λ depends on whether an asymmetrical or a symmetrical measure is required. The asymmetrical λ_a is useful if attention is focused on one variable (the explanatory variable) and we want to assess how helpful that variable is in predicting the level of the response variable. The symmetrical λ is useful for assessing mutual predictability.

For 2 x 2 tables, one of the measures in Section 5.6 should be used.

Further Comments

For a fuller discussion of measures of association for unordered contingency tables, see Bishop, Fienberg and Holland (1975, Chapter 11). They include some of the other measures based on χ^2 that we have not discussed here as well as giving a full coverage of the 2 x 2 case. They also include information about the standard errors of the measures of association. They also discuss measures based on other considerations than those mentioned here.

For those not wanting to go the full distance, Everitt (1977, Section 3.7) provides a concise readable discussion and gives some useful references.

Example 8.4 Measuring Association for Example 8.1

In Example 8.1, we compared the voting intentions of 500 people from each of two parliamentary constituencies. For the data in Table 8.4, we found that $\chi^2 = 152.67$ indicating a reliable difference between the two constituencies. A predictive measure seems reasonable here, but first, it won't hurt to calculate ϕ^2 and C. Since $n = 1000$, ϕ^2 will be 152.67/1000 or 0.15. C will also be 0.15, since there are $r = 2$ rows and $c = 5$ columns in Table 8.4, so $q = 2$ (the smaller of r and c) and

$$C = \frac{\chi^2}{n(q-1)} = \frac{152.67}{1000} = 0.15.$$

These measures indicate a small association between constituency and voting intention.

Of the predictive measures, the asymmetrical version λ_a seems more appropriate here, since we have controlled the size of the samples drawn from the two constituencies, which means we are more likely to want to use the data to predict voting intention given knowledge about constituency rather than the other way round. Treating constituency as the explanatory variable, then, we find from Table 8.4 that the largest row frequencies are 150 and 170, so $\Sigma rm_i = 150 + 170 = 320$,

$\max(u) = 300$, the largest column marginal total, and $n = 1000$, so

$$\lambda_a = \frac{320 - 300}{1000 - 300} = 0.03$$

This indicates that only 3% of our errors in predicting voting intention can be eliminated if we know the constituency concerned.

Example 8.5 Measuring Association for Example 8.2

For Pearson's data shown in Table 8.5, we found that $\chi^2 = 181.55$, so $\phi^2 = 181.55/1000 = 0.18$. To calculate C, we note that there are 5 rows and 5 columns, so $q = 5$ and

$$C = \frac{\chi^2}{n(q-1)} = \frac{181.55}{1000 \times 4} = 0.05$$

Both measures indicate a small association between coat colour of mother and daughter.

Lambda will also be useful here. If we want to predict coat colour of daughter from that of the mother, we find

$$\lambda_a = \frac{(13 + 95 + 230 + 101 + 42) - 481}{1000 - 481} = 0,$$

indicating no predictive association at all. This is reasonable in this case, since the most likely colour of the daughter's coat is bay, no matter what the colour of the mother's coat.

To predict the colour of the mother's coat from that of the daughter, we find

$$\lambda_a = \frac{(11 + 75 + 230 + 113 + 39) - 447}{1000 - 447} = 0.04.$$

This way round, there is something, but not much, to be gained in predictive terms from knowing the colour of the daughter's coat.

Finally, the symmetrical version of λ is obtained as follows for these data.

$$\lambda = \frac{(13+95+230+101+42)+(11+75+230+113+39)-481-447}{2000-481-447}$$

$$= 0.02,$$

indicating a very slight degree of n ual predictability.

8.4 MEASURING AGREEMENT BETWEEN TWO OBSERVERS

Too much agreement kills a chat
Eldridge Cleaver, *Soul on Ice*

Suppose two observers independently categorize a number of items using the same set of categories. This might occur if we asked two educational psychologists to interview a group of children and assess each child's stage of development using the standard Piagetian categories 'sensory motor', 'pre-operational', 'concrete-operational' and 'formal operational'. In such a case we might want to assess the degree to which the two psychologists agree. As a second example, we might wish to compare two psychiatrists' independent classifications of a group of patients as suffering from either endogenous depression, reactive depression or obsessional neurosis. Alternatively, these patients may be classified by two purportedly identical forms of a psychological test and we may wish to assess the agreement between the tests. In this case, the 'observers' are the two forms of the test and the agreement we wish to assess is generally referred to as the reliability of the test.

If there is an underlying ordering in the categories that we wish to focus attention on, then Kendall's tau *b* discussed in Section 5.6 provides an appropriate measure of agreement. In the Piagetian example, the four stages mentioned represent increasingly sophisticated performance. In assessing agreement between the two psychologists, we might want to exploit this ordering. If one psychologist classifies a child as being at the sensory motor stage while the other one classifies the same child as being at the formal operational stage, this would represent much greater disagreement than that between sensory motor and pre-operational. We should probably not want to ignore this ordinal information, so τ_b will be a useful index of agreement in this case. (See Exercise 5.5 for another example of the use of tau *b* to measure agreement.)

When there is no underlying ordering that we wish to focus on, as in the second example above, τ_b will not be appropriate. Neither will the other measures of association introduced in the previous section. This is because agreement is a very special sort of association. To see this, consider the data in Table 8.10. In (a), there is perfect agreement between the two psychiatrists, while in (b) there is no agreement at all. In both cases, however, there is perfect association, since it is always possible to predict completely accurately the classification given by one of the psychiatrists given knowledge of the other's. Our measures of association reflect this – for example, $\lambda = 1$ in both cases.

So we need a different way of measuring agreement. When discussing agreement we shall always assume that the data have been recorded in a contingency table for which the categories used by one observer form the rows and the categories used by the other observer form the columns. In addition we shall require that the order of the rows be identical to that of the columns, as in Table 8.10. It doesn't matter what this common order is, since we are not focusing on any underlying ordering of the categories, but if the order of the rows is changed the order of the columns

Table 8.10. Hypothetical data illustrating possible agreement between two psychiatrists in classifying 30 patients

(a)

		Psychiatrist *B*			
		ED	RD	ON	t_i
Psychiatrist *A*	ED	10			10
	RD		10		10
	ON			10	10
	u_i	10	10	10	$30 = n$

$\lambda = 1; \kappa = 1$

(b)

		Psychiatrist *B*			
		ED	RD	ON	t_i
Psychiatrist *A*	ED		10		10
	RD			10	10
	ON	10			10
	u_i	10	10	10	$30 = n$

$\lambda = 1; \kappa = -0.5$

must follow suit. With this convention, it is easy to see whether there is any agreement between the two observers, since agreement will be reflected by having large frequencies in the NW–SE diagonal, as in Table 8.10a while disagreement will be reflected by having small or zero frequencies in this diagonal, as in Table 8.10(b). In what follows, the sum of these diagonal cells will be labelled D (for diagonal), so in (a) we have $D = 10 + 10 + 10 = 30$, while in (b) we have $D = 0 + 0 + 0 = 0$.

The simplest measure of agreement is given by the proportion of times the two observers agree, which is just D/n. For (a), this is $30/30 = 1$, while for (b) it is $0/30 = 0$. This simple measure works well for this example. Unfortunately, it will not do as a general measure of agreement, since the possible values it can take are affected by the marginal totals. To see this, consider the hypothetical data in Table 8.11, where our two psychiatrists simply use the categories endogenous depression (ED) and reactive depression (RD). In (a) 60/100 or 60% of the classifications agree, while in (b) only 40% agree. But if you consider in addition the marginal totals, it is clear that the psychiatrists in (a) show the smallest possible agreement given the constraints imposed by the margins, while the psychiatrists in (b) show the largest possible agreement given the constraints. In (a), the marginal totals are reflecting

Table 8.11. Hypothetical data illustrating possible agreement between two psychiatrists in classifying 100 patients

		(a) Psychiatrist B				(b) Psychiatrist B		
		ED	RD	t_i		ED	RD	t_i
Psychiatrist A	ED	60	20	80	ED	20	60	80
	RD	20		20	RD		20	20
	u_i	80	20	$100 = n$	u_i	20	80	$100 = n$
		$\kappa = -0.25$				$\kappa = 0.12$		

the fact that both psychiatrists have a marked tendency to classify these patients as endogenous depressives, so they cannot help but agree. In (b), psychiatrist A has a preference for classifying people as endogenous depressive while psychiatrist B shows the reverse tendency: in this case, they cannot help disagreeing. So our figures of 60% and 40% are merely reflecting the information in the marginal totals.

In most cases, we don't want a measure of agreement that is so dependent on the marginal totals. Several measures have been suggested that take into account the information in the marginal totals. We shall consider here only the most popular of these, Cohen's kappa.

Cohen's Kappa

Jacob Cohen (1960) suggested that a measure of agreement could be obtained by comparing the observed agreement D with the 'chance agreement' that would be expected if the two observers were totally independent. Now, this chance agreement is given by the expected frequency for each of the diagonal cells, calculated as in the Chi-Square Test for Independence. So in Table 8.11(a), the expected frequency E for the first diagonal cell will be $80 \times 80/100 = 64$, the row marginal total multiplied by the column marginal total and divided by n, the total number of patients. For the second diagonal cell in (a), E will be $20 \times 20/100 = 4$.

The first stage in obtaining a measure of agreement is to subtract the sum of the expected frequencies for the diagonal cells, ΣE, from the sum of the observed frequencies, D. For (a) we have $\Sigma E = 64 + 4 = 68$ and $D = 60$, so the difference will be $60 - 68 = -8$. The negative value here reflects the fact that we have a smaller amount of agreement in (a) than would be expected by chance, given the constraints imposed by the marginal totals.

For Table 8.11(b), the expected frequencies for the two diagonal cells are $80 \times 20/100 = 16$ and $20 \times 80/100 = 16$, so ΣE will be 32, and the difference $D - \Sigma E$ will be $40 - 32 = 8$, the positive value reflecting the fact that here we have more agreement than would be expected by chance.

As usual, it helps to have a measure of agreement for which the maximum value is 1. To achieve this, we divide $D - \Sigma E$ by $n - \Sigma E$. This gives the measure that

Cohen labels κ (the Greek letter kappa). For the data in (a), we have $n = 100$ and $\Sigma E = 68$, so $\kappa = -8/32 = -0.25$. For the data in (b), we have $n = 100$ and $\Sigma E = 32$, so $\kappa = 8/68 = 0.12$.

Rather than use the procedure outlined above it is generally quicker to calculate kappa using the following equivalent formula.

$$\kappa = \frac{nD - \Sigma t_i u_i}{n^2 - \Sigma t_i u_i}, \tag{8.9}$$

where t_i and u_i are the marginal totals, n is the total number of observations and D is the sum of the frequencies in the diagonal cells. The $\Sigma t_i u_i$ instructs us to multiply together the row and column marginal totals converging on each diagonal cell and then add them. To illustrate, in Table 8.11(a), we have $n = 100$, $D = 60$ and

$$\Sigma t_i u_i = 80 \times 80 + 20 \times 20 = 6800,$$

so

$$\kappa = \frac{100 \times 60 - 6800}{10000 - 6800} = -0.25,$$

as obtained above using the more elaborate procedure.

As a further illustration, returning to the data in Table 8.10(a), we have $n = 30$, $D = 30$ and $\Sigma t_i u_i = 10 \times 10 + 10 \times 10 + 10 \times 10 = 300$, so

$$\kappa = \frac{30 \times 30 - 300}{900 - 300} = 1,$$

indicating perfect agreement. For the data in Table 8.10(b), we have $n = 30$, $D = 0$ and $\Sigma t_i u_i = 300$, so

$$\kappa = \frac{30 \times 0 - 300}{900 - 300} = -0.5,$$

indicating much less agreement than would be expected by chance.

From these examples, it should be clear that kappa only takes its maximum value of 1 in cases of perfect agreement between the two observers, as in Table 8.10(a). This will occur when the only non-zero cells in the table occur on the main diagonal. In all other cases, kappa will be less than 1; the smaller kappa gets the more disagreement there is between the two observers, negative values reflecting less than chance agreement.

Further Comments

For a full discussion of kappa, see Cohen (1960). Bishop, Fienberg, and Holland (1975, Section 11.4) give a detailed discussion of kappa and other measures of agreement and disagreement. They also discuss some suggestions for generalizing kappa to provide an index of agreement among more than two observers.

In some cases, we may want to measure agreement between observers when the categories are not specified in advance. For example, we may ask the observers simply to divide the items into as many categories as seem sensible to them. Here, kappa won't be appropriate, since it depends on the observers using exactly the same categories. A measure of agreement for this type of situation is discussed by Brennan and Light (1974) and Hubert (1977).

Example 8.6 Measuring Agreement Using Kappa

As part of a study of the image of women reflected by Hollywood films in the sixties, two people independently classify the treatment of the leading female character in 50 movies using the following categories: woman presented as slave (Slave); woman presented as in total control of her destiny (Controller); woman presented as being a victim of her circumstances (Victim). Some hypothetical data are shown in Table 8.12. There is no underlying ordering in the categories used that we wish to focus attention on, so kappa will provide a useful measure of agreement between the two people.

To calculate kappa, we find $D = 15 + 5 + 10 = 30$, $n = 50$ and $\Sigma t_i u_i = 20 \times 30 + 10 \times 5 + 20 \times 15 = 950$, so from formula 8.9,

$$\kappa = \frac{nD - \Sigma t_i u_i}{n^2 - \Sigma t_i u_i} = \frac{50 \times 30 - 950}{2500 - 950} = 0.35,$$

indicating moderate agreement between the two people in their use of these categories. In such a study, a much higher amount of agreement would be desirable before any firm conclusions may be drawn about the treatment of women in the cinema.

Table 8.12. Hypothetical data for Example 8.6

		Person 2			
		Slave	Controller	Victim	t_i
	Slave	15		5	20
Person 1	Controller	5	5		10
	Victim	10		10	20
	u_i	30	5	15	$50 = n$

8.5 SUMMARY OF SUGGESTED PROCEDURE

General Points

1. Do you have *either* one-sample data *or* two or more independent samples? If not, look elsewhere; see the table at the front of the book for suggestions.
2. Do you wish to test a predicted ordering of the samples? If so, try the tests in Chapter 4 or 5.

3. Are the scores on the response variable ordinal? If so try the tests in Chapters 2, 3, or 4.
4. For one-sample data, if the response variable has two categories, try the Binomial Test in Chapter 3. Otherwise, try the one-sample Chi-Square Test.
5. If the explanatory variable has two or more levels, try the Chi-Square Test for Independence. In this case, a measure of association or agreement may be useful.

Chi-Square Test for Independence

1. This test assesses whether two variables are independent or whether they are associated in any way. The data should be recorded in the form of a contingency table, with the levels of one variable (the explanatory variable) forming the rows and the levels of the other variable (the response variable) forming the columns.
2. Select significance level α.
3. For each cell in the contingency table, calculate the expected frequency, E, by multiplying together the row and column marginal totals converging on the cell and dividing by n, the total number of observations. If any of the E's is less than 1 or if more than one in five of the E's is less than 5, the test may not be accurate.
4. Compute $(O - E)^2/E$ for each cell, where O is the observed frequency and E is the expected frequency.
5. Compute $$\chi^2 = \sum \frac{(O - E)^2}{E} \qquad (8.1)$$
6. Find r, the number of rows in the contingency table, and c, the number of columns.
7. Calculate $df = (r - 1) \times (c - 1)$ and compare the obtained value of χ^2 with the relevant approximate critical value given in Table G to complete the test.
8. If you require a measure of the degree of association, see below.

One-Sample Chi-Square Test

1. This test compares a single sample of k observed frequencies, O, with a set of predicted expected frequencies, E. The prediction generally involves a set of predicted proportions (as in Example 8.3) from which the E's are computed by multiplying each predicted proportion by n, the total number of observations.
2. Select significance level α.
3. Compute $(O - E)^2/E$ for each of the k categories.
4. Compute $$\chi^2 = \sum \frac{(O - E)^2}{E} \qquad (8.1)$$
5. Find $df = k - 1$, where k is the number of categories, and compare the obtained value of χ^2 with the relevant approximate critical value given in Table G to complete the test.

Measures of Association for Unordered Contingency Tables

1. For a predictive measure of association use one of the lambda measures in 3.
2. *Measures based on* χ^2

   For a general measure of association that doesn't have a simple interpretation compute Pearson's *mean square contingency coefficient* by calculating

   $$\phi^2 = \chi^2/n \tag{8.3}$$

   For a better measure that lies between 0 and 1, use Cramér's measure, given by

   $$C = \frac{\chi^2}{n(q-1)} \tag{8.4}$$

   where q is the number of rows in the contingency table or the number of columns (whichever is smaller).
3. *Goodman and Kruskal's lambda measures*

   If the distinction between the explanatory and the response variable is important and you wish to estimate how much the error in predicting the response category may be reduced by knowing the explanatory category, use the asymmetrical version λ_a. Otherwise, use the symmetrical version λ.

   (a) *Asymmetrical version,* λ_a.

   Make sure the levels of the explanatory variable form the rows of the contingency table.

   Find rm_i, the largest frequency in the ith row, and $\max(u)$, the largest column marginal total.

   $$\text{Compute } \lambda_a = \frac{\Sigma rm_i - \max(u)}{n - \max(u)} \tag{8.6}$$

   (b) *Symmetrical version,* λ

   Find rm_i, the largest frequency in the ith row, cm_i, the largest frequency in the ith column, $\max(u)$, the largest column marginal total and $\max(t)$, the largest row marginal total.

   $$\text{Compute } \lambda = \frac{\Sigma rm_i + \Sigma cm_i - \max(u) - \max(t)}{2n - \max(u) - \max(t)} \tag{8.8}$$

Measuring Agreement Between Two Observers Using Cohen's Kappa

1. The following procedure provides a measure of agreement between two observers when they each independently classify the same n items using the same categories. Alternatively, it may be used to assess the reliability between two tests that classify the same n individuals using the same categories.
2. Record the data in a contingency table making sure that the categories are recorded in the same order for the rows and the columns. If you wish to focus attention on any underlying ordering of the categories, use Kendall's tau b as described in Chapter 5. Otherwise, compute Cohen's kappa as shown below.

3. Find D, the sum of the diagonal entries in the contingency table. Find $\Sigma t_i u_i$, where t_i and u_i are the row and column marginal totals converging on the ith diagonal cell.

$$\text{Compute } \kappa = \frac{nD - \Sigma t_i u_i}{n^2 - \Sigma t_i u_i} \tag{8.9}$$

8.6 EXERCISES

Section 8.1

1. From central police records, 100 crimes are cross-classified according to the nature of the crime and the city in which it was committed. Some hypothetical data are shown below. Are there differences between the cities in the types of crime committed?

	Type of crime			
	Burglary	Larceny	Assault	Robbery
El Paso	5	5	5	5
Houston	4	12	14	5
Albuquerque	11	13	1	20

2. Using the data of Exercise 1, show that the obtained value of χ^2 is the same no matter what order the rows or the columns of the contingency table are recorded in.
3. Using the data from Exercise 4.5, calculate χ^2 from formula 8.1 and check that it is nearly equal to the value obtained previously. You have now demonstrated that the Chi-Square Test for Independence and the Kruskal–Wallis Test are almost equivalent when one of the variables has only two categories.
4. In a study of the interpretation of ambiguous doubly quantified sentences, Bill Beveridge (1977) asked 24 people to read a sentence and state whether it was true or false. Twelve of the people read the sentence in a context that stressed the grammatical subject of the sentence – subject topicalization (ST). The remaining 12 read the sentence in a context that stressed the grammatical object – object topicalization (OT). The results are shown below. (a) Use the Chi-Square Test to assess whether the two topicalization conditions differ in the proportion of true judgements. (b) Use the normal approximation to the Fisher Exact Test (without a continuity correction). (c) Check that the value of χ^2 obtained in (a) is almost identical to the square of the z score obtained in (b). They should differ by a factor of $n/(n-1)$.

	'True'	'False'
ST	10	2
OT	4	8

Section 8.2

5. 108 critics independently name their favourite Arthur Penn film. Are there differences in preference between the films named below?

The Left-Handed Gun	*Mickey One*	*Night Moves*	*Little Big Man*	*The Miracle Worker*	*The Chase*
20	1	25	30	15	17

6. Reanalyse the data of Exercise 5 to decide whether the later coloured films are preferred to the earlier black-and-white films (these being *The Left-Handed Gun, Mickey One,* and *The Miracle Worker*). You'll need to group the data into the two categories 'black-and-white' and 'coloured' before carrying out the χ^2 test. Check that the same conclusion is obtained using the normal approximation to the Binomial Test.

Section 8.3

7. Calculate C and λ_a for the data in Table 8.1. What does λ_a tell you?
8. Estimate the degree to which our error in guessing the type of crime committed may be reduced by knowing the city in which it occurred using the data in Exercise 1.

Section 8.4

9. Two careers officers independently interview the same fifty students. For each student they decide whether the most appropriate carreer would be in teaching, industry or the civil service. From the hypothetical data below, estimate how much the two officers agree.

		Officer *B* Teaching	Industry	Civil Service
Officer *A*	Teaching	10	5	
	Industry	5	10	
	Civil Service	5	1	14

CHAPTER 9

Only a little more
I have to write,
Then I'll give o'er
And bid the world good-night.
Robert Herrick

Postscript

If you have got this far, you will probably have started to be aware of many topics not covered in this book. Some of the references given in the 'Further Comments' sections of previous chapters give useful information about such topics. However, some of these references are rather difficult for the mathematically squeamish. In this final brief chapter, I hope to provide you with a way of going beyond the topics covered here at a fairly gentle pace.

The next step for most people ought to be to find out about the use of parametric techniques in statistics, particularly the analysis of variance. Such techniques are important in their own right as well as providing a stepping-stone to the more complicated nonparametric techniques, which frequently assume a knowledge of analysis of variance. The most straightforward introduction to analysis of variance is the book by Keppel (1973).

After this, I suggest going right back to the basics and looking at Tukey's (1977) many interesting and simple suggestions about how to describe and compare different sets of data without using any of the complicated techniques you will now know about. At the same time, you might complement this by a more careful look at probability theory as presented by Mosteller, Rourke, and Thomas (1970).

If you want to go into the nonparametric techniques suggested in this book in more depth, try Bradley (1968) and Lehmann (1975), which you should be able to cope with by now. Bradley, for example, suggests some simple ways of generalizing the Friedman and Kruskal–Wallis Tests to cover the addition of a third variable (see Bradley's Section 5.15). Lehmann gives a very full coverage of the tests comparing ordinal variables, giving more information than I have been able to provide and suggesting ways of generalizing the tests to cover more variables.

In some cases, you may wish to use Kendall's S statistic to assess trends that are more complicated than the simple monotonic type covered here. Ferguson (1965) shows how this can be done in a very straightforward way.

For a good introduction to some of the more complicated ways of analysing categorical data, see Everitt (1977). The log-linear approach introduced in Everitt's Chapter 4 and 5 provides a good way of tackling categorical data when more than two variables are involved. These chapters give the flavour of the approach, providing an appetizer for the more complete coverage by Fienberg (1977). For the real enthusiast, there is no better source than Bishop, Fienberg, and Holland (1975). This is well worth looking at, since it is very readable, despite covering more research situations than most of us will ever be aware of.

Finally, the best way of learning about a statistical technique is to make use of it in a practical context that you are familiar with. Only then will you properly appreciate the sense in the quotation from Norton Juster at the beginning of Chapter 1.

APPENDIX

Tables for the Test Statistics

TABLE A. CRITICAL VALUES OF S FOR THE WILCOXON RANK-SUM TEST

t_1 is the number of observations in the larger sample
t_2 is the number of observations in the smaller sample
The table may be used for all cases for which both t_1 and t_2 are less than 26.

Examples For a *two-tailed test* with $t_1 = 11$, $t_2 = 10$ and $\alpha = 0.05$, reject the null hypothesis if the obtained S is larger than or equal to 58 or if it is smaller than or equal to −58.

For a *one-tailed test* with $t_1 = 11$, $t_2 = 10$ and $\alpha = 0.05$, if an upper tail test is required, reject the null hypothesis if the obtained S is larger than or equal to 48. If a lower tail test is required, reject if the obtained S is smaller than or equal to −48.

For some cases, such as $t_1 = 5$, $t_2 = 1$, no entries appear. This means that, for the given significance levels, none of the possible values of S would lead to rejection of the null hypothesis.

		One-tailed significance level, α					
		0.100	0.050	0.025	0.010	0.005	0.001
		Two-tailed significance level, α					
t_1	t_2	0.200	0.100	0.050	0.020	0.010	0.002
3	2	6					
3	3	7	9				
4	2	8					
4	3	10	12				
4	4	10	14	16			
5	2	8	10				
5	3	11	13	15			
5	4	12	16	18	20		
5	5	15	17	21	23		
6	2	10	12				
6	3	12	14	16			
6	4	14	18	20	22	24	
6	5	16	20	24	26	28	
6	6	18	22	26	30	32	
7	2	12	14				
7	3	13	17	19	21		
7	4	16	20	22	26	28	
7	5	19	23	25	29	33	
7	6	20	26	30	34	36	42
7	7	23	27	33	37	41	47
8	2	12	14	16			
8	3	14	18	20	24		
8	4	18	22	24	28	30	
8	5	20	24	28	32	36	40
8	6	22	28	32	36	40	46
8	7	24	30	36	42	44	52
8	8	26	34	38	46	50	56
9	1	9					
9	2	14	16	18			
9	3	17	19	23	25	27	
9	4	18	24	28	30	34	
9	5	21	27	31	35	39	43
9	6	24	30	34	40	44	50
9	7	27	33	39	45	49	57
9	8	28	36	42	50	54	62
9	9	31	39	47	53	59	67
10	1	10					
10	2	14	18	20			

		One-tailed significance level, α					
		0.100	0.050	0.025	0.010	0 .005	0.001
		Two-tailed significance level, α					
t_1	t_2	0.200	0.100	0.050	0.020	0 .010	0.002
10	3	18	22	24	28	30	
10	4	20	26	30	34	36	40
10	5	24	28	34	38	42	48
10	6	26	32	38	44	48	54
10	7	28	36	42	48	52	60
10	8	32	40	46	54	58	68
10	9	34	42	50	58	64	74
10	10	36	46	54	62	68	80
11	1	11					
11	2	16	20	22			
11	3	19	23	27	31	33	
11	4	22	28	32	36	40	44
11	5	25	31	37	41	45	51
11	6	28	34	40	48	52	58
11	7	31	39	45	53	57	65
11	8	34	42	50	58	62	72
11	9	37	45	53	63	67	79
11	10	38	48	58	66	74	86
11	11	41	53	61	71	79	91
12	1	12					
12	2	16	20	22			
12	3	20	26	28	32	34	
12	4	24	30	34	38	42	48
12	5	26	34	38	44	48	56
12	6	30	38	44	50	54	64
12	7	32	42	48	56	60	70
12	8	36	44	52	62	66	78
12	9	38	48	56	66	72	84
12	10	42	52	62	72	78	92
12	11	44	56	66	76	84	98
12	12	46	60	70	82	90	104
13	1	13					
13	2	18	22	24	26		
13	3	21	27	31	35	37	
13	4	26	32	36	42	46	50
13	5	29	35	41	47	51	59
13	6	32	40	46	54	58	68
13	7	35	43	51	59	65	75

TABLE A (*continued*)

		One-tailed significance level, α					
		0.100	0.050	0.025	0.010	0.005	0.001
		Two-tailed significance level, α					
t_1	t_2	0.200	0.100	0.050	0.020	0.010	0.002
13	8	38	48	56	64	70	82
13	9	41	51	61	71	77	89
13	10	44	56	64	76	82	96
13	11	47	59	69	81	89	103
13	12	50	62	74	86	94	110
13	13	53	67	79	91	101	117
14	1	14					
14	2	18	22	26	28		
14	3	22	28	32	38	40	
14	4	26	34	38	44	48	54
14	5	30	38	44	50	56	64
14	6	34	42	50	58	62	72
14	7	36	46	54	64	68	80
14	8	40	50	60	68	76	88
14	9	44	54	64	74	82	96
14	10	46	58	68	80	88	102
14	11	50	62	74	86	94	110
14	12	52	66	78	92	100	118
14	13	56	70	82	96	106	124
14	14	58	74	86	102	112	132
15	1	15					
15	2	20	24	28	30		
15	3	25	31	35	39	41	
15	4	28	36	40	46	50	58
15	5	31	39	47	53	59	67
15	6	36	44	52	60	66	76
15	7	39	49	57	67	73	85
15	8	42	54	62	72	80	92
15	9	45	57	67	79	87	101
15	10	48	62	72	84	92	108
15	11	51	65	77	91	99	117
15	12	54	70	82	96	106	124
15	13	59	73	87	101	111	131
15	14	62	78	92	108	118	138
15	15	65	81	97	113	123	145
16	1	16					
16	2	22	26	30	32		
16	3	26	32	36	42	44	
16	4	30	36	42	50	54	60
16	5	34	42	50	56	62	70
16	6	38	46	54	64	70	80
16	7	40	52	60	70	76	90
16	8	44	56	66	76	84	98
16	9	48	60	70	82	90	106
16	10	52	64	76	88	98	114
16	11	54	68	82	94	104	122
16	12	58	72	86	100	110	130
16	13	60	78	90	106	118	138
16	14	64	82	96	112	124	146
16	15	68	86	100	118	130	154
16	16	70	90	106	124	136	160
17	1	17					
17	2	22	28	30	34		
17	3	27	33	39	43	47	51
17	4	32	38	46	52	56	64
17	5	35	45	51	59	65	75
17	6	40	50	58	66	72	84
17	7	43	53	63	73	81	93
17	8	46	58	68	80	88	102
17	9	49	63	75	87	95	111
17	10	54	68	80	94	102	120
17	11	57	73	85	99	109	129
17	12	60	76	90	106	116	136
17	13	63	81	95	111	123	145
17	14	68	84	100	118	130	152
17	15	71	89	105	123	135	161
17	16	74	94	110	130	142	168
17	17	77	97	115	135	149	175
18	1	18					
18	2	24	28	32	36		
18	3	28	36	40	46	50	54
18	4	32	40	48	54	60	66
18	5	36	46	54	62	68	78
18	6	40	52	60	70	76	88
18	7	44	56	66	78	84	98
18	8	48	62	72	84	92	108
18	9	52	66	78	90	100	116
18	10	56	70	84	98	106	126
18	11	60	76	88	104	114	134
18	12	62	80	94	110	122	142
18	13	66	84	100	116	128	150
18	14	70	88	104	122	136	160
18	15	74	94	110	130	142	168
18	16	76	98	116	136	148	176
18	17	80	102	120	142	156	184
18	18	84	106	126	148	162	192
19	1	17	19				
19	2	24	30	34	36	38	
19	3	29	37	43	49	51	57
19	4	34	42	50	58	62	70

TABLE A (*continued*)

		One-tailed significance level, α					
		0.100	0.050	0.025	0.010	0.005	0.001
		Two-tailed significance level, α					
t_1	t_2	0.200	0.100	0.050	0.020	0.010	0.002
19	5	39	49	57	65	71	81
19	6	42	54	64	74	80	92
19	7	47	59	69	81	89	103
19	8	50	64	76	88	96	112
19	9	55	69	81	95	105	121
19	10	58	74	86	102	112	132
19	11	63	79	93	109	119	141
19	12	66	84	98	116	126	148
19	13	69	87	103	121	133	157
19	14	72	92	110	128	140	166
19	15	77	97	115	135	147	175
19	16	80	102	120	140	156	184
19	17	83	105	125	147	161	191
19	18	86	110	130	154	168	200
19	19	91	115	135	159	175	207
20	1	18	20				
20	2	26	32	36	38	40	
20	3	30	38	44	50	54	60
20	4	36	44	52	60	64	74
20	5	40	50	60	68	74	86
20	6	44	56	66	76	84	96
20	7	48	62	72	84	92	108
20	8	52	66	78	92	100	118
20	9	56	72	84	100	108	128
20	10	60	76	90	106	116	136
20	11	64	82	96	114	124	146
20	12	68	86	102	120	132	156
20	13	72	92	108	126	140	164
20	14	76	96	114	134	146	172
20	15	80	100	120	140	154	182
20	16	82	106	124	146	162	190
20	17	86	110	130	154	168	200
20	18	90	114	136	160	176	208
20	19	94	120	142	166	182	216
20	20	98	124	146	172	190	224
21	1	19	21				
21	2	26	32	36	40	42	
21	3	33	41	47	53	57	61
21	4	38	46	54	62	68	76
21	5	41	53	61	71	77	89
21	6	46	58	68	80	88	102
21	7	51	65	75	87	97	111
21	8	56	70	82	96	104	122
21	9	59	75	89	103	113	133
21	10	64	80	94	110	122	142
21	11	67	85	101	117	129	151
21	12	70	90	106	124	136	162
21	13	75	95	113	131	145	171
21	14	78	100	118	138	152	180
21	15	83	105	123	145	159	189
21	16	86	110	130	152	168	198
21	17	89	115	135	159	175	207
21	18	94	118	140	166	182	216
21	19	97	123	147	173	189	225
21	20	100	128	152	178	196	232
21	21	105	133	157	185	205	241
22	1	20	22				
22	2	28	34	38	42	44	
22	3	34	42	48	54	58	64
22	4	38	48	56	66	70	80
22	5	44	54	64	74	82	94
22	6	48	60	72	84	90	106
22	7	52	66	78	92	100	116
22	8	58	72	86	100	108	128
22	9	62	78	92	108	118	138
22	10	66	84	98	114	126	148
22	11	70	88	104	122	134	158
22	12	74	94	110	130	142	168
22	13	78	98	116	136	150	178
22	14	82	104	122	144	158	186
22	15	86	108	128	150	166	196
22	16	90	114	134	158	174	206
22	17	92	118	140	164	182	214
22	18	96	124	146	172	188	224
22	19	100	128	152	178	196	232
22	20	104	132	158	186	204	242
22	21	108	138	162	192	212	250
22	22	112	142	168	198	218	260
23	1	21	23				
23	2	28	36	40	44	46	
23	3	35	43	51	57	61	67
23	4	40	50	58	68	74	84
23	5	45	57	67	77	85	97
23	6	50	64	74	86	94	110
23	7	55	69	81	95	103	121
23	8	60	76	88	104	114	132
23	9	63	81	95	111	121	143
23	10	68	86	102	120	130	154
23	11	73	91	107	127	139	163
23	12	76	96	114	134	148	174

TABLE A (*continued*)

		One-tailed significance level, α					
		0.100	0.050	0.025	0.010	0.005	0.001
		Two-tailed significance level, α					
t_1	t_2	0.200	0.100	0.050	0.020	0.010	0.002
23	13	81	103	121	141	155	183
23	14	84	108	126	148	164	194
23	15	89	113	133	157	171	203
23	16	92	118	138	164	180	212
23	17	97	123	145	171	187	221
23	18	100	128	150	178	196	232
23	19	103	133	157	185	203	241
23	20	108	138	162	192	210	250
23	21	111	143	169	199	219	259
23	22	116	148	174	206	226	268
23	23	119	151	179	213	233	277
24	1	22	24				
24	2	30	36	42	46	48	
24	3	36	46	52	60	64	70
24	4	40	52	62	70	76	86
24	5	48	60	70	80	88	100
24	6	52	66	78	90	98	114
24	7	56	72	84	98	108	126
24	8	62	78	92	108	118	136
24	9	66	84	98	116	126	148
24	10	70	90	106	124	136	160
24	11	74	94	112	132	144	170
24	12	78	100	118	138	152	180
24	13	84	106	124	146	162	190
24	14	88	110	132	154	170	200
24	15	92	116	138	162	178	210
24	16	96	122	144	168	186	220
24	17	100	126	150	176	194	230
24	18	104	132	156	184	202	240
24	19	108	136	162	190	210	248
24	20	112	142	168	198	218	258
24	21	116	146	174	204	226	268
24	22	120	152	180	212	234	276
24	23	122	156	186	218	242	286
24	24	126	162	192	226	248	296
25	1	23	25				
25	2	32	38	44	48	50	
25	3	37	47	55	61	65	73
25	4	44	54	64	74	80	90
25	5	49	61	71	83	91	105
25	6	54	68	80	92	102	118
25	7	59	75	87	103	111	131
25	8	64	80	94	110	122	142
25	9	69	87	101	119	131	153
25	10	72	92	108	128	140	164
25	11	77	97	115	135	149	175
25	12	82	104	122	144	158	186
25	13	85	109	129	151	167	197
25	14	90	114	136	160	176	206
25	15	95	119	141	167	183	217
25	16	98	126	148	174	192	228
25	17	103	131	155	181	201	237
25	18	106	136	160	190	208	246
25	19	111	141	167	197	217	257
25	20	114	146	174	204	224	266
25	21	119	151	179	211	233	275
25	22	122	156	186	218	240	286
25	23	127	161	191	225	249	295
25	24	130	166	198	232	256	304
25	25	135	171	203	241	265	315

TABLE B. THE STANDARD NORMAL DISTRIBUTION

(i) Area under the normal curve to the right of z

Examples The *one-tailed* probability of obtaining a z larger than or equal to 2.13 is 0.0166. This is also the one-tailed probability of obtaining a z smaller than or equal to −2.13.

For a *two-tailed* probability, double the tabulated value. Thus the probability of obtaining a z larger than or equal to 2.13 or smaller than or equal to −2.13 is 2 x 0.0166 = 0.0332.

z	.00	.01	.02	.03	.04	.05	.06	.07	.08	.09
.0	.5000	.4960	.4920	.4880	.4840	.4801	.4761	.4721	.4681	.4641
.1	.4602	.4562	.4522	.4483	.4443	.4404	.4364	.4325	.4286	.4247
.2	.4207	.4168	.4129	.4090	.4052	.4013	.3974	.3936	.3897	.3859
.3	.3821	.3783	.3745	.3707	.3669	.3632	.3594	.3557	.3520	.3483
.4	.3446	.3409	.3372	.3336	.3300	.3264	.3228	.3192	.3156	.3121
.5	.3085	.3050	.3015	.2981	.2946	.2912	.2877	.2843	.2810	.2776
.6	.2743	.2709	.2676	.2643	.2611	.2578	.2546	.2514	.2483	.2451
.7	.2420	.2389	.2358	.2327	.2296	.2266	.2236	.2206	.2177	.2148
.8	.2119	.2090	.2061	.2033	.2005	.1977	.1949	.1922	.1894	.1867
.9	.1841	.1814	.1788	.1762	.1736	.1711	.1685	.1660	.1635	.1611
1.0	.1587	.1562	.1539	.1515	.1492	.1469	.1446	.1423	.1401	.1379
1.1	.1357	.1335	.1314	.1292	.1271	.1251	.1230	.1210	.1190	.1170
1.2	.1151	.1131	.1112	.1093	.1075	.1056	.1038	.1020	.1003	.0985
1.3	.0968	.0951	.0934	.0918	.0901	.0885	.0869	.0853	.0838	.0823
1.4	.0808	.0793	.0778	.0764	.0749	.0735	.0721	.0708	.0694	.0681
1.5	.0668	.0655	.0643	.0630	.0618	.0606	.0594	.0582	.0571	.0559
1.6	.0548	.0537	.0526	.0516	.0505	.0495	.0485	.0475	.0465	.0455
1.7	.0446	.0436	.0427	.0418	.0409	.0401	.0392	.0384	.0375	.0367
1.8	.0359	.0351	.0344	.0336	.0329	.0322	.0314	.0307	.0301	.0294
1.9	.0287	.0281	.0274	.0268	.0262	.0256	.0250	.0244	.0239	.0233
2.0	.0228	.0222	.0217	.0212	.0207	.0202	.0197	.0192	.0188	.0183
2.1	.0179	.0174	.0170	.0166	.0162	.0158	.0154	.0150	.0146	.0143
2.2	.0139	.0136	.0132	.0129	.0125	.0122	.0119	.0116	.0113	.0110
2.3	.0107	.0104	.0102	.0099	.0096	.0094	.0091	.0089	.0087	.0084
2.4	.0082	.0080	.0078	.0075	.0073	.0071	.0069	.0068	.0066	.0064
2.5	.0062	.0060	.0059	.0057	.0055	.0054	.0052	.0051	.0049	.0048
2.6	.0047	.0045	.0044	.0043	.0041	.0040	.0039	.0038	.0037	.0036
2.7	.0035	.0034	.0033	.0032	.0031	.0030	.0029	.0028	.0027	.0026
2.8	.0026	.0025	.0024	.0023	.0023	.0022	.0021	.0021	.0020	.0019
2.9	.0019	.0018	.0018	.0017	.0016	.0016	.0015	.0015	.0014	.0014
3.0	.0013	.0013	.0013	.0012	.0012	.0011	.0011	.0011	.0010	.0010
3.1	.0010	.0009	.0009	.0009	.0008	.0008	.0008	.0008	.0007	.0007
3.2	.0007	.0007	.0006	.0006	.0006	.0006	.0006	.0005	.0005	.0005
3.3	.0005	.0005	.0005	.0004	.0004	.0004	.0004	.0004	.0004	.0003
3.4	.0003	.0003	.0003	.0003	.0003	.0003	.0003	.0003	.0003	.0002

(ii) Critical values of z

Examples For a *two-tailed test* with $\alpha = 0.05$, reject the null hypothesis if z is larger than or equal to 1.96 or if z is smaller than or equal to −1.96.

For a *one-tailed test* with $\alpha = 0.05$, if an upper tail test is required, reject the null hypothesis if z is larger than or larger than or equal to 1.645. If a lower tail test is required, reject if z is smaller than or equal to −1.645.

					One-tailed significance level, α					
	0.1000	0.0500	0.0250	0.0125	0.0100	0.0050	0.0025	0.0010	0.0005	0.0001
					Two-tailed significance level, α					
	0.2000	0.1000	0.0500	0.0250	0.0200	0.0100	0.0050	0.0020	0.0010	0.0002
z	1.282	1.645	1.960	2.241	2.326	2.576	2.807	3.090	3.291	3.719

TABLE C. CRITICAL VALUES OF S FOR THE FISHER EXACT TEST

The table may be used for any 2 x 2 contingency table for which the marginal totals t_1, t_2, u_1 and u_2 are all less than 19. The data must first be rearranged so that $t_1 \geqslant t_2$, $u_1 \geqslant u_2$ and $t_1 \geqslant u_1$.

Examples To use the table with the data given in the contingency table on the left, rearrange the data to give the equivalent contingency table on the right for which the obtained S is $7 \times 3 - 2 \times 0 = 21$.

7	0	7
2	3	5
9	3	

7	2	$9 = t_1$
0	3	$3 = t_2$
7	5	
u_1	u_2	

For a *two-tailed test* with $\alpha = 0.05$, reject the null hypothesis if the obtained S is larger than or equal to 21 or if it is smaller than or equal to −21. (For the data given, we should therefore reject the null hypothesis.)

For a *one-tailed test* with $\alpha = 0.05$, if an upper tail test is required, reject the null hypothesis if the obtained S is larger than or equal to 21 (which it is in the example). If a lower tail test is required, no critical value is given, so we should never be able to reject the null hypothesis.

							One-tailed α					
				Two-tailed α			Upper tail			Lower tail		
t_1	t_2	u_1	u_2	0.050	0.010	0.001	0.005	0.010	0.001	0.005	0.010	0.001
3	3	3	3				9			-9		
4	3	4	3	12			12					
4	4	4	4	16			16			-16		
5	2	5	2	10			10					
5	3	5	3	15			15					
5	4	5	4	16	20		20	20		-16		
5	5	5	5	25	25		25	25		-25	-25	
6	2	6	2	12			12					
6	3	5	4	15			15					
6	3	6	3	18			18					
6	4	5	5	20			20			-20		
6	4	6	4	24	24		24	24				
6	5	6	5	25	30		30	30		-25		
6	6	6	6	36	36		24	36		-24	-36	
7	2	7	2	14			14					
7	3	6	4	18			18					
7	3	7	3	21	21		21	21				
7	4	6	5	24			24			-20		
7	4	7	4	28	28		28	28				
7	5	6	6	30			30	30		-30	-30	
7	5	7	5	25	35		23	35		-25		
7	6	7	6	29	36	42	29	42	42	-36	-36	
7	7	7	7	35	49	49	35	49	49	-35	-49	-49
8	2	8	2	16			16					
8	3	7	4	21			21					
8	3	8	3	24	24		24	24				
8	4	6	6				24			-24		
8	4	7	5	28			28					
8	4	8	4	32	32		32	32				
8	5	7	6	30	35		35	35		-30		
8	5	8	5	27	40	40	27	40	40	-25		
8	6	7	7	42	42		42	42		-42	-42	
8	6	8	6	34	36	48	34	48	48	-36	-36	
8	7	8	7	34	49	56	41	41	56	-34	-49	
8	8	8	8	48	64	64	48	48	64	-48	-48	-64
9	2	9	2	18			18					
9	3	7	5	21			21					
9	3	8	4	24			24					

TABLE C (*continued*)

				Two-tailed α			One-tailed α Upper tail			One-tailed α Lower tail		
t_1	t_2	u_1	u_2	0.050	0.010	0.001	0.050	0.010	0.001	0.050	0.010	0.001
9	3	9	3	27	27		27	27				
9	4	7	6	28			28			-24		
9	4	8	5	32	32		32	32				
9	4	9	4	36	36		36	36				
9	5	7	7	35			35			-35		
9	5	8	6	30	40		40	40		-30		
9	5	9	5	31	45	45	31	45	45			
9	6	8	7	33	42		33	48		-42	-42	
9	6	9	6	36	54	54	39	54	54	-36		
9	7	8	8	40	56		40	56	56	-40	-56	-56
9	7	9	7	47	47	63	47	47	63	-49	-49	
9	8	9	8	47	55	64	38	55	72	-47	-64	-64
9	9	9	9	63	63	81	45	63	81	-45	-63	-81
10	2	9	3	18			18					
10	2	10	2	20			20					
10	3	8	5	24			24					
10	3	9	4	27			27					
10	3	10	3	30	30		30	30				
10	4	7	7				28			-28		
10	4	8	6	32			32					
10	4	9	5	36	36		36	36				
10	4	10	4	26	40	40	26	40	40			
10	5	8	7	35	40		40	40		-35		
10	5	9	6	45	45		30	45		-30		
10	5	10	5	35	50	50	35	50	50			
10	6	8	8	48	48		48	48		-48	-48	
10	6	9	7	38	54	54	38	54	54	-42		
10	6	10	6	36	44	60	44	44	60	-36		
10	7	9	8	39	56	63	46	63	63	-39	-56	
10	7	10	7	49	49	70	53	53	70	-49	-49	
10	8	9	9	54	72	72	54	54	72	-54	-54	-72
10	8	10	8	46	62	80	44	62	80	-46	-64	
10	9	10	9	52	62	81	52	71	71	-62	-62	-81
10	10	10	10	60	80	100	60	80	80	-60	-80	-80
11	2	10	3	20			20					
11	2	11	2	22			22					
11	3	9	5	27			27					
11	3	10	4	30			30					
11	3	11	3	33	33		33	33				
11	4	8	7	32			32					
11	4	9	6	36			36					
11	4	10	5	40	40		40	40				
11	4	11	4	29	44	44	29	44	44			
11	5	8	8	40			40			-40		
11	5	9	7	35	45		45	45		-35		

TABLE C (*continued*)

				Two-tailed α			One-tailed α Upper tail			Lower tail		
t_1	t_2	u_1	u_2	0.050	0.010	0.001	0.050	0.010	0.001	0.050	0.010	0.001
11	5	10	6	34	50		34	50				
11	5	11	5	39	55	55	39	55	55			
11	6	9	8	37	48		37	54		-48	-48	
11	6	10	7	42	60	60	43	60	60	-42		
11	6	11	6	36	49	66	49	49	66	-36		
11	7	9	9	45	63		45	63		-45	-63	
11	7	10	8	52	56	70	52	52	70	-56	-56	
11	7	11	7	41	59	77	41	59	77	-49		
11	8	10	9	53	61	72	61	61	80	-53	-72	-72
11	8	11	8	50	64	88	50	69	88	-45	-64	
11	9	10	10	70	70	90	50	70	90	-50	-70	-90
11	9	11	9	59	61	79	59	79	79	-61	-61	-81
11	10	11	10	58	68	89	68	68	89	-58	-79	-100
11	11	11	11	77	77	99	55	77	99	-55	-77	-99
12	2	11	3	22			22					
12	2	12	2	24			24					
12	3	9	6	27			27					
12	3	10	5	30			30					
12	3	11	4	33	33		33	33				
12	3	12	3	36	36		36	36				
12	4	8	8				32			-32		
12	4	9	7	36			36					
12	4	10	6	40	40		40	40				
12	4	11	5	44	44		44	44				
12	4	12	4	32	48	48	32	48	48			
12	5	9	8	40	45		45	45		-40		
12	5	10	7	35	50		50	50		-35		
12	5	11	6	38	55	55	38	55	55			
12	5	12	5	43	43	60	43	43	60			
12	6	9	9	54	54		54	54		-54	-54	
12	6	10	8	42	60		42	60		-48		
12	6	11	7	42	66	66	48	66	66	-42		
12	6	12	6	54	54	72	54	54	72	-36		
12	7	10	9	51	63	70	51	70	70	-44	-63	
12	7	11	8	56	58	77	58	58	77	-56	-56	
12	7	12	7	46	65	84	46	65	84	-49		
12	8	10	10	60	80	80	60	60	80	-60	-60	-80
12	8	11	9	52	68	88	48	68	88	-52	-72	
12	8	12	8	56	64	76	56	76	76	-64	-64	
12	9	11	10	57	69	90	57	78	99	-69	-69	-90
12	9	12	9	60	66	87	66	66	87	-60	-81	-81
12	10	11	11	66	88	110	66	88	88	-66	-88	-88
12	10	12	10	56	76	98	54	76	98	-56	-78	-100
12	11	12	11	63	86	98	63	86	109	-75	-75	-98
12	12	12	12	72	96	120	72	96	120	-72	-96	-120

TABLE C (*continued*)

t_1	t_2	u_1	u_2	Two-tailed α 0.050	Two-tailed α 0.010	Two-tailed α 0.001	One-tailed α Upper tail 0.050	One-tailed α Upper tail 0.010	One-tailed α Upper tail 0.001	One-tailed α Lower tail 0.050	One-tailed α Lower tail 0.010	One-tailed α Lower tail 0.001
13	2	12	3	24			24					
13	2	13	2	26	26		26	26				
13	3	10	6	30			30					
13	3	11	5	33			33					
13	3	12	4	36	36		36	36				
13	3	13	3	39	39		39	39				
13	4	9	8	36			36					
13	4	10	7	40			40					
13	4	11	6	44	44		44	44				
13	4	12	5	48	48		48	48				
13	4	13	4	35	52	52	35	52	52			
13	5	9	9	45			45			-45		
13	5	10	8	40	50		50	50		-40		
13	5	11	7	37	55		37	55				
13	5	12	6	42	60	60	42	60	60			
13	5	13	5	47	47	65	47	47	65			
13	6	10	9	54	60		41	60		-54	-54	
13	6	11	8	47	66		47	66		-48		
13	6	12	7	42	53	72	53	53	72	-42		
13	6	13	6	40	59	78	40	59	78			
13	7	10	10	70	70		50	70		-50	-70	
13	7	11	9	57	63	77	57	77	77	-63	-63	
13	7	12	8	56	64	84	64	64	84	-56		
13	7	13	7	49	71	91	51	71	91	-49		
13	8	11	10	59	67	88	67	67	88	-59	-80	-80
13	8	12	9	54	72	96	54	75	96	-51	-72	
13	8	13	8	62	64	83	62	83	83	-64	-64	
13	9	11	11	77	77	99	55	77	99	-55	-77	-99
13	9	12	10	64	86	90	64	86	108	-68	-90	-90
13	9	13	9	59	73	95	73	73	95	-59	-81	
13	10	12	11	64	87	97	74	97	97	-64	-87	-110
13	10	13	10	61	77	100	61	84	107	-77	-77	-100
13	11	12	12	84	108	108	60	84	108	-60	-84	-108
13	11	13	11	71	95	119	71	95	119	-73	-97	-121
13	12	13	12	69	94	119	81	106	131	-69	-94	-119
13	13	13	13	91	117	143	91	91	117	-91	-91	-117
14	2	12	4	24			24					
14	2	13	3	26			26					
14	2	14	2	28	28		28	28				
14	3	11	6	33			33					
14	3	12	5	36			36					
14	3	13	4	39	39		39	39				
14	3	14	3	42	42		42	42				
14	4	9	9				36			-36		
14	4	10	8	40			40					

TABLE C (*continued*)

t_1	t_2	u_1	u_2	Two-tailed α 0.050	Two-tailed α 0.010	Two-tailed α 0.001	One-tailed α Upper tail 0.050	One-tailed α Upper tail 0.010	One-tailed α Upper tail 0.001	One-tailed α Lower tail 0.050	One-tailed α Lower tail 0.010	One-tailed α Lower tail 0.001
14	4	11	7	44			44					
14	4	12	6	48	48		48	48				
14	4	13	5	34	52		34	52				
14	4	14	4	38	56	56	38	56	56			
14	5	10	9	45			50			-45		
14	5	11	8	40	55		55	55		-40		
14	5	12	7	41	60		41	60				
14	5	13	6	46	65	65	46	65	65			
14	5	14	5	51	51	70	51	51	70			
14	6	10	10	60			60	60		-60	-60	
14	6	11	9	46	66		46	66		-54		
14	6	12	8	48	72	72	52	72	72	-48		
14	6	13	7	58	58	78	58	58	78	-42		
14	6	14	6	44	64	84	44	64	84			
14	7	11	10	56	70		56	77		-49	-70	
14	7	12	9	63	84	84	63	63	84	-63	-63	
14	7	13	8	56	70	91	49	70	91	-56		
14	7	14	7	49	77	77	56	77	77	-49		
14	8	11	11	66	88		66	88	88	-66	-88	-88
14	8	12	10	58	74	96	52	74	96	-58	-80	
14	8	13	9	60	72	104	60	82	104	-72	-72	
14	8	14	8	64	68	90	68	68	90	-64	-64	
14	9	12	11	62	76	99	62	85	108	-76	-76	-99
14	9	13	10	67	90	94	71	94	94	-67	-90	-90
14	9	14	9	58	80	103	57	80	103	-58	-81	
14	10	12	12	72	96	120	72	96	120	-72	-96	-120
14	10	13	11	62	86	106	82	82	106	-62	-86	-110
14	10	14	10	68	92	100	68	92	116	-76	-100	-100
14	11	13	12	68	93	107	68	93	118	-82	-107	-107
14	11	14	11	71	96	121	79	104	129	-71	-96	-121
14	12	13	13	78	104	130	78	104	130	-78	-104	-130
14	12	14	12	90	92	118	90	90	116	-92	-92	-118
14	13	14	13	88	101	128	74	101	128	-88	-115	-142
14	14	14	14	112	112	140	84	112	140	-84	-112	-140
15	2	13	4	26			26					
15	2	14	3	28			28					
15	2	15	2	30	30		30	30				
15	3	11	7	33			33					
15	3	12	6	36			36					
15	3	13	5	39			39					
15	3	14	4	42	42		42	42				
15	3	15	3	45	45		45	45				
15	4	10	9	40			40					
15	4	11	8	44			44					
15	4	12	7	48	48		48	48				

TABLE C (*continued*)

t_1	t_2	u_1	u_2	Two-tailed α 0.050	Two-tailed α 0.010	Two-tailed α 0.001	One-tailed α Upper tail 0.050	Upper tail 0.010	Upper tail 0.001	Lower tail 0.050	Lower tail 0.010	Lower tail 0.001
15	4	13	6	52	52		52	52				
15	4	14	5	37	56		37	56				
15	4	15	4	41	60	60	41	60	60			
15	5	10	10	50			50			-50		
15	5	11	9	45	55		55	55		-45		
15	5	12	8	60	60		60	60				
15	5	13	7	45	65		45	65				
15	5	14	6	50	70	70	50	70	70			
15	5	15	5	55	55	75	55	55	75			
15	6	11	10	60	66		66	66		-60	-60	
15	6	12	9	51	72		51	72		-54		
15	6	13	8	48	78	78	57	78	78	-48		
15	6	14	7	63	63	84	63	63	84			
15	6	15	6	48	69	90	48	69	90			
15	7	11	11	77	77		55	77		-55	-77	
15	7	12	10	62	70	84	62	84	84	-70	-70	
15	7	13	9	63	69	91	69	69	91	-63		
15	7	14	8	56	76	98	54	76	98	-56		
15	7	15	7	61	83	83	61	83	83	-49		
15	8	12	11	65	73	96	73	73	96	-65	-88	
15	8	13	10	58	80	104	58	81	104	-57	-80	
15	8	14	9	66	72	112	66	89	112	-72	-72	
15	8	15	8	64	74	97	74	74	97	-64		
15	9	12	12	84	84	108	60	84	108	-60	-84	-108
15	9	13	11	69	93	99	69	93	117	-75	-99	-99
15	9	14	10	66	90	102	78	78	102	-66	-90	
15	9	15	9	63	81	111	63	87	111	-57	-81	
15	10	13	12	70	95	105	80	105	105	-70	-95	-120
15	10	14	11	65	90	110	65	90	115	-85	-85	-110
15	10	15	10	75	100	125	75	100	125	-75	-100	-100
15	11	13	13	91	117	117	91	91	117	-91	-91	-117
15	11	14	12	76	102	128	76	102	128	-80	-106	-132
15	11	15	11	87	95	113	87	113	113	-69	-95	-121
15	12	14	13	87	102	129	87	114	141	-75	-102	-129
15	12	15	12	90	99	126	72	99	126	-90	-117	-117
15	13	14	14	98	126	154	98	126	126	-98	-126	-126
15	13	15	13	85	111	139	83	111	139	-85	-113	-141
15	14	15	14	94	109	138	94	123	152	-80	-109	-138
15	15	15	15	105	135	165	105	135	165	-105	-135	-165
16	2	14	4	28			28					
16	2	15	3	30			30					
16	2	16	2	32	32		32	32				
16	3	12	7	36			36					
16	3	13	6	39			39					
16	3	14	5	42			42					

TABLE C (*continued*)

				Two-tailed α			One-tailed α Upper tail			One-tailed α Lower tail		
t_1	t_2	u_1	u_2	0.050	0.010	0.001	0.050	0.010	0.001	0.050	0.010	0.001
16	3	15	4	45	45		45	45				
16	3	16	3	48	48		48	48				
16	4	10	10				40			-40		
16	4	11	9	44			44					
16	4	12	8	48			48					
16	4	13	7	52	52		52	52				
16	4	14	6	56	56		56	56				
16	4	15	5	40	60		40	60				
16	4	16	4	44	64	64	44	64	64			
16	5	11	10	50			55			-50		
16	5	12	9	45	60		60	60		-45		
16	5	13	8	44	65		44	65				
16	5	14	7	49	70		49	70				
16	5	15	6	54	75	75	54	75	75			
16	5	16	5	59	59	80	59	59	80			
16	6	11	11	66			66	66		-66	-66	
16	6	12	10	60	72		50	72		-60		
16	6	13	9	54	78		56	78		-54		
16	6	14	8	62	84	84	62	84	84	-48		
16	6	15	7	68	68	90	68	68	90			
16	6	16	6	52	74	96	52	74	96			
16	7	12	11	61	77		61	84		-54	-77	
16	7	13	10	68	70	91	68	91	91	-70	-70	
16	7	14	9	63	75	98	75	75	98	-63		
16	7	15	8	59	82	105	59	82	105	-56		
16	7	16	7	66	89	89	66	89	89	-49		
16	8	12	12	72	96		72	96	96	-72	-96	-96
16	8	13	11	64	80	104	80	80	104	-64	-88	
16	8	14	10	64	80	112	64	88	112	-80	-80	
16	8	15	9	72	96	96	72	96	96	-72	-72	
16	8	16	8	64	80	104	56	80	104	-64		
16	9	13	12	67	92	108	67	92	117	-83	-83	-108
16	9	14	11	74	99	126	76	101	126	-74	-99	-99
16	9	15	10	65	85	110	85	85	110	-65	-90	
16	9	16	9	69	81	119	69	94	119	-81	-81	
16	10	13	13	78	104	130	78	104	130	-78	-104	-130
16	10	14	12	88	94	114	88	88	114	-68	-94	-120
16	10	15	11	84	98	110	72	98	124	-84	-84	-110
16	10	16	10	74	100	134	82	108	134	-74	-100	
16	11	14	13	89	100	127	73	100	127	-89	-116	-143
16	11	15	12	78	105	132	84	111	138	-78	-105	-132
16	11	16	11	94	95	121	95	95	122	-94	-94	-121
16	12	14	14	112	112	140	84	112	140	-84	-112	-140
16	12	15	13	96	100	128	96	124	152	-100	-100	-128
16	12	16	12	88	108	136	80	108	136	-88	-116	-144

TABLE C (*continued*)

				Two-tailed α			One-tailed α Upper tail			One-tailed α Lower tail		
t_1	t_2	u_1	u_2	0.050	0.010	0.001	0.050	0.010	0.001	0.050	0.010	0.001
16	13	15	14	95	108	137	79	108	137	-95	-124	-153
16	13	16	13	92	111	140	92	121	150	-82	-111	-140
16	14	15	15	120	120	150	90	120	150	-90	-120	-150
16	14	16	14	104	134	164	104	134	164	-106	-136	-166
16	15	16	15	101	132	163	116	116	147	-101	-132	-163
16	16	16	16	128	160	192	96	128	160	-96	-128	-160
17	2	15	4	30			30					
17	2	16	3	32			32					
17	2	17	2	34	34		34	34				
17	3	12	8	36			36					
17	3	13	7	39			39					
17	3	14	6	42			42					
17	3	15	5	45	45		45	45				
17	3	16	4	48	48		48	48				
17	3	17	3	31	51	51	31	51	51			
17	4	11	10	44			44					
17	4	12	9	48			48					
17	4	13	8	52			52					
17	4	14	7	56	56		56	56				
17	4	15	6	60	60		60	60				
17	4	16	5	43	64	64	43	64	64			
17	4	17	4	47	68	68	47	68	68			
17	5	11	11	55			55			-55		
17	5	12	10	50	60		60	60		-50		
17	5	13	9	65	65		65	65		-45		
17	5	14	8	48	70		48	70				
17	5	15	7	53	75	75	53	75	75			
17	5	16	6	58	58	80	58	58	80			
17	5	17	5	63	63	85	63	63	85			
17	6	12	11	66	72		72	72		-66	-66	
17	6	13	10	60	78		55	78		-60		
17	6	14	9	54	84	84	61	84	84	-54		
17	6	15	8	67	67	90	67	67	90	-48		
17	6	16	7	50	73	96	50	73	96			
17	6	17	6	56	79	102	56	79	102			
17	7	12	12	84	84		60	84		-60	-84	
17	7	13	11	67	77	91	67	91	91	-77	-77	
17	7	14	10	70	74	98	74	74	98	-70	-70	
17	7	15	9	63	81	105	57	81	105	-63		
17	7	16	8	64	88	112	64	88	112	-56		
17	7	17	7	71	71	95	71	71	95			
17	8	13	12	71	96	104	79	79	104	-71	-96	
17	8	14	11	63	87	112	62	87	112	-63	-88	
17	8	15	10	70	80	120	70	95	120	-80	-80	
17	8	16	9	72	78	103	78	78	103	-72		

TABLE C (*continued*)

				Two-tailed α			One-tailed α Upper tail			One-tailed α Lower tail		
t_1	t_2	u_1	u_2	0.050	0.010	0.001	0.050	0.010	0.001	0.050	0.010	0.001
17	8	17	8	64	86	111	61	86	111	-64		
17	9	13	13	91	117	117	65	91	117	-65	-91	-117
17	9	14	12	74	100	108	74	100	126	-82	-108	-108
17	9	15	11	73	99	109	83	109	109	-73	-99	
17	9	16	10	66	90	118	66	92	118	-64	-90	
17	9	17	9	75	81	127	75	101	127	-81	-81	
17	10	14	13	76	103	130	86	113	140	-76	-103	-130
17	10	15	12	93	96	120	69	96	123	-93	-93	-120
17	10	16	11	79	106	133	79	106	133	-83	-110	-110
17	10	17	10	73	100	116	89	116	116	-73	-100	
17	11	14	14	98	126	154	98	98	126	-98	-98	-126
17	11	15	13	87	109	137	81	109	137	-87	-115	-143
17	11	16	12	92	104	132	92	120	148	-76	-104	-132
17	11	17	11	93	103	121	75	103	131	-93	-121	-121
17	12	15	14	93	110	139	93	122	151	-81	-110	-139
17	12	16	13	98	105	134	105	105	134	-98	-127	-156
17	12	17	12	88	115	144	88	117	146	-86	-115	-144
17	13	15	15	105	135	165	105	135	165	-105	-135	-165
17	13	16	14	92	118	148	88	118	148	-92	-122	-152
17	13	17	13	101	131	139	101	131	161	-109	-109	-139
17	14	16	15	100	131	148	100	131	162	-86	-117	-148
17	14	17	14	103	134	165	114	114	145	-103	-134	-165
17	15	16	16	112	144	176	112	144	176	-112	-144	-176
17	15	17	15	97	129	161	95	127	159	-97	-129	-161
17	16	17	16	107	140	173	107	140	173	-124	-157	-190
17	17	17	17	119	153	187	119	153	187	-119	-153	-187
18	2	16	4	32			32					
18	2	17	3	34			34					
18	2	18	2	36	36		36	36				
18	3	13	8	39			39					
18	3	14	7	42			42					
18	3	15	6	45			45					
18	3	16	5	48	48		48	48				
18	3	17	4	51	51		51	51				
18	3	18	3	33	54	54	33	54	54			
18	4	11	11				44			-44		
18	4	12	10	48			48					
18	4	13	9	52			52					
18	4	14	8	56	56		56	56				
18	4	15	7	60	60		60	60				
18	4	16	6	42	64		42	64				
18	4	17	5	46	68	68	46	68	68			
18	4	18	4	50	50	72	50	50	72			
18	5	12	11	55			60			-55		
18	5	13	10	50	65		65	65		-50		

TABLE C (*continued*)

				Two-tailed α			One-tailed α Upper tail			One-tailed α Lower tail		
t_1	t_2	u_1	u_2	0.050	0.010	0.001	0.050	0.010	0.001	0.050	0.010	0.001
18	5	14	9	70	70		70	70				
18	5	15	8	52	75		52	75				
18	5	16	7	57	80	80	57	80	80			
18	5	17	6	62	62	85	62	62	85			
18	5	18	5	44	67	90	44	67	90			
18	6	12	12	72			72	72		-72	-72	
18	6	13	11	66	78		54	78		-66		
18	6	14	10	84	84		60	84		-60		
18	6	15	9	66	90	90	66	90	90	-54		
18	6	16	8	72	72	96	72	72	96			
18	6	17	7	54	78	102	54	78	102			
18	6	18	6	60	84	84	60	84	84			
18	7	13	12	66	84		66	91		-59	-84	
18	7	14	11	73	77	98	73	98	98	-77	-77	
18	7	15	10	70	80	105	80	80	105	-70		
18	7	16	9	63	87	112	62	87	112	-63		
18	7	17	8	69	94	119	69	94	119	-56		
18	7	18	7	76	76	101	76	76	101			
18	8	13	13	78	104		78	104	104	-78	-104	-104
18	8	14	12	70	86	112	86	86	112	-70	-96	
18	8	15	11	68	88	120	68	94	120	-62	-88	
18	8	16	10	76	80	128	76	102	128	-80	-80	
18	8	17	9	72	84	110	84	84	110	-72		
18	8	18	8	66	92	118	66	92	118	-64		
18	9	14	13	72	99	117	72	99	126	-90	-90	-117
18	9	15	12	81	108	135	81	108	135	-81	-108	
18	9	16	11	72	99	117	90	90	117	-72	-99	
18	9	17	10	72	90	126	72	99	126	-90	-90	
18	9	18	9	81	108	135	81	108	135	-81		
18	10	14	14	84	112	140	84	112	140	-84	-112	-140
18	10	15	13	94	102	130	94	122	122	-74	-102	-130
18	10	16	12	76	104	120	76	104	132	-92	-120	-120
18	10	17	11	82	110	142	86	114	142	-82	-110	
18	10	18	10	72	100	124	96	96	124	-72	-100	
18	11	15	14	96	107	136	78	107	136	-96	-125	-154
18	11	16	13	89	114	143	89	118	147	-85	-114	-143
18	11	17	12	100	103	132	100	129	129	-103	-103	-132
18	11	18	11	82	111	140	82	111	140	-92	-121	-121
18	12	15	15	120	120	150	90	120	150	-90	-120	-150
18	12	16	14	102	132	138	102	132	162	-108	-108	-138
18	12	17	13	96	114	144	84	114	144	-96	-126	-156
18	12	18	12	96	114	144	96	126	156	-84	-114	-144
18	13	16	15	102	133	146	115	115	146	-102	-133	-164
18	13	17	14	97	120	151	97	128	159	-89	-120	-151
18	13	18	13	107	138	169	110	141	172	-107	-138	-169

TABLE C (*continued*)

							One-tailed α					
				Two-tailed α			Upper tail			Lower tail		
				0.050	0.010	0.001	0.050	0.010	0.001	0.050	0.010	0.001
t_1	t_2	u_1	u_2									
18	14	16	16	128	160	160	96	128	160	-96	-128	-160
18	14	17	15	110	142	174	110	142	174	-114	-146	-178
18	14	18	14	100	132	156	92	124	156	-100	-132	-164
18	15	17	16	108	141	174	123	156	189	-108	-141	-174
18	15	18	15	105	138	171	105	138	171	-126	-126	-159
18	16	17	17	136	170	204	102	136	170	-102	-136	-170
18	16	18	16	118	152	186	118	152	186	-120	-154	-188
18	17	18	17	114	149	184	131	166	201	-114	-149	-184
18	18	18	18	144	180	216	108	144	216	-108	-144	-216

TABLE D. CRITICAL VALUES OF $W+$ FOR THE WILCOXON SIGNED-RANK TEST

The table may be used for all values of n (the number of paired observations) less than 51.

Examples For a *two-tailed test* with $n = 15$ and $\alpha = 0.05$, reject the null hypothesis either if the obtained $W+$ is smaller than or equal 25 or if the obtained $W-$ is smaller than or equal to 25.

For a *one-tailed test* with $n = 15$ and $\alpha = 0.05$, if a lower tail test is required, reject the null hypothesis if the obtained $W+$ is smaller than or equal to 30. If an upper tail test is required, reject if the obtained $W-$ is smaller than or equal to 30.

	One-tailed significance level, α						
	0.100	0.050	0.025	0.010	0.005	0.0025	0.0005
	Two-tailed significance level, α						
n	0.200	0.100	0.050	0.020	0.010	0.005	0.001
4	0						
5	2	0					
6	3	2	0				
7	5	3	2	0			
8	8	5	3	1	0		
9	10	8	5	3	1	0	
10	14	10	8	5	3	1	
11	17	13	10	7	5	3	0
12	21	17	13	9	7	5	1
13	26	21	17	12	9	7	2
14	31	25	21	15	12	9	4
15	36	30	25	19	15	12	6
16	42	35	29	23	19	15	8
17	48	41	34	27	23	19	11
18	55	47	40	32	27	23	14
19	62	53	46	37	32	27	18
20	69	60	52	43	37	32	21
21	77	67	58	49	42	37	25
22	86	75	65	55	48	42	30
23	94	83	73	62	54	48	35
24	104	91	81	69	61	54	40
25	113	100	89	76	68	60	45
26	124	110	98	84	75	67	51
27	134	119	107	92	83	74	57
28	145	130	116	101	91	82	64
29	157	140	126	110	100	90	71
30	169	151	137	120	109	98	78
31	181	163	147	130	118	107	86
32	194	175	159	140	128	116	94
33	207	187	170	151	138	126	102
34	221	200	182	162	148	136	111
35	235	213	195	173	159	146	120
36	250	227	208	185	171	157	130
37	265	241	221	198	182	168	140
38	281	256	235	211	194	180	150
39	297	271	249	224	207	192	161
40	313	286	264	238	220	204	172
41	330	302	279	252	233	217	183
42	348	319	294	266	247	230	195
43	365	336	310	281	261	244	207
44	384	353	327	296	276	258	220
45	402	371	343	312	291	272	233
46	422	389	361	328	307	287	246
47	441	407	378	345	322	302	260
48	462	426	396	362	339	318	274
49	482	446	415	379	355	334	289
50	503	466	434	397	373	350	304

TABLE E. CRITICAL VALUES OF $N+$ FOR THE SIGN TEST

The table may be used for all values of n (the number of paired observations) less than 51.

Examples For a *two-tailed test* with $n = 16$ and $\alpha = 0.05$, reject the null hypothesis either if the obtained $N+$ is smaller than or equal to 3 or if the obtained $N-$ is smaller than or equal to 3.

For a *one-tailed test* with $n = 16$ and $\alpha = 0.05$, if a lower tail test is required, reject the null hypothesis if the obtained $N+$ is smaller than or equal to 4. If an upper tail test is required, reject if the obtained $N-$ is smaller than or equal to 4.

	One-tailed significance level, α					
	0.100	0.050	0.025	0.010	0.005	0.0005
	Two-tailed significance level, α					
n	0.200	0.100	0.050	0.020	0.010	0.001
4	0					
5	0	0				
6	0	0	0			
7	1	0	0	0		
8	1	1	0	0	0	
9	2	1	1	0	0	
10	2	1	1	0	0	
11	2	2	1	1	0	0
12	3	2	2	1	1	0
13	3	3	2	1	1	0
14	4	3	2	2	1	0
15	4	3	3	2	2	1
16	4	4	3	2	2	1
17	5	4	4	3	2	1
18	5	5	4	3	3	1
19	6	5	4	4	3	2
20	6	5	5	4	3	2
21	7	6	5	4	4	2
22	7	6	5	5	4	3
23	7	7	6	5	4	3
24	8	7	6	5	5	3
25	8	7	7	6	5	4
26	9	8	7	6	6	4
27	9	8	7	7	6	4
28	10	9	8	7	6	5
29	10	9	8	7	7	5
30	10	10	9	8	7	5
31	11	10	9	8	7	6
32	11	10	9	8	8	6
33	12	11	10	9	8	6
34	12	11	10	9	9	7
35	13	12	11	10	9	7
36	13	12	11	10	9	7
37	14	13	12	10	10	8
38	14	13	12	11	10	8
39	15	13	12	11	11	8
40	15	14	13	12	11	9
41	15	14	13	12	11	9
42	16	15	14	13	12	10
43	16	15	14	13	12	10
44	17	16	15	13	13	10
45	17	16	15	14	13	11
46	18	16	15	14	13	11
47	18	17	16	15	14	11
48	19	17	16	15	14	12
49	19	18	17	15	15	12
50	19	18	17	16	15	13

TABLE F. CRITICAL VALUES OF K FOR THE KRUSKAL–WALLIS TEST WITH 3 INDEPENDENT SAMPLES

t_1 is the number of observations in the largest sample
t_3 is the number of observations in the smallest sample
The table may be used for any case for which t_1, t_2, and t_3 are all less than 6. The test is inherently two-tailed.

Examples For $t_1 = 4$, $t_2 = 2$, $t_3 = 2$ and $\alpha = 0.05$, reject the null hypothesis if the obtained K is larger than or equal to 5.33.

For some cases, such as $t_1 = 3$, $t_2 = 1$, $t_3 = 1$, no entries appear. This means that, for the given significance levels, none of the possible values of K would lead to rejection of the null hypothesis.

			Significance level, α						
t_1	t_2	t_3	0.200	0.100	0.050	0.025	0.010	0.005	0.001
2	2	1	3.60						
2	2	2	3.71	4.57					
3	2	1	3.52	4.29					
3	2	2	3.93	4.50	4.71				
3	3	1	3.29	4.57	5.14				
3	3	2	3.78	4.56	5.36	5.56			
3	3	3	3.47	4.62	5.60	5.96	7.20	7.20	
4	1	1	3.57						
4	2	1	3.16	4.50					
4	2	2	3.67	4.46	5.33	5.50			
4	3	1	3.21	4.06	5.21	5.83			
4	3	2	3.44	4.51	5.44	6.00	6.44	7.00	
4	3	3	3.39	4.71	5.73	6.15	6.75	7.32	8.02
4	4	1	3.27	4.17	4.97	6.17	6.67		
4	4	2	3.46	4.55	5.45	6.08	7.04	7.28	
4	4	3	3.42	4.55	5.60	6.39	7.14	7.60	8.33
4	4	4	3.50	4.65	5.69	6.62	7.65	8.00	8.65
5	1	1	3.86						
5	2	1	3.33	4.20	5.00				
5	2	2	3.36	4.37	5.16	6.00	6.53		
5	3	1	3.22	4.02	4.96	6.04			
5	3	2	3.41	4.65	5.25	6.00	6.82	7.19	
5	3	3	3.44	4.53	5.65	6.32	7.08	7.52	8.24
5	4	1	3.09	3.99	4.99	5.78	6.95	7.36	
5	4	2	3.36	4.54	5.27	6.04	7.12	7.57	8.11
5	4	3	3.32	4.55	5.63	6.41	7.45	7.91	8.50
5	4	4	3.33	4.62	5.62	6.67	7.76	8.14	9.00
5	5	1	3.24	4.11	5.13	6.00	7.31	7.75	
5	5	2	3.39	4.51	5.34	6.35	7.27	8.13	8.69
5	5	3	3.43	4.55	5.71	6.49	7.54	8.24	9.06
5	5	4	3.31	4.52	5.64	6.67	7.77	8.37	9.32
5	5	5	3.42	4.56	5.78	6.74	8.00	8.72	9.68

TABLE G. CRITICAL VALUES OF χ^2

Example With $\alpha = 0.050$ and 4 degrees of freedom, reject the null hypothesis if the obtained χ^2 is larger than or equal to 9.488. The distribution is inherently two-tailed.

	Significance level, α						
df	0.200	0.100	0.050	0.025	0.010	0.005	0.001
1	1.642	2.706	3.841	5.024	6.635	7.879	10.828
2	3.219	4.605	5.991	7.378	9.210	10.597	13.816
3	4.642	6.251	7.815	9.348	11.345	12.838	16.266
4	5.989	7.779	9.488	11.143	13.277	14.860	18.467
5	7.289	9.236	11.071	12.833	15.086	16.750	20.515
6	8.558	10.645	12.592	14.449	16.812	18.548	22.458
7	9.803	12.017	14.067	16.013	18.475	20.278	24.322
8	11.030	13.362	15.507	17.535	20.090	21.955	26.125
9	12.242	14.684	16.919	19.023	21.666	23.589	27.877
10	13.442	15.987	18.307	20.483	23.209	25.188	29.588
11	14.631	17.275	19.675	21.920	24.725	26.757	31.264
12	15.812	18.549	21.026	23.337	26.217	28.300	32.909
13	16.985	19.812	22.362	24.736	27.688	29.820	34.528
14	18.151	21.064	23.685	26.119	29.141	31.319	36.123
15	19.311	22.307	24.996	27.488	30.578	32.801	37.697
16	20.465	23.542	26.296	28.845	32.000	34.267	39.252
17	21.615	24.769	27.587	30.191	33.409	35.719	40.790
18	22.760	25.989	28.869	31.526	34.805	37.157	42.312
19	23.900	27.204	30.144	32.852	36.191	38.582	43.820
20	25.038	28.412	31.410	34.170	37.566	39.997	45.315
21	26.171	29.615	32.671	35.479	38.932	41.401	46.797
22	27.301	30.813	33.924	36.781	40.289	42.796	48.268
23	28.429	32.007	35.173	38.076	41.638	44.181	49.728
24	29.553	33.196	36.415	39.364	42.980	45.559	51.179
25	30.675	34.382	37.653	40.647	44.314	46.928	52.620
26	31.795	35.563	38.885	41.923	45.642	48.290	54.052
27	32.912	36.741	40.113	43.195	46.963	49.645	55.476
28	34.027	37.916	41.337	44.461	48.278	50.993	56.892
29	35.139	39.088	42.557	45.722	49.588	52.336	58.301
30	36.250	40.256	43.773	46.979	50.892	53.672	59.703
40	47.269	51.805	55.759	59.342	63.691	66.766	73.402
50	58.164	63.167	67.505	71.420	76.154	79.490	86.661
60	68.972	74.397	79.082	83.298	88.379	91.952	99.607
70	79.715	85.527	90.531	95.023	100.425	104.215	112.317
80	90.405	96.578	101.879	106.629	112.329	116.321	124.839
90	101.054	107.565	113.145	118.136	124.116	128.299	137.208
100	111.667	118.498	124.342	129.561	135.807	140.169	149.449

TABLE H. CRITICAL VALUES OF S FOR THE JONCKHEERE TEST WITH 3 INDEPENDENT SAMPLES

t_1 is the number of observations in the largest sample
t_3 is the number of observations in the smallest sample
The table may be used for any case for which t_1, t_2, and t_3 are all less than 6.

Examples For a *two-tailed test* with $t_1 = 4$, $t_2 = 2$, $t_3 = 2$ and $\alpha = 0.05$, reject the null hypothesis either if the obtained S is larger than or equal to 16 or if it is smaller than or equal to -16.

For a *one-tailed test* with $t_1 = 4$, $t_2 = 2$, $t_3 = 2$ and $\alpha = 0.05$, if an upper tail test is required, reject the null hypothesis if the obtained S is larger than or equal to 14. If a lower tail test is required, reject if the obtained S is smaller than or equal to 14.

			One-tailed significance level, α				
			0.100	0.050	0.025	0.010	0.005
			Two-tailed significance level, α				
t_1	t_2	t_3	0.200	0.100	0.050	0.020	0.010
2	1	1	5				
2	2	1	6	8			
2	2	2	8	10	12		
3	1	1	7	7			
3	2	1	9	9	11		
3	2	2	10	12	14	16	16
3	3	1	9	11	13	15	
3	3	2	11	15	17	19	21
3	3	3	13	17	19	23	23
4	1	1	7	9			
4	2	1	10	12	14	14	
4	2	2	12	14	16	18	20
4	3	1	11	13	15	17	19
4	3	2	14	16	20	22	24
4	3	3	15	19	23	25	27
4	4	1	14	16	18	22	22
4	4	2	16	20	22	26	28
4	4	3	18	22	26	30	32
4	4	4	20	24	28	32	36
5	1	1	9	11	11		
5	2	1	14	16	16	18	
5	2	2	14	16	18	22	22
5	3	1	13	15	19	21	23
5	3	2	15	19	21	25	27
5	3	3	17	21	25	29	31
5	4	1	15	19	21	25	27
5	4	2	18	22	24	28	30
5	4	3	19	25	29	33	35
5	4	4	22	28	32	36	40
5	5	1	17	21	25	27	31
5	5	2	19	25	27	33	35
5	5	3	21	27	31	37	39
5	5	4	25	31	35	41	45
5	5	5	27	33	39	45	49

TABLE I. CRITICAL VALUES OF S FOR THE KENDALL TEST

The table may be used for all values of n less than 41.

Examples For a *two-tailed test*, with $n = 15$ and $\alpha = 0.05$, reject the null hypothesis if the obtained S is larger than or equal to 41 or if it is smaller than or equal to -41.

For a *one-tailed test* with $n = 15$ and $\alpha = 0.05$, if an upper tail test is required, reject the null hypothesis if the obtained S is larger than or equal to 35. If a lower tail test is required, reject the null hypothesis if the obtained S is smaller than or equal to -35.

	One-tailed significance level, α				
	0.100	0.050	0.025	0.010	0.005
	Two-tailed significance level, α				
n	0.200	0.100	0.050	0.020	0.010
4	6	6	8	8	8
5	8	8	10	10	12
6	9	11	13	13	15
7	11	13	15	17	19
8	12	16	18	20	22
9	14	18	20	24	26
10	17	21	23	27	29
11	19	23	27	31	33
12	20	26	30	36	38
13	24	28	34	40	44
14	25	33	37	43	47
15	29	35	41	49	53
16	30	38	46	52	58
17	34	42	50	58	64
18	37	45	53	63	69
19	39	49	57	67	75
20	42	52	62	72	80
21	44	56	66	78	86
22	47	61	71	83	91
23	51	65	75	89	99
24	54	68	80	94	104
25	58	72	86	100	110
26	61	77	91	107	117
27	63	81	95	113	125
28	68	86	100	118	130
29	70	90	106	126	138
30	75	95	111	131	145
31	77	99	117	137	151
32	82	104	122	144	160
33	86	108	128	152	166
34	89	113	133	157	175
35	93	117	139	165	181
36	96	122	146	172	190
37	100	128	152	178	198
38	105	133	157	185	205
39	109	139	163	193	213
40	112	144	170	200	222

TABLE J. CRITICAL VALUES OF ρ FOR THE SPEARMAN TEST

The table may be used for all values of n less than 31.

Examples For a *two-tailed test*, with $n = 15$ and $\alpha = 0.05$, reject the null hypothesis if the obtained ρ is larger than or equal to 0.521 or if it is smaller than or equal to −0.521.

For a *one-tailed test* with $n = 15$ and $\alpha = 0.05$, if an upper tail test is required, reject the null hypothesis if the obtained ρ is larger than or equal to 0.446. If a lower tail test is required, reject if the obtained ρ is smaller than or equal to −0.446.

	One-tailed significance level, α					
	0.100	0.050	0.025	0.010	0.005	0.001
	Two-tailed significance level, α					
n	0.200	0.100	0.050	0.020	0.010	0.002
4	1.000	1.000				
5	.800	.900	1.000	1.000		
6	.657	.829	.886	.943	1.000	
7	.571	.714	.786	.893	.929	1.000
8	.524	.643	.738	.833	.881	.952
9	.483	.600	.700	.783	.833	.917
10	.455	.564	.648	.745	.794	.879
11	.427	.536	.618	.709	.755	.845
12	.406	.503	.587	.678	.727	.818
13	.385	.484	.560	.648	.703	.791
14	.367	.464	.538	.626	.679	.771
15	.354	.446	.521	.604	.657	.750
16	.341	.429	.503	.585	.635	.729
17	.328	.414	.488	.566	.618	.711
18	.317	.401	.474	.550	.600	.692
19	.309	.391	.460	.535	.584	.675
20	.299	.380	.447	.522	.570	.660
21	.292	.370	.436	.509	.556	.647
22	.284	.361	.425	.497	.544	.633
23	.278	.353	.416	.486	.532	.620
24	.271	.344	.407	.476	.521	.608
25	.265	.337	.398	.466	.511	.597
26	.259	.331	.390	.457	.501	.586
27	.255	.324	.383	.449	.492	.576
28	.250	.318	.375	.441	.483	.567
29	.245	.312	.369	.433	.475	.557
30	.240	.306	.362	.426	.467	.548

TABLE K. CRITICAL VALUES OF Q FOR THE FRIEDMAN TEST WITH 3 OR 4 RELATED SAMPLES

The table may be used for all values of n less than 14 with 3 samples or for all values of n less than 9 with 4 samples. The test is inherently two-tailed.

Examples For 3 samples ($k = 3$) with 10 related sets of observations ($n = 10$) and $\alpha = 0.05$, reject the null hypothesis if the obtained Q is larger than or equal to 6.20.

For 4 samples ($k = 4$) with $n = 5$ and $\alpha = 0.05$, reject the null hypothesis if the obtained Q is larger than or equal to 7.80.

	Significance level, α						
n	0.200	0.100	0.050	0.025	0.010	0.005	0.001
				$k = 3$			
2	4.00						
3	4.67	6.00	6.00				
4	4.50	6.00	6.50	8.00	8.00	8.00	
5	3.60	5.20	6.40	7.60	8.40	10.00	10.00
6	4.00	5.33	7.00	8.33	9.00	10.33	12.00
7	3.71	5.43	7.14	7.71	8.86	10.29	12.29
8	4.00	5.25	6.25	7.75	9.00	9.75	12.25
9	3.56	5.56	6.22	8.00	9.56	10.67	12.67
10	3.80	5.00	6.20	7.80	9.60	10.40	12.60
11	3.82	5.09	6.55	7.82	9.46	10.36	13.27
12	3.50	5.17	6.50	8.00	9.50	10.17	12.50
13	3.85	4.77	6.62	7.54	9.39	10.31	12.92
				$k = 4$			
2	5.40	6.00	6.00				
3	5.40	6.60	7.40	8.20	9.00	9.00	
4	4.80	6.30	7.80	8.40	9.60	10.20	11.10
5	5.16	6.36	7.80	8.76	9.96	10.92	12.60
6	4.80	6.40	7.60	8.80	10.20	11.40	13.00
7	4.89	6.43	7.80	9.00	10.37	11.40	13.80
8	4.80	6.30	7.65	9.00	10.50	11.85	13.95

TABLE L. CRITICAL VALUES OF J FOR THE COMBINED S TEST

m is the number of S scores being combined
n is the number of observations making up each S score
The table may be used for all values of m between 2 and 10 and all values of n between 3 and 8.

Examples For a *two-tailed test*, with $m = 2$, $n = 4$ and $\alpha = 0.05$, reject the null hypothesis if the obtained J is larger than or equal to 10 or if it is less than or equal to 10.

For a *one-tailed test* with $m = 2$, $n = 4$ and $\alpha = 0.05$, if an upper tail test is required, reject the null hypothesis if the obtained J is larger than or equal to 8. If a lower tail test is required, reject if the obtained J is smaller than or equal to 8.

	One-tailed significance level, α						
	0.100	0.050	0.025	0.010	0.005	0.001	0.0005
	Two-tailed significance level, α						
	0.200	0.100	0.050	0.020	0.010	0.002	0.001
				$n = 3$			
m							
2	6	6					
3	7	7	9	9	9		
4	6	8	10	10	12	12	
5	7	9	11	11	13	15	15
6	8	10	12	12	14	16	16
7	9	11	11	13	15	17	17
8	8	10	12	14	16	18	18
9	9	11	13	15	17	19	21
10	10	12	14	16	18	20	22
				$n = 4$			
2	8	8	10	12	12		
3	8	10	12	14	14	16	18
4	10	12	14	16	16	20	20
5	10	12	14	18	18	22	22
6	12	14	16	18	20	24	24
7	12	14	18	20	22	26	26
8	12	16	18	22	24	28	28
9	14	16	20	22	24	28	30
10	14	18	20	24	26	30	32
				$n = 5$			
2	10	12	14	16	16	18	20
3	12	14	16	18	20	22	24
4	12	16	18	20	22	26	28
5	14	18	20	22	26	30	32
6	14	18	22	26	28	32	34
7	16	20	24	26	30	34	36
8	16	20	24	28	32	38	40
9	18	22	26	30	34	40	42
10	18	24	28	32	34	42	44

TABLE L (*continued*)

	One-tailed significance level, α						
	0.100	0.050	0.025	0.010	0.005	0.001	0.0005
	Two-tailed significance level, α						
	0.200	0.100	0.050	0.020	0.010	0.002	0.001
				$n = 6$			
m							
2	12	14	16	20	20	24	26
3	13	17	19	23	25	29	31
4	16	20	22	26	28	34	36
5	17	21	25	29	33	37	41
6	18	24	28	32	36	42	44
7	21	25	29	35	37	45	47
8	22	26	32	36	40	48	50
9	23	29	33	39	43	51	53
10	24	30	34	40	46	54	56
				$n = 7$			
2	14	18	20	24	26	30	32
3	17	21	25	29	31	37	39
4	20	24	28	32	36	42	44
5	21	27	31	37	39	47	49
6	22	28	34	40	44	52	54
7	25	31	37	43	47	55	59
8	26	32	38	46	50	60	64
9	27	35	41	49	53	63	67
10	30	36	44	50	56	66	70
				$n = 8$			
2	16	20	24	28	30	36	38
3	20	26	30	34	38	44	46
4	22	28	34	40	44	50	54
5	26	32	38	44	48	56	60
6	28	34	40	48	52	62	66
7	30	38	44	52	56	68	72
8	32	40	46	54	60	72	76
9	34	42	50	58	64	76	80
10	34	44	52	62	68	80	86

ACKNOWLEDGEMENTS FOR TABLES

Table A. Adapted from Table 1 in L. R. Verdooren, Extended critical values for Wilcoxon's test statistic. *Biometrika*, 1963, **50**, 177–186.

Table D. Reproduced from part of Table 1 in R. L. McCornack, Extended tables of the Wilcoxon Matched Pair Signed Rank Statistic. *Journal of the American Statistical Association*, 1965, **60**, 864–871.

Table F. Adapted from Table F in C. H. Kraft and C. van Eeden, *A Nonparametric Introduction to Statistics*, Macmillan, New York, 1968.

Table H. Values where any $t_i = 1$ computed by the author. Other values reproduced from part of Table I in R. E. Odeh, On Jonckheere's k-sample test against ordered alternatives. *Technometrics*, 1971, **13**, 912–918.

Table I. Reproduced from Table III in L. Kaarsemaker and A. van Wijngaarden, Tables for use in rank correlation. *Statistica Neerlandica*, 1953, **7**, 41–54.

Table J. Reproduced, with corrections, from Table 3 in G. J. Glasser and R. F. Winter, Critical values of the coefficient of rank correlation for testing the hypothesis of independence, *Biometrika*, 1961, **48**, 444–448.

Table K. Adapted from Table A.15 in M. Hollander and D. A. Wolfe, *Nonparametric Statistical Methods*, Wiley, New York, 1973.

References

Bannister, D. and Mair, J. M. M. (1968). *The Evaluation of Personal Constructs*, London: Academic Press.

Benjafield, J. and Green, T. R. G. (1978). Golden section relations in interpersonal *Psychol.*, **67**, 11–15.

Benjafield, J. and Green, T. R. G. (1978). Golden section relations in interpersonal judgement. *Br. J. Psychol.*, **69**, 25–35.

Beveridge, W. N. (1977). Topicalization and the interpretation of ambiguous doubly quantified sentences. Unpublished undergraduate dissertation, University of Newcastle upon Tyne.

Bishop, Y. M. M., Fienberg, S. E., and Holland, P. W. (1975). *Discrete Multivariate Analysis: Theory and Practice*, Cambridge, Massachusetts: The MIT Press.

Bradley, J. V. (1968). *Distribution-Free Statistical Tests*, Englewood Cliffs, N.J.: Prentice-Hall, Inc.

Brennan, R. L. and Light, R. J. (1974). Measuring agreement when two observers classify people into categories not defined in advance. *Br. J. math. statist. Psychol.*, **27**, 154–163.

Buckley, H. C. (1978). Smoking and locus of control. Unpublished undergraduate dissertation, University of Newcastle upon Tyne.

Byer, A. J. and Abrams, D. (1953). A comparison of the triangular and two-sample taste-test methods. *Food Technol.*, **7**, 185–187.

Chambers, L. and Rowlands, E. (1975). The child's memory for unitized and serialized scenes. Unpublished undergraduate dissertation, University of Newcastle upon Tyne.

Cohen, J. (1960). A coefficient of agreement for nominal scales. *Educ. psychol. Measur.*, **20**, 37–46.

Everitt, B. S. (1977). *The Analysis of Contingency Tables*, London: Chapman and Hall.

Ferguson, G. A. (1965). *Nonparametric Trend Analysis*, Montreal: McGill University Press.

Fienberg, S. E. (1977). *The Analysis of Cross-Classified Categorical Data*, Cambridge, Mass.: The MIT Press.

Fleiss, J. L. (1973). *Statistical Methods for Rates and Proportions*, New York: Wiley.

Fransella, F. and Bannister, D. (1977). *A Manual for Repertory Grid Technique*, London: Academic Press.

Gart, J. J. (1969). An exact test for comparing matched proportions in crossover designs. *Biometrika*, **56**, 75–80.

Goodman, L. A. and Kruskal, W. H. (1954). Measures of association for cross classifications. *J. Amer. Statist. Assoc.*, **49**, 732–764.

Goodman, L. A. and Kruskal, W. H. (1963). Measures of association for cross classifications III: Approximate sampling theory. *J. Amer. Statist. Assoc.*, **58**, 310–364.

Goodman, L. A. and Kruskal, W. H. (1972). Measures of association for cross classifications, IV: Simplification of asymptotic variances. *J. Amer. Statist. Assoc.*, **67**, 415–421.

Grant, P. (1975). Self esteem in alcoholism and drug addiction. Unpublished undergraduate dissertation, University of Newcastle upon Tyne.

Haber, A. and Runyon, R. P. (1973). *General Statistics* (2nd Edn.), Reading, Massachusetts: Addison-Wesley.

Hays, W. L. (1963). *Statistics for Psychologists*, New York: Holt, Rinehart and Winston.

Hodges, J. L., Jr. and Lehmann, E. L. (1970). *Basic concepts of probability and statistics*, (2nd edn.) San Francisco: Holden-Day.

Hollander, M. and Wolfe, D. A. (1973). *Nonparametric Statistical Methods*, New York: Wiley.

Hubert, L. (1977). Nominal scale response agreement as a generalized correlation. *Br. J. math. statist. Psychol.*, **30**, 98–103.

Jonckheere, A. R. (1954a). A distribution-free *k*-sample test against ordered alternatives. *Biometrika*, **41**, 133–145.

Jonckheere, A. R. (1954b). A test of significance for the relation between *m* rankings and *k* ranked categories. *Br. J. statist. Psychol.*, **7**, 93–100.

Jonckheere, A. R. (1970) Techniques for ordered contingency tables. In J. B. Riemersma & H. C. van der Meer (eds.), *Proceedings of the NUFFIC International Summer Session in Science, 'Het Oude Hof'*, The Hague.

Jonckheere, A. R. and Bower, G. H. (1967). Non-parametric trend tests for learning data. *Br. J. math. statist. Psychol.*, **20**, 163–186.

Kendall, M. G. (1970). *Rank Correlation Methods*, (4th edition.) London: Griffin.

Kendall, M. G. and Stuart, A. (1973). *The Advanced Theory of Statistics*, Vol. 2 (3rd edn.) London: Griffin.

Keppel, G. (1973). *Design and Analysis: A Researcher's Handbook*, Englewood Cliffs, N.J.: Prentice-Hall, Inc.

Leach, C. (1974). The importance of instructions in assessing sequential effects in impression formation. *Br. J. soc. clin. Psychol.*, **13**, 151–156.

Lehmann, E. L. (1975). *Nonparametrics: Statistical Methods Based on Ranks*, San Francisco: Holden-Day.

Lowenstein, C. C. (1978). Body image in anorexics and 'normal' women and 'normal' men. Unpublished undergraduate dissertation, University of Newcastle upon Tyne.

Luchins, A. S. (1958). Definitiveness of impression and primacy-recency in communications. *J. soc. Psychol.*, **48**, 275–290.

McKane, W. A. (1977). Dogmatism in teachers and its effect on the academic self-concept of the pupils. Unpublished undergraduate dissertation, University of Newcastle upon Tyne.

Mosteller, F. and Rourke, R. E. K. (1973). *Sturdy Statistics*, Reading, Massachusetts: Addison-Wesley.

Mosteller, F., Rourke, R. E. K. and Thomas, G. B. Jr. (1970). *Probability with Statistical Applications*, (2nd ed.) Reading, Massachusetts: Addison-Wesley.

Poulton, E. C. (1973). Unwanted range effects from using within-subject experimental designs. *Psychol. Bull.*, **80**, 113–121.

Rotter, J. B. (1966). Generalized expectancies for internal versus external control of reinforcement. *Psychological Monographs*, **80**, 1–28.

Somers, R. H. (1962). A new asymmetrical measure of association for ordinal variables. *Amer. Sociological Rev.*, **27**, 799–811.

Stirling, E. A. (1977). The Application of Linguistic Models in the Investigation of Perceptual and Memory Processes in Normal Readers. Unpublished Ph.D. Thesis, University of Birmingham.

Tukey, J. W. (1977). *Exploratory Data Analysis*, Reading, Massachusetts: Addison-Wesley.

Wonnacott, T. H., and Wonnacott, R. J. (1972). *Introductory Statistics*, (2nd edn.) New York: Wiley.

Answers to Exercises

'. . . the answers make you wise, but the questions make you human.'
Yves Montand to Barbra Streisand in *On a Clear Day You Can See Forever*

CHAPTER 1

1. (a), (b), (d), (f), and (g) are continuous; (c) and (e) are discrete.

2. (a)

No. of visits	0	1	2	3	4	5	6
Frequency	4	2	3	1	2	5	3
Relative frequency	0.20	0.10	0.15	0.05	0.10	0.25	0.15

(b) 0.15; (c) Mean = 3.1; Median = 3.5; Mode = 5;
(d) Range = 6; S.D. = 2.19.

3. (a) Mean = 3; Variance = 3.2.
(b) Mean = 6; Variance = 3.2.
(c) Adding a constant to each score adds the same constant to the mean.
(d) Adding a constant has no effect on the variance.
(e) Mean = 6; Variance = 12.8.
(f) Mean = 9; Variance = 28.8.
(g) Multiplying each score by a constant has the effect of multiplying the mean by the same constant.
(h) Multiplying each score by a constant multiplies the variance by the square of that constant – e.g. by 2^2 in (e) and by 3^2 in (f).

4. (c) Mean = 42; Variance = 169.04.
(d) Median = 43.

5. (a) 0.2; (b) 0.5.

6. (a) 0.8; (b) 3/25;
(c) 0; (d) 12/600 = 0.02.

7. Only (b) is experimental.

CHAPTER 2

1. $S = 50$. With $\alpha = 0.05$, critical value for an upper tail test is 40; so, reject null hypothesis – prediction confirmed.
2. $S = 30$. With $\alpha = 0.05$, critical values for a two-tailed test are –26 and 26; so reject null hypothesis – decision makers prevaricate more.
4.

S	–9	–7	–5	–3	–1	1	3	5	7	9
prob	1/20	1/20	2/20	3/20	3/20	3/20	3/20	2/20	1/20	1/20

5. $S = 108$. (a) With $\alpha = 0.01$, critical values for a two-tailed test are –90 and +90; reject null hypothesis – speed instructions speed things up. (b) Critical values of z are –2.576 and +2.576. Obtained $z = 3.09$. Same conclusion, so approximation accurate.
6. (a) $S = 46$. With $\alpha = 0.05$, critical value is 40; so reject null hypothesis. (b) $S = 52$, $z = 2.20$, which is larger than critical value of 1.645, so reject null hypothesis.
7. $S = -89$, $z = -1.19$, which is larger than lower tail critical value of –1.645 ($\alpha = 0.05$), so prediction not supported.
8. (1) *H-L* estimate = 7, $\delta = 0.625$; (2) *H-L* estimate = 5.5, $\delta = 0.833$; (5) *H-L* estimate = 25.5, $\delta = 0.750$; (6a) *H-L* estimate = 7, $\delta = 0.575$; (6b) *H-L* estimate = 5, $\delta = 0.650$, (7) $\delta = 0.223$.
9. $S = -38$. With $\alpha = 0.05$, critical value is –59, so cannot reject null hypothesis.
10. Obtained $z = -1.15$. Same conclusion.
11. $S = 90$. With $\alpha = 0.05$, two-tailed critical values are –120 and 120, so cannot reject null hypothesis – no feeling of knowing.
12. (9) $\delta = -0.345$; (11) $\delta = 0.402$.
13. Examples 2.1, 2.2, 2.11, 2.12, are experimental; 2.3, 2.4, 2.5, 2.10 are correlational.

CHAPTER 3

1. $W+ = 9$; critical value = 5; so cannot reject null hypothesis.
2. $W+ = 105.5$; $z = -1.765$. For $\alpha = 0.2$, critical values of $z = \pm 1.282$; so reject null hypothesis – theory not supported.
3. It does make a difference; ranking high to low is wrong.
4.

$W+$	0	1	2	3	4	5	6	7	8	9	10
prob	1/32	1/32	1/32	2/32	2/32	3/32	3/32	3/32	3/32	3/32	3/32
							11	12	13	14	15
							2/32	2/32	1/32	1/32	1/32

5. $N+ = 1$; critical value = 1; so reject null hypothesis.

6. $N+ = 10$, $N- = 16$; critical value = 9 if $\alpha = 0.2$; so cannot reject null hypothesis – theory supported. Signed-Rank Test probably more reasonable for these data, since magnitudes give important information.
7.

$N+$	0	1	2	3	4	5
prob	1/32	5/32	10/32	10/32	5/32	1/32

9. (a) *H-L* estimate is –6; median is –5.
   (b) *H-L* estimate is 0.588; median is 0.587.
10. $n = 25$, $p = 0.2$. For Bill, $z = 3.25$; prob = 0.0006; so Bill isn't guessing. Mike has fewer correct than expected by chance, so he is guessing.
11. McNemar Test. With $\alpha = 0.05$, critical value is 9. $B = 10$, so cannot reject null hypothesis – no evidence that A is more likely to accept than B.
12. $n = 50$, $p = 1/3$, $z = 2.35$. Using one-tailed test with $\alpha = 0.05$, critical value of z is 1.645, so we reject null hypothesis and conclude that there is evidence of discrimination. Estimate is 0.5.
13. Reliable order effect, since with $t_1 = 6$, $t_2 = 3$, $u_1 = 5$, $u_2 = 4$, obtained S equals critical value of 15 for $\alpha = 0.05$.
    No treatment effect, since with $t_1 = 8$, $t_2 = 1$, $u_1 = 5$, $u_2 = 4$, and $S = 5$ it is not possible to reject null hypothesis.
14. For $t_1 = 7$, $t_2 = 5$, critical values of S for two-tailed test with $\alpha = 0.05$ are –25 and 25.
    (a) There is no difference between the two forms, since $S = 5$.
    (b) There is a reliable difference between first and second born, since $S = 31$.

CHAPTER 4

1. With $\alpha = 0.05$, critical value = 5.69. $K = 2.35$ – not significant.
2. With $\alpha = 0.05$, critical value = 7.815. $K = 8.54$; therefore the treatments differ.
3. With $\alpha = 0.05$, critical value = 5.991. $K = 14.24$. Therefore the films differ.
5. With $\alpha = 0.05$, critical value = 7.815. $K = 7.32$ – not significant.
6. No.
7. 2413
8. BAC
9. (a) All samples differ reliably; (b) A and B don't differ, C larger than B and A, D larger than B, A, and C; (c) B smaller than the others, A and C don't differ, D larger than the others; (d) B smaller than the others, A smaller than C and D, which don't differ; (e) B and A don't differ, A and C don't differ, but B smaller than C, and D larger than the others; (f) B and A don't differ, but both are reliably smaller than C and D, which don't differ; (g) B smaller than the others, A and C don't differ, C and D don't differ, but A smaller than D; (h) D larger than the others, which don't differ; (i) B smaller than the others, which don't differ; (j) B, A, and C don't differ, C and D don't differ, but D larger than B and A; (k) B and A don't differ, A, C, and D don't differ, but B smaller than C and D; (1) no differences between the samples; (m) only B and D differ.
10. Only Example 4.1 is experimental.

CHAPTER 5

1. $S = 18$. With $\alpha = 0.05$, critical value for an upper tail test is 25; cannot reject null hypothesis – prediction not supported.
2. $S = 45$; $z = 1.73$; with $\alpha = 0.05$, critical value for an upper tail test is 1.645, so reject null hypothesis – prediction supported.
3. $S = -74$; $S_c = -64.25$; $z = -1.74$; with $\alpha = 0.05$, critical value for a lower tail test is -1.645; so reject null hypothesis – prediction supported.
4. (a) $S = 17$. With $\alpha = 0.05$, critical values for a two-tailed test are -15 and 15; so reject the null hypothesis – the two tasks are positively correlated.
   (b) Yes, even when there are ties.
5. $S = -11$, indicating no agreement (Why?)
6. $S = 27$. With $\alpha = 0.05$, critical value for an upper tail test is 21, so the two judges agree.
7. $S = 9$. With $\alpha = 0.05$, critical value for an upper tail test is 9, so reliable evidence of learning.
8. $S = -360$; $z = -4.02$, much smaller than any standard critical value, so strong evidence of increasing conservation with age.
9. $S = -87$; $S_c = -81.5$; $z = -2.81$. With $\alpha = 0.05$, two-tailed critical values are -1.96 and 1.96; so reject null hypothesis – evidence of improvement with age.
10. $S = -720$; $S_c = -700$; $z = -2.77$. With $\alpha = 0.05$, and lower tail test, reject null hypothesis – prediction supported. (To calculate S here, must first record data in form of an ordered contingency table.)
11. (4) $\rho = 0.929$. Critical values are -0.786 and 0.786; so reject null hypothesis.
    (5) $\rho = -0.370$. Judges don't agree.
    (6) $\rho = 0.455$. Critical value is 0.564, so no agreement. (Different conclusion from Kendall Test – why?)
12. $\delta = 0.664$.
13. $\delta = 0.220$.
14. $\tau_b = -0.312$.

CHAPTER 6

1. $Q = 6.5$; with $\alpha = 0.05$, critical value is 6.5, so reject null hypothesis – the problems differ.
2. (a) $Q = 19.63$; with $\alpha = 0.05$ and 3 df, critical value is 7.815, so there are differences between the films. (b) $W = .65$.
4. With $\alpha = 0.02$ for each comparison, there are no differences, mainly because of the small number of subjects. $\overline{\text{ABC}}$.
5. LP $\overline{\text{Sc RB BS}}$ (using $\alpha = 0.02$ for each comparison).
6. $Q = 14.56$; with $\alpha = 0.05$, there are differences between the films. $\overline{\text{LP Sc RB}}$ BS (using $\alpha = 0.02$ for each comparison).

CHAPTER 7

1. $J = 31$. From Table L, with $n = 6$, $m = 3$ and $\alpha = 0.05$, one-tailed critical value is 17, so reject null hypothesis – the group is learning.

2. $J = 8$. From Table L with $n = 3$, $m = 4$ and $\alpha = 0.05$, one-tailed critical value is 8, so reject null hypothesis – prediction confirmed.
3. $J = 90$; Variance of $S = 521.05$; Variance of $J = 1563.15$; $z = 2.28$. Using two-tailed test with $\alpha = 0.05$, reject null hypothesis – Method I is better.
5. $J = 24$; Variance of $J = 74$; $z = 2.67$ (using continuity correction). Using one-tailed test with $\alpha = 0.05$, reject null hypothesis – the group is learning.
6. The S's are 7, 10 and 7; the variances of S are 13, 16.67, and 15.67. $J = 24$; Variance of $J = 45.33$; $z = 3.56$; the group is learning.
7. The S's are 8, –5, 0 and 2; the variances of S are 36, 45, 12, and 16. $J = 5$; Variance of $J = 109$; $z = 0.48$ – the data are in line with the all-or-none theory.
8. The S's are 84, –11 and 96; the variances of S are 895.30, 5819.00, 1981.94. $J^* = 6.26$; Variance of $J^* = 6.36$; $z = 2.48$. Method I is better.
9. (1) $\Sigma z_i^2 = 11.96$; $z^2 = 11.31$; $H = 0.65$. With $\alpha = 0.05$ and 2 df, critical value is 5.991 – so no difference between subjects.
   (3) $\Sigma z_i^2 = 6.72$; $z^2 = 5.20$; $H = 1.52$. With $\alpha = 0.05$ and 2 df, critical value is 5.991 – so no difference between schools.
   (8) $\Sigma z_i^2 = 12.55$; $z^2 = 6.15$; $H = 6.40$. With $\alpha = 0.05$ and 2 df, critical value is 5.991 – so the schools differ.

CHAPTER 8

1. $\chi^2 = 22.92$, df = 6. With $\alpha = 0.05$, critical value is 12.592, so reject null hypothesis – the cities differ.
4. (a) $\chi^2 = 6.17$; df = 1. (b) $z = 2.43$. (c) $z^2 = 5.91 = 6.17 \times 23/24$.
5. $\chi^2 = 27.56$; df = 5. With $\alpha = 0.05$, critical value is 11.071, so reject null hypothesis – there are differences between the films.
6. $\chi^2 = 12$; df = 1. With $\alpha = 0.05$, critical value is 3.841, so the earlier films are liked less than the later ones.
7. $C = 0.27$. $\lambda_a = 0.23$. Hence, 23% of the errors in guessing the most sympathetic character can be eliminated by knowing the film concerned.
8. $\lambda_a = 0.13$.
9. $\kappa = 0.52$.

Index

TIES	EXPLANATORY VARIABLE	RESPONSE VARIABLE	NAME OF TEST	EXACT TABLE	EXAMPLE OF USE	Conti correc
None	Ordinal	Ordinal	KENDALL	*I*	5.6, 5.7	1
Ties in one variable	Ordinal with ties	Ordinal	JONCKHEERE	*H*	5.1, 5.2, 5.3, 5.8	1
	Two sample	Ordinal	RANK-SUM	*A*	2.1, 2.2, 2.3	1
Ties in both variables	Ordinal with ties	Ordinal with ties	JONCKHEERE (with ties)	None	5.4	Non
	Ordinal with ties	Two category	JONCKHEERE (with two cat. response variable)	None	5.5	$\frac{2n - }{2(k}$
	Two sample	Ordinal with ties	RANK-SUM (with ties)	None	2.4, 2.5	$\frac{2n - u}{2(k}$
	Two sample	Two sample	FISHER EXACT	*C*	2.10, 2.11, 2.12	$n/$